Table of Contents

KU-040-136

Foreword

The management of golf courses is becoming more complex. The demand for higher quality playing surfaces, the need for more precise management techniques, and increased environmental awareness are just three of the factors contributing to this trend. As a result, it is important that all members of the golf course maintenance staff have an understanding of the principles of turfgrass and landscape management.

This book is designed to provide landscape management information for the entire golf course operation. For the professional manager, the book is a handy reference to quickly search for the answers to the most common landscape management questions. The book also provides maintenance staff with an understanding of the practical information they need to work effectively in this rapidly changing field.

CHAPTER 1

Soil

The soil is a complex mixture of organic and inorganic chemicals and serves as a major source of both the water and nutrients needed for the growth of the plant.

Soil Structure

A soil is made up of minerals called sand, silt and clay. The difference between the three is both physical and chemical. Physically, they differ in size (Table 1 and Figure 1).

When a soil is analyzed, as it would be in a physical soil test, the relative amount of sand, silt and clay content is determined using a set of sieves. The resulting percentages of sand, silt and clay place the soil in what is called a soil texture group (Figure 2).

Terms such as loam, sandy loam and clay loam are some of the names for soil texture groups. For example, if a soil contains about 60 percent sand, 20 percent silt and 20 percent clay, it is called a sandy loam. A clay has about 20 percent sand, 20 percent silt and 60 percent clay. Most consider a sandy loam the best soil texture for plant because it has good drainage and good soil nutrient-holding characteristics.

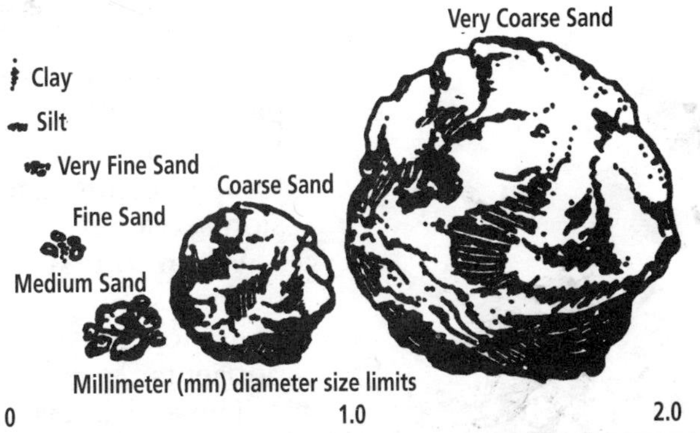

The most important direct effects of soil structure on a turf are on the rate at which water enters the soil, the amount of water the soil holds, and the rate at which water drains through the soil. As the percentage of sand in a soil increases, water enters the soil quicker, the soil holds less water and the water moves faster through the soil.

Sandy soils tend to be droughty and require fairly frequent irrigation. The presence of very small clay particles in any significant amount in a soil dramatically slows water infiltration and increases the amount of water held in that soil (Table 2).

While these soils hold water, they are poorly drained, and puddles develop even after a short rain. Generally, plants root deeper in sandy soils than in high clay soils, with adequate irrigation.

Several kinds of clay minerals are found in soils. One particular clay can cause serious problems, especially for athletic fields. This clay shrinks when dried. If a soil has a high percentage of this clay, cracks several inches across and sometimes several feet deep may open in the soil during dry periods. These cracks create a severe safety hazard. When these soils are wetted, the clay expands and the cracks disappear.

Figure 1. Relative Sizes of Mineral Soil Particles

Very Coarse Sand

Clay
Silt
Very Fine Sand
Coarse Sand
Fine Sand
Medium Sand

Millimeter (mm) diameter size limits

0   1.0   2.0

Table 1. Soil Particle Size Range

Particle	Size (mm)	Number of particles per gram	Surface area in 1 gram (sq. cm.)
Very coarse sand	2.00-1.00	90	11
Coarse sand	1.00-0.50	720	23
Medium sand	0.50-0.25	5,700	45
Fine sand	0.25-0.10	46,000	91
Very fine sand	0.10-0.05	722,000	227
Silt	0.05-0.002	5,776,000	454
Clay	0.002	90,260,853,000	8,000,000

Figure 2. Soil Classification Triangle

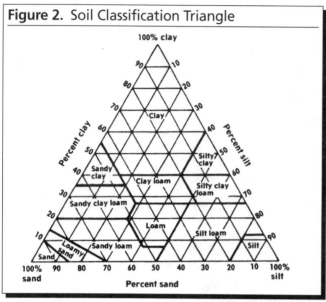

Soil Chemistry

The ability of a soil to hold and supply nutrients to a plant is dependent on the amount of clay and, to some degree, the amount of organic matter it contains. Both clay particles and organic matter have a negative charge. Since most plant nutrients have a positive charge, the nutrients are held to their surface for future use by plants.

Soils high in sand content do not hold many nutrients, so fertilizer programs are more critical. As an extreme example, plants grown on a very sandy soil may need to be fertilized with small amounts of fertilizer every one or two weeks, while other plants grown on soils containing moderate amounts of clay can go four, six or even eight weeks between fertilizer applications.

Soil Test

A soil test can be valuable to develop any fertility program. Depending on the test selected, it can determine the level of essential plant nutrients in the sampled soil, describe any salt problem, determine the pH and identify the soil's texture class.

Which lab? If the soil sample was sent to 10 different labs there might be 10 slightly different answers. Not all labs have the same analytical equipment nor use the same techniques. It does not make sense to compare results from different labs. Pick a dependable lab and stick with it. Every state has a land grant university with a soil test lab. Information for soil testing is available from the local office of the cooperative extension service.

When to test. Soil nutrient levels do not stay the same. Plants remove nutrients. Some nutrients are leached through the root system. Rain or irrigation may dilute nutrient concentrations. Microorganisms use up nutrients.

The soil is ever changing, especially during the growing season. In order to get the most dependable test results possible, test when the system is fairly stable—usually January and February, when the last fertilizer application was weeks prior and the next is weeks away. Plants are dormant, so the whole system is fairly stable. Soil test every 2 or 3 years at the same time of the year should be sufficient.

How to soil test. The soil should come from the plant's rootzone. In most cases, this is just a few inches deep. The sample should represent a fairly uniform area. A sample shouldn't be made up of soil from a sandy area together with soil from a high clay area. These two soils should be treated separately.

On golf courses, greens wouldn't be included with tees or fairways, but soil from all 18 greens could be put together into one sample if all the greens had basically the same construction. There may be enough variation in soils across a golf course that each fairway can be sampled separately. It even may be that a front lawn will be different from the back. (Figure 3)

How to evaluate results. One single soil test may be of limited value.

It's important to know the soil pH because of its impact on nutrient availability. The soil texture class information is needed to determine the rate of material needed to adjust pH. Soil salinity levels are important, especially if they are too high. By soil testing the same area each

Table 2. Water Infiltration Rates

Soil Type	Inches Per Hour
Sand	2.0
Sandy Loam	1.0
Loam	0.5
Silt Loam	0.4
Clay Loam	0.3
Clay	0.2

year, at the same time, it can be determined if salt levels are increasing or decreasing and if the pH level is going up or down. If the level of a particular nutrient is increasing over the years, the fertilizer program can be adjusted to reduce the amount of that nutrient. The trends of soil test results over several seasons are important.

Soil Drainage

Poor soil drainage, both surface and internal, can be one of the worst continual problems for all plants. Roots simply won't grow in wet soils.

Surface drainage may be adequate if the grade is at least 1 percent. This means that for water to run downhill, the slope should drop at least one foot for every 100 feet in distance.

While surface drainage is important and will aid in keeping plants from becoming waterlogged, especially during periods of heavy rainfall, the internal drainage characteristics of soil are most important.

Several factors may prevent soil from draining well internally. The most common problem is the clay content. Clay holds water, and the higher the percentage of clay, the more water is held and poorer the drainage.

Another common cause of poor drainage is compaction caused by traffic. The more traffic an area receives, the slower the drainage. Only high sand areas, such as golf course putting greens or athletic fields, can withstand fairly high traffic and maintain good drainage.

Soils high in calcium and/or sodium may tend to be poorly drained. These two elements may cause the soil to lose its desirable structure, and its good drainage characteristics. If a soil has lost its structure because of high sodium, adding gypsum may improve internal drainage. Since gypsum is calcium sulfate, application to a high calcium soil won't help.

Tile Systems

When internal soil drainage is extremely limited, it may be desirable to install a tile system. In the past, both clay and concrete tiles have been used, but now plastic tubing has become very popular.

The system design depends on such factors as the area's topography and the soil texture type. A system is composed of a main collector line and a number of laterals. (Figure 4). Generally, the tile line must have a minimum of a 0.5% fall. This is a drop of 6 inches for every 100 feet of tile. It is suggested when tile lines join, they join at a 45 degree angle. This will help keep the flowing at the fastest rate out of the ground.

The distance between the systems lateral lines is determined by the distance water will travel laterally in the soil. The more clay in the soil, the closer the lateral lines may need to be.

The minimum depth of the system may depend on activities such as aerification. Usually 2 feet is the minimum depth.

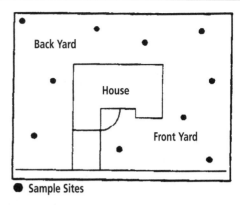

Figure 3. Example of How to Take a Soil Sample

● Sample Sites

Step. 1. Soil samples should not include any surface debris. Scrape away the ¼ to ½ inch of plant debris that occurs at the soil surface before taking a sample.

Step 2. The final sample sent to the lab should represent the soil from the whole lawn. Since urban soils tend to be variable, a series of small samples should be taken from selected sites around your home (see Figure 3). If there is a great difference between the front and back yards, you may wish to sample them separately.

Step 3. Remove a small sample of soil from each of the selected sites. There's no need to go deeper than about 6 inches.

Step 4. Mix all the soil from the selected sites together in a plastic bucket forming one large sample. Fill the plastic sample bag with about 1 cup of soil.

Step 5. Fill out the soil sample information sheet completely.

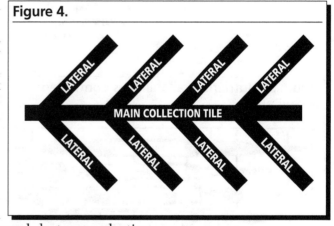

Figure 4.

The whole system is covered with gravel, course sand, or other material to help keep soil from entering and clogging up the lines. A drainage specialist should be called to help design the system.

Special-Use Areas

The two most intensely-trafficked athletic fields are golf course putting greens and football fields. Turf on these fields must be kept in an optimum growing condition. The root system must be as deep and extensive as possible. Another desirable quality is that these two areas be playable even after a heavy rain. This has led to the construction of 100% sand putting greens and football fields. They may not all be 100% sand. Many are built using a mixture of sand from 80 to 95% sand and the rest peat. The peat is just enough to hold moisture for seed germination or for initial sprig growth. The sand must be clean and fit a certain size criteria (Table 3).

These high sand greens and fields are now in use all over the country. They have proven to be very successful.

Soil pH

The pH of the soil has one important effect on the growth of turf—it controls the availability of nutrients in the soil. It doesn't matter if the nutrients are provided by the application of a liquid or dry fertilizer, or if the nutrients are supplied by the decomposition of soil minerals. Availability to the grass plant is controlled to a large degree by the soil pH (Figure 5).

Most nutrients are available in greatest supply around a pH of 6.5. As an indirect effect of pH, some microorganisms in the soil are necessary for the conversion of some plant nutrients from an unavailable form to a form the plant can use. These conversions are slower in both high and low pH soils.

One of the most common nutrient problems associated with an excessively high or low pH is iron deficiency. Many times there is enough iron in the soil, but it is not available to the plant. It is rare to have minor nutrient problems not directly related to pH.

Soil Modification

Physical

The goal of physically modifying a soil is to provide better internal drainage. Sand is the most commonly-used material to improve drainage. Very fine sand should not be used. An ideal sand should have a diameter of about one-half millimeter—fairly coarse.

Sands are sold under names like cement sand, mortar sand, sugar sand, bedding sand, foundation sand, etc. These names do not relate to any physical particle size and do not necessarily assure quality. The fine sands, when mixed with clay and dried out, can form a very hard surface.

In order to improve soil drainage significantly, large quantities of a good quality sand must be used. For example, if the soil to be modified

Table 3. Sand Particle Sizes

Particle Size	Ideal Percent
2.00 – 1.00mm	10% or less
1.00 – 0.50mm	At Least
0.50 – 0.25mm	80%
0.25 – 0.10mm	
less than 0.10mm	10% or less

Figure 5. Nutrient Availability as Controlled by Soil pH

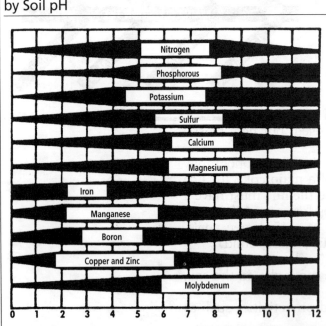

is a clay loam containing 20 percent sand, 20 percent silt and 60 percent clay and is mixed with an equal quantity of sand, the resulting soil would have a composition of 60 percent sand, 10 percent silt and 30 percent clay. This new soil will have better drainage, but it takes large amounts of sand to modify a clay soil. A few inches of sand spread over a soil and then roto-tilled into it probably won't improve drainage significantly.

An ideal soil contains about 5 percent organic matter. Some soils high in clay and low in organic matter have poor drainage. Mixing organic matter into these soils may improve drainage as much as adding sand. Decomposed or composted organic matter should be used. Fresh organic matter is not as desirable. The organisms that decompose organic matter have a high nitrogen requirement, so any plants growing in soils containing fresh organic matter usually have severe nitrogen deficiencies until the organic matter has decomposed.

Chemical

If a soil test indicates that pH is less than 6.5, limestone is usually recommended. Limestone is calcium carbonate ($CaCO_2$), and since calcium is a necessary plant nutrient, when limestone is used, calcium is also supplied to the plant. If dolomitic limestone is used, magnesium, as well as calcium, is supplied. The higher the amount of clay in a soil, the more limestone is needed to change the pH (Table 4).

Soils that have a pH higher than 6.5 may be modified with sulfur (Table 5).

Sulfur lowers pH. Three commonly-used forms of sulfur are powder, flake, and granular. The powder form works fastest, but is messiest. With sulfur application, if internal soil drainage is not good, the soluble salt levels of the soil may be increased. This may be one reason why sulfur recommendations may not be very common.

In some soils, a salt buildup can create serious problems. The primary source of salt is irrigation water. Plants vary in ability to tolerate high soil salt levels. The first symptom of a salt problem is reduced growth. As salt levels increase, a white salt deposit typically is seen on the soil surface. A soil test can determine soluble salt levels.

The only way to reduce a soil salt problem is to improve internal soil drainage so that salts are leached out of the rootzone. Aerification and/or use of a soil wetting agent may also aid in reducing soil salt levels.

Table 4. Amount of Ground or Dolomitic Limestone Needed Per 1,000 Square Feet To Raise pH to 6.5

Soil pH	Soil Texture Class		
	Sand	Loam	Clay
6.0	20	35	50
5.5	45	75	100
5.0	65	110	150
4.5	80	150	200
4.0	100	175	230

Table 5. Amount of Elemental Sulfer Needed Per 1,000 Square Feet To Lower pH To 6.5

Soil pH	Soil Texture Class	
	Sandy	Clay
8.5	35-46	45-60
8.0	25-35	35-50
7.5	10-15	20-25

Soil Organisms

While sand, silt and clay are the non-living part of the soil, organisms such as worms, nematodes, algae, fungi and bacteria are living parts of the soil.

The most common soil organisms are bacteria and fungi. As many as 100 million bacteria per teaspoon of soil may be present, although a few thousand is the usual population. Fungi populations are harder to estimate because they grow in thread-like strands and don't exist as individuals.

One of the most important functions of soil organisms is the conversion of the organic form of nitrogen to an inorganic form the plant can use. Bacteria converts organic nitrogen to ammonium, which they use as their food supply. As long as there is a large supply of carbon, such as non-decomposed organic material, these bacteria will use up all available nitrogen. This is why it is never recommended that any non-decomposed organic material be incorporated into the soil.

If the soil supply of carbon is limited and there is more nitrogen than this group of bacteria can use, another group of bacteria convert the ammonium nitrogen to the nitrate form. All plants prefer the nitrate form of nitrogen.

Soil organisms assist in the degradation process. Bacteria use many pesticides as sources of the nitrogen and carbon that they require as food material. Bacteria also aid in keeping many forms of fungi under control. ❦

Notes

CHAPTER 2

Plant Growth

All plants have the same basic requirements. They need a supply of water, a fairly continuous source of nutrients, a certain quality and quantity of light and the proper temperature.

Plants make their own food or carbohydrates through a process called **photosynthesis**. In this process the plant uses carbon dioxide (CO_2) and water (H_2O) in the presence of light to make a sugar with some oxygen released as a by- product. Only plant cells containing the green pigment chlorophyll can carry on photosynthesis. The carbohydrates may be used right away to support plant growth or they may be stored as a food reserve to get the plant through stress periods as well as through summer or winter dormancy.

The process which turns carbohydrates into the energy the plant needs to grow is called **respiration**. The difference between photosynthesis and respiration is as follows:

Photosynthesis	Respiration
1. Produces food	Uses food for plant energy
2. Energy is stored	Energy is used
3. Occurs in cells with chlorophyll	Occurs in all cells
4. Oxygen is released	Oxygen is used
5. Water is used	Water is produced
6. Carbon dioxide is used	Carbon dioxide is produced
7. Occurs in sunlight	Occurs anytime

The third basic process is called transpiration. This describes the movement of water from the time it enters the roots until it exits the plant as water vapor through small holes in the leaves called stomata. This process is responsible for the transport of nutrients from the soil up through the root system to all parts of the plant. As water is changed from a liquid to a vapor form in the transpiration process, the plant is cooled.

Effect of Light

Light has three characteristics that affect plant growth. These are light quantity, light quality and light duration. Light quantity simply refers to the intensity of sunlight. It's highest during summer. The higher the intensity, up to a point, the higher the level of photosynthesis.

Sunlight is made up of a whole range of different wavelengths. Each wavelength is a different color in the spectrum. Those in the red and blue wavelengths have the greatest effect on plant growth. Most artificially-produced light is not the wavelengths that plants need.

Light duration refers to the length of time the plant is exposed to sunlight. This may also be called photoperiod. The length of a plant's pho-

Figure 1.

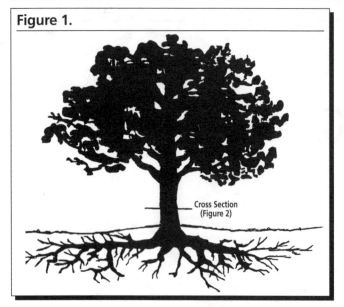

Cross Section
(Figure 2)

Figure 2.

Cross section of a tree trunk, showing A, the heartwood, composed of dead xylem cells; B, the sapwood, which has many living xylem cells that conduct water and nutrients upward, C, the annual rings composed of summer and spring wood; D, the medullary rays, which transfer water and food radially; E, the cambium from which are formed xylem cells on the inside and phloem tissue on the outside; F; the phloem cells, which conduct food downward; G, the cork cambium, which produces cork cells to form the outer bark, H.

toperiod can determine what part of the year the plant flowers and it also may prepare a plant for dormancy. Photoperiod triggers the growth of cells that cause leaves of deciduous plants to turn color in the fall and drop off.

Effect of Temperature

The rates of photosynthesis and respiration can be effected by temperature. Plants have optimum temperature ranges in which they grow at their best rates. Plant growth slows when temperatures are above or below the optimum range. Some plants won't flower unless they are exposed to so many hours of cold temperatures. Low temperatures may also cause plants to reduce their use of carbohydrates and to increase carbohydrate storage for winter dormancy.

Parts of the Plant

Roots

The root system originates at the lower end of the embryo of a seedling plant. Some plants, especially trees, tend to have a primary root that grows deep into the soil. This is called a tap root and gives these plants great stability. Smaller secondary and fibrous roots developing from the main tap root are responsible for taking up water and nutrients.

Other woody plants and grasses do not develop a strong tap root but produce a very fibrous root system composed of a great number of very small roots.

The part of the root system that is active in water and nutrient uptake is usually in the top one foot of soil for woody plants and in the top few inches for grasses. A tree's root system usually extends a few feet out from the spread of the branches (Figure 1).

Stems

The stem is responsible for the transport of water and nutrients up from the root system to the leaves (Figure 2). This occurs in conducting tissue called xylem. The carbohydrates manufactured in the leaves are transported to the rest of the plant through conducting tissue called phloem. There is a layer of tissue between the xylem and the phloem called the cambium layer. Cambium produces new xylem and new phloem cells. Old xylem becomes wood and old phloem becomes bark in wood plants.

The turfgrass plant has a very compressed stem that's contained in the crown (Figure 3).

Leaves

A healthy leaf system is critical to the life of every plant. Any injury or reduction of the leaf system can be serious. At the beginning of the growing season, the leaves are all new and carbohydrate production is high. It has to be high to support the flush of growth that nearly every plant produces. Some southern plants may continue fairly high growth rates all summer, but growth rates of plants in the North may slow down as the days get warmer during the summer. In the fall, as a reaction to cooler temperatures and to photoperiod, food material from the leaves is stored in other plant parts to keep the plant alive through the winter.

Leaves do not last long. Deciduous trees keep theirs only one growing season, and by the end of the season they may show a lot of wear and tear. Grass leaves are constantly being replaced during the whole growth season. The grass plant always has some new leaves. Leaves of evergreen plants do not last long, either. Because they are not replaced all at once, it only seems that they last forever.

Seasonal Growth Cycles

Winter Annuals

These are annual plants that complete their life cycle over the winter. They come up from seed in early fall, grow through the fall, stay green but dormant during the winter and resume growth in the spring. They quickly produce flowers and seed. Their seed lays dormant through the hot summer.

Annual bluegrass follows this pattern, as do many weeds.

Summer Annuals

These plants complete their life cycles over the summer months. Their seed germinates in the spring, growth continues all summer; flowering and seed production are in the early fall. Their seed lies dormant all through the winter. Many annual flowers and weeds like crabgrass, goosegrass, etc. follow this pattern.

Cool-Season Grasses

These are perennial plants that have two favorable growth periods a year in most locations. Growth starts in the spring and remains at high levels until it gets too hot. These heat- sensitive plants escape heat damage by going into a summer dormancy. Food material manufactured and stored in the plant during the spring growing period are used to keep the plant alive during the hot summer. During their dormancy, lawns may turn brown. When the cooler weather returns in early fall, the plants renew growth using the food material which was stored last spring. Food material stored from fall growth gets the plants through the cold winter months. Lawns may or may not stay green all winter.

Warm-Season Grasses

The growth cycle of the southern grasses are nearly opposite that of the cool-season grasses. For warm-season grass, the green-up occurs in middle to late spring. They experience optimum growth through all the hot months. In the fall, their growth slows down. At this point in time, the plant is storing food material for the winter months. With freezing

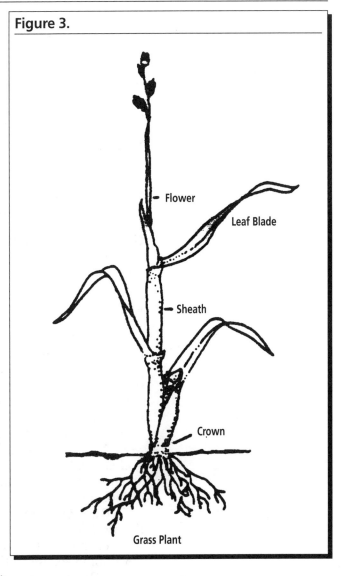

Figure 3.

Flower

Leaf Blade

Sheath

Crown

Grass Plant

weather, the southern grasses go completely dormant.

While warm-season turfgrasses are considered to be perennial, their root systems are annual. Each winter when the plant goes dormant, its root system stops functioning. In the spring, the southern grass plant must grow a new root system. It is critical that the plant store enough food material from the fall so that the plant can grow a new root system and an initial set of leaves in the spring.

Woody Plants

These plants follow the usual growth in summer, go-dormant-in-the-winter pattern. The deciduous plants drop all of their leaves each fall. Evergreen plants hold leaves all year. They drop their needles or leaves a few at a time, nearly all year around.

Growth Substances

Growth substances in plants are often naturally occurring (plant products). They stimulate growth or enhance growth in some way and thus are different from the materials identified as growth regulators. When present or when added in small amounts, hormones inhibit or promote certain physiological processes. These hormones are produced by a plant organ and then transported to a specific site where change in plant development takes place.

Both natural and synthetic growth substances regulate or influence cell division and differentiation (change to create different tissues), root and shoot growth, flowering, senescence and nucleic acid synthesis. Certain herbicides and fungicides affect growth through hormonal activity.

Five groups of growth substances have been identified:

AUXIN (Indole-3-acetic acid)—Promotes growth through cell division and elongation. Important in inhibiting leaf senescence and phloem and xylem tissue differentiation. Leaf primoirda and young leaves are the site of biosynthesis.

GIBBERELLINS (Gibberellic acid)—Promote stem elongation through cell division and cell elongation. These chemicals are classified according to structure rather than biological activity. Young tissue and developing seeds are the sites of biosynthesis.

CYTOKININ (Zeaton)—Promotes call division and delay of leaf senescence. A growth promoter in tissue culture. Root tips and developing seeds are the site of biosynthesis.

ETHYLENE—A gas that forms in tissue that is undergoing stress. Important in the ripening of fruit. Little known as to the effects on turfgrass.

ABSCISIC ACID—Considered an inhibitor of growth. Known to close stomates of plants under water stress. Counteracts some of the effects of auxins and gibberellins. Synthesizes in mature leaves usually under stress.

Growth of fine turf under ideal temperature and moisture conditions is not difficult. But when it's either too hot or too cold or too wet or too dry, stress develops within grass plants and causes trouble. Add to this stress additional unfavorable soil aeration from turf use and resulting soil compaction, and the net result is weakened grass plants. Careful fertilization and watering practices are necessary for turf to recover to a normal healthy condition. The fine-tuning of growth by appropriate use of growth regulators and growth substances throughout the season is beneficial. ❧

CHAPTER 3

Turfgrasses

Any grass plant that can survive regular mowing, at a reasonably low height, may be considered a turfgrass. Many plants in the grass family qualify as a turfgrass.

For the turfgrass plant to fulfill its mission of forming a dense, dark, green turf, it must be furnished with optimum or at least near-optimum growing conditions. Turfgrass is very sensitive to its environment, and any dramatic changes may severely limit its ability to survive.

Nearly all commonly-used turfgrass plants are perennials, living more than one or two growing seasons. They require nutrients, water, optimum temperature and air.

Two groups of turfgrasses are used for turf areas throughout the country (Figure 1 and Table I). These are the warm-season grasses, which have an optimum or ideal growing temperature of 80 degrees to 95 degrees F; and the cool-season grasses, which do best from 60 degrees to 75 degrees (Table 2).

These two groups of grasses react differently to the annual variation in temperatures (Figure 2). The cool-season grasses, because of their lower optimum temperature requirements, undergo high growth rates in the spring and the fall regardless of whether or not they are grown in the North or South.

Warm-season grasses experience peak growth period in the summer, when the cool-season grass growth rates are reduced. The season of high stress for the warm-season grass plant is winter while the period of high stress for the cool-season grass plant is the summer.

A plant reacts to many stress situations by entering a state of dormancy. It is normal for a warm-season grass plant to turn brown in early winter and remain brown or dormant until early to mid-spring. The plant is not dead, but has retreated to its growing points—basically its crown, stolons and rhizomes (Figure 3). The cool-season plant normally enters dormancy by turning brown during the heat of summer. When cool weather returns in the early fall, cool-season grass plants renew growth.

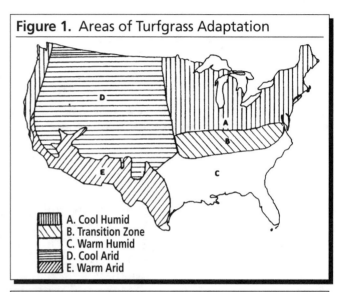

Figure 1. Areas of Turfgrass Adaptation

A. Cool Humid
B. Transition Zone
C. Warm Humid
D. Cool Arid
E. Warm Arid

Table 1. Turfgrasses

WARM-SEASON

Common Name	Scientific Name
Common Bermudagrass	Cynodon dactylon
Hybrid Bermudagrass	C. dactylon x C transvaalensis
St. Augustinegrass	Stenolaphrum secundatum
Zoysiagrass	Zoysia japonica or Z. tenuifolia
Centipedegrass	Eremochloa ophuroides
Bahiagrass	Paspalum notatum
Kikuyugrass	Pennisetum clandestinum
Buffalograss	Buchloe dactyloides
Paspalum	Paspalum vaginatum
Texas Bluegrass	Poa arachnifera

COOL-SEASON

Kentucky Bluegrass	Poa pratensis
Rough Bluegrass	Poa trivialis
Creeping Red Fescue	Festuca rubra ssp. rubra
Chewings Fescue	Festuca rubra ssp. cumnutata
Sheeps Fescue	Festuca ovina ssp. ovina
Hard Fescue	Festuca ovina ssp. cluriuscula
Tall Fescue	Festuca arundinacea
Blue Fescue	Fesruca ovina ssp. glaca
Perennial Ryegrass	Lolium perenne
Annual Ryegrass	Lolium multiflorum
Creeping Bentgrass	Agrostis palustris
Colonial Bentgrass	Agrostis tenuis
Velvet Bentgrass	Agrostis canina
Red Top	Agrostis alba

Table 2. Temperature Differences

	Warm-Season	Cool-Season
Ideal Shoot Growth	80-95°F	60-75°F
Ideal Root Growth	75-85°F	50-65°F
Upper Limit Shoot Growth	120°F	90°F
Upper Limit Root Growth	110°F	77°F
Lower Limit Shoot Growth	65°F	40°F
Lower Limit Root Growth	50°F	33°F

Figure 2. Seasonal Turfgrass Growth Pattern

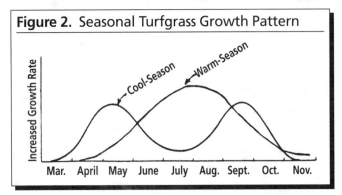

All the turfgrass plants spread in one or more of three ways (Figure 4 and Table 3). An above-ground lateral stem is called a stolon. A below-ground lateral stem is called a rhizome. Both structures are able to produce nodes which can produce a new plant. These lateral stems are organs that store carbohydrates for survival through periods of dormancy. Once favorable weather returns, the nodes produce new plants.

Tillering is the third type of vegetative reproduction. The new plant is produced at the base of the original. This is the slowest method of spreading. These grasses tend to form clumps and sometimes are called bunch grasses.

Warm-Season Grass

Bermudagrass

Bermudagrass originated in Africa, where it evolved under a fairly hot-dry climate. Bermudagrasses go dormant with the first cold weather in the fall and don't renew growth until soil temperatures get back up to at least 60 degrees Fahrenheit.

None of the bermudas have any significant shade tolerance, but thrive under full sun. They are the most popular turfgrass in the South. Bermudagrass varieties range in leaf texture from medium to fine. They grow in a wide variety of soils and are fairly salt tolerant. They will survive extended periods of low rainfall and will even survive some flooding.

More and more improved seeded bermuda varieties are being developed. Most seed is available in a hulled (hull removed) or in an unhulled (hull remains) form. Hulled bermuda germinates faster, but unhulled bermuda seed will last longer during unfavorable weather before it germinates. Several popular bermudagrass varieties do not produce seed and must be either sprigged or sodded.

Bermudagrass spreads by both stolons and rhizomes. They are all aggressive growers and need routine edging around sidewalks, trees and buildings.

St. Augustine

Compared to many other turfgrasses, St. Augustine varieties are more course textured, but are very shade tolerant. St. Augustinegrass proceeds a high quality turf in shady areas where other warm-season turfgrasses will not grow.

St. Augustinegrass is native to the coastal regions of both the Gulf of Mexico and the Mediterranean. Although far less cold tolerant than bermudagrass, it stays green longer after the first frost. It is not unusual to find green St. Augustinegrass in the winter in protected areas or under tree leaves. Planting range is limited by its lack of cold tolerance, which varies greatly among varieties. St. Augustine grows well in a wide range of soil types and generally prefers a soil with a near natural pH.

Figure 3. Diagram of a Grass Plant

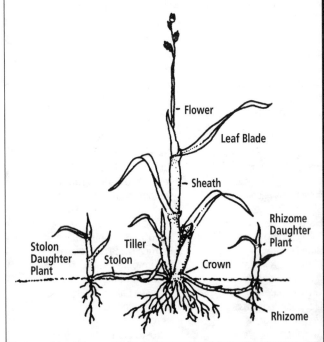

St. Augustine spreads by stolons. A few seeded St. Augustines tend to be the more dwarf types that also have poor cold tolerance.

St. Augustine has been plagued by a viral disease called St. Augustine Decline (SAD). Resistance has proven to be the best answer for the SAD problem. Breeding new varieties for resistance to chinch bug is also a high priority.

Centipedegrass

Centipedegrass was introduced from China. It spreads by stolons and has a leaf texture between that of St. Augustine and bermudagrass.

It is not as shade tolerant as St. Augustine, but more so than bermuda. Centipede has excellent drought tolerance, but low wear tolerance and a slow growth rate.

Bahiagrass

This South American turfgrass spreads by stolons and rhizomes. It has excellent drought tolerance, but forms what is considered a low-quality turf.

It is suitable for use on utility turf areas such as roadsides. One reason bahia is considered undesirable is that it produces tall seed heads after mowing.

Zoysiagrass

Zoysiagrass, native of the Orient, is not as shade tolerant as St. Augustine but has better shade tolerance by far than bermuda. Zoysia spreads by rhizomes and stolons but has a fairly low growth rate. If established with plugs, it may take up to two seasons to fill in, depending on the sprig or plug rate. As a rule of thumb, zoysia spreads about 6 inches a year.

Zoysia is used for tees and fairways on golf courses and for home lawns, especially in the transition zone. But its overall use is fairly limited.

Buffalograss

The only turfgrass native to the North American Great Plains, from Texas to Canada, buffalograss is a warm-season grass that spreads by stolons. It has fine blue-green leaf blades. It will not form a turf as dense as bermuda but, left unmowed, usually won't get more than 4 or 5 inches tall.

Buffalograss can survive extreme drought conditions but may turn brown during dry summer periods and green up again with rain. It can be used for golf course roughs or other low-maintenance areas. New improved buffalograss selections are being introduced and may be adaptable for home lawns. Buffalo has little shade tolerance.

Buffalograss is established from seed, called burrs, or from sod or plugs. The seeds are larger than other grass seed and overall production is low, making the price higher. Buffalograss is the only dioecious turf-

Table 3: Types of Lateral Stems

Variety	Rhizome	Stolon	Tiller
Bluegrass	X		
Bermudagrass	X	X	
Buffalograss		X	
Fescues			X
Ryegrass			X
Zoysiagrass	X	X	
Bentgrass		X	
St. Augustinegrass		X	
Centipedegrass		X	

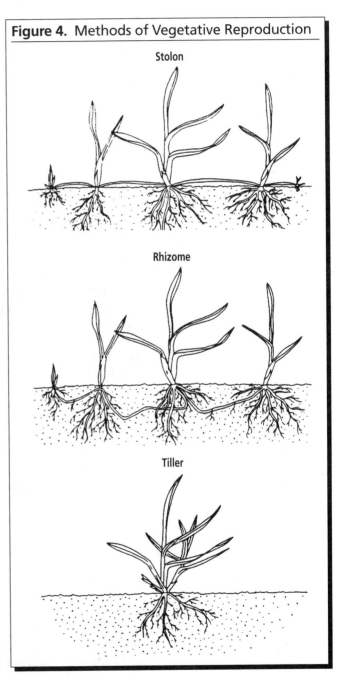

Figure 4. Methods of Vegetative Reproduction

Stolon

Rhizome

Tiller

grass—there are male and female plants. The male flower is produced on the end of a stalk, while the female flower is produced at the base of the plant.

Buffalograss has no particular insect or disease problems. Its biggest threat may be over-watering and over-fertilizing.

Tall Fescue

Tall fescue is a northern turfgrass tough enough to take southern summers if managed correctly. Additional information on tall fescue is included in the cool-season turfgrasses section of this book.

Tall fescue originated in Europe and is one of the most heat and drought tolerant of the cool-season grasses. It is a bunch grass that spreads by tillers, needs little edging and won't invade a flower or shrub bed.

Its greatest asset is its ability to grow well in fairly dense shade and survive winters in the upper South. It stays green all winter. Tall fescue grows best during spring and fall.

Long, hot summers give tall fescue its biggest test. Watering every three or four days during the summer to keep the soil cool should keep it from going into summer dormancy. More watering could increase potential for disease. Mowing at 2 inches or higher keeps the growing point cooler.

The old standard tall fescue variety has been Kentucky 31 and it's still available. There are now several new varieties with finer leaf blades and improved heat and shade tolerance. For best results, use a mixture of three or four new turf-type tall fescues.

Paspalum

Paspalum raginatum is from a family of grasses that also includes both bahiagrass and dallisgrass. This grass has a very high salt tolerance and may be used in fairways and roughs on courses with relatively high salt exposure.

Kikuyugrass

Kikuyugrass has found use on courses in selected areas even though most consider it a weed. It spreads by both stolons and rhizomes and is used mostly in hot, dry locations.

Texas Bluegrass

This is a true bluegrass that is native to west central Texas. It stays green all year around and seems to stand up well to the long, hot Texas summer. This turfgrass is currently in research. Named varieties may be available in a few years.

Cool-Season Turfgrass

Bentgrass

There are three distinct groups of bentgrass used mostly on golf courses. They are creeping bentgrass, colonial bentgrass and velvet bentgrass—all natives of Europe and Asia. Prostrate growth habit makes them ideal for golf course use. They have fairly high maintenance needs and some salt tolerance, but poor shade tolerance.

Creeping Bentgrass

This is by far the most popular of the bentgrasses. Creeping bentgrass is used for more putting greens than any other turfgrass. It spreads by stolons and may be maintained as low as 1/8 inch under ideal conditions.

The creeping bentgrasses may be divided into two groups: those established from seed, and those grown from sprigs or stolons. Over the years, Penncross has proven to be the most popular, but new seeded varieties are offering stiff competition. Efforts to develop a bentgrass with increased heat and disease tolerance, especially for use in the South, are under way.

Colonial Bentgrass

This bentgrass is more upright in growth form than creeping bentgrass and has been used on some courses in tees and fairways.

Velvet Bentgrass

Many consider that you've not played golf until you've putted on good velvet bentgrass greens. Velvet is one of the finest textured turfgrasses used for a putting surface. Its upright growth habit and fine blade leaves produce a very dense putting surface.

Unfortunately, its use is subject to specific climactic conditions. In fact, most of it is limited to upper New England and the Pacific Northwest.

Bluegrass

Kentucky Bluegrass

This is the "number one" cool-season turfgrass. It's a native of Europe and Asia and came to North America several hundred years ago. This turfgrass has been and is used for about every conceivable area, except golf course putting greens. Bluegrass will grow in some shade. Kentucky bluegrass spreads by rhizome and can be established from seed or sod.

Selective breeding programs have produced many varieties which vary widely in their characteristics. As many as 20 to 30 are available. Some are dwarf in growth pattern; some grow better than others in the shade, and so on. Breeding programs are trying to develop bluegrasses with more disease, insect, heat and drought resistance.

Each year, several new varieties make it to the market. Which is the best? That is a hard question. Many state universities with turf programs have test plots and turf field days. These are good places to evaluate new grasses.

Another approach is to use a blend of three or four different varieties. The turf will have the advantage of all the good attributes of the different bluegrasses and the good characteristics of one may offset negative characteristics of the others. Bluegrasses work well in a mixture. Not only can several bluegrasses be mixed, but bluegrass can also be used with any other cool-season, seeded turfgrass.

Rough (Poa trivialis)

This bluegrass is from northern Europe and differs considerably from Kentucky bluegrass, in that rough bluegrass spreads by stolons rather than by rhizomes like Kentucky bluegrass. It also grows better under cooler, wetter conditions than Kentucky bluegrass. Perhaps the most popular use of rough bluegrass, or as it is more commonly called, Poa trivialis, is to overseed dormant bermuda turf in the South.

Annual (Poa annua)

This turfgrass is about the only one classified as both a desirable turfgrass and a weed—perhaps more often referred to as a weed. This plant is a winter annual; it normally germinates in the early fall, lives through the winter, produces seed in early spring and then dies. The problem is if the summer isn't too hot and dry, annual may perform more like a perennial. It may not die and can become a weed.

Annual bluegrass can form a very dense turf, making it ideal for use on golf courses. Some northern golf courses rely almost totally on annual bluegrass turf. As long as the summer remains cool, this grass does well. But if the weather turns hot, and especially when accompanied by high humidity, there is a great chance this grass will die, and die very quickly.

Ryegrass

Perennial

This is a short-lived perennial bunch grass with a variety of uses. It has a fairly high wear resistance, making it desirable in seed mixtures for athletic fields. It also germinates as quickly as any turfgrass and is a good addition to a mixture. In this way, soil erosion can be controlled while the slower germinating turfgrasses become established. One of the main uses for perennial ryegrass is for overseeding dormant bermudagrass athletic fields, including bermuda putting greens in the South. Even whole golf courses may be overseeded.

Annual

Annual ryegrass is not used as much as it once was. It still may be used alone as a temporary turf for erosion control. Its highly aggressive seedling growth makes it undesirable for use in a mixture. Annual ryegrass may also be known as Italian ryegrass.

Tall Fescue

While tall fescue was included previously on warm season turfgrasses, it is a true cool-season turfgrass with very special qualities. Tall fescue has a fair amount of heat tolerance. It is also very drought tolerant and salt tolerant. It is a bunch grass that spreads by tillers and has some shade tolerance. Many newer turf-type tall fescues are on the market. Several of these may be used together in a mixture. Mixtures with Kentucky bluegrass are fairly common.

Fine Fescues

Several grasses could be called fine fescue. The most widely used is creeping red fescue. Red fescue has shade and drought tolerance, making it popular in seed mixtures. It has short rhizomes.

Another fine fescue, chewings fescue, is much like red, except it doesn't have rhizomes. Neither are seeded alone but are used with other cool-season turfgrasses such as Kentucky bluegrass.

Sheeps fescue, also a fine fescue, is a bunch grass with stiff, bluish-green leaves.

Festuca ovina var. glauca is commonly called blue fescue. This is an ornamental grass that forms about a six-inch ball of bluish, very narrow leaves. It is used only as an ornamental accent plant in the cool-season parts of the country. ❧

Check the **Seed Pocket Guide**
published every July in *Landscape Management* magazine
for a complete up-to-date listing of all commercially available varieties.

CHAPTER 4

Turfgrass Selection

There are dozens of different turfgrasses on the market. Some are very much alike, but some are very different. It's worth some effort to determine which will make the best turf for the purpose intended.

The best way to begin this selection process is to answer three basic questions:

What is the environment like? Sunny or shady? Are the soils acid or alkaline? Does it get extremely cold or extremely hot? Check the lists on this page plus pages 18 and 19. Note how the turfgrasses differ in their reaction to these different environmental factors.

What is the function of the turf? As an example, sports activities require a very low-cut turf, so turfgrass that can take low mowing should be used. Also, a cultivar needed for a sports field should be fairly wear resistant.

What maintenance is involved? Some turfgrasses, because of the way they grow, or in some cases lack of disease or insect resistance, cost more to maintain. The presence or absence of an irrigation system can make a difference in the selection of a turfgrass. It's difficult to grow a turfgrass that has low drought resistance without an irrigation system. In deciding which turfgrass is best for a particular location or use, compare the strengths and weaknesses of all the available turfgrasses.

Step One
Location Evaluation

Geographic

Turfgrasses are divided into two main groups. One group is the Cool-Season Turfgrasses and they grow best in the Northern Zone (Table 1, page 11).

The other group is the Warm-Season Turfgrasses and they perform best in the Southern Zone. In addition, there is an area that runs roughly east-west across the country that, as far as turfgrasses are concerned, is neither north nor south, called the Transition Zone. Depending on geographic factors, either cool- and warm-season turfgrasses may be used.

The map identified as Figure 1 (chapter 3, page 11) is not "set in concrete". Over the years, there have been many maps drawn in an attempt to accurately define the areas that should be planted with cool-season turfgrasses and the areas that should have warm-season turfgrasses.

Table 1. Fertility Requirements

Warm-Season		Cool-Season	
Buffalo	Lo	Bentgrass	Hi
Centipede	Lo	Bluegrass	Med
Common Bermuda	Med-Hi	Fine Fescue	Lo
Hybrid Bermuda	Hi	Ryegrass	Med
St. Augustine	Med	Tall Fescue	Lo-Med
Tall Fescue	Med		
Zoysia	Lo-Med		

Table 2. Leaf Texture

Warm-Season		Cool-Season	
Buffalo	Fine	Bentgrass	Fine
Centipede	Med-Coarse	Bluegrass	Med
Common Bermuda	Med	Fine Fescue	Fine
Hybrid Bermuda	Fine	Ryegrass	Med
St. Augustine	Coarse	Tall Fescue	Med
Tall Fescue	Med		
Zoysia	Fine-Med		

Table 3. Shade Tolerance

Warm-Season		Cool-Season	
Buffalo	Lo	Bentgrass	Med
Centipede	Med-Hi	Bluegrass	Lo-Med
Common Bermuda	Lo	Fine Fescue	Hi
Hybrid Bermuda	Lo-Med	Ryegrass	Lo-Med
St. Augustine	Hi	Tall Fescue	Med
Tall Fescue	Hi		
Zoysia	Med-Hi		

Table 4. Wear Tolerance

Warm-Season		Cool-Season	
Buffalo	Med-Hi	Bentgrass	Lo
Centipede	Lo	Bluegrass	Med
Common Bermuda	Hi	Fine Fescue	Med
Hybrid Bermuda	Med-Hi	Ryegrass	Hi
St. Augustine	Lo	Tall Fescue	Med-Hi
Tall Fescue	Mead		
Zoysia	Hi		

Table 5. Mowing Height

Warm-Season		Cool-Season	
Buffalo	Hi	Bentgrass	Lo
Centipede	Med-Hi	Bluegrass	Med
Common Bermuda	Med	Fine Fescue	Med
Hybrid Bermuda	Lo	Ryegrass	Med
St. Augustine	Hi	Tall Fescue	Med
Tall Fescue	Hi		
Zoysia	Med		

Table 6. Cold Tolerance

Warm-Season		Cool-Season	
Buffalo	Hi	Bentgrass	Lo
Centipede	Med-Hi	Bluegrass	Med
Common Bermuda	Med	Fine Fescue	Med-Hi
Hybrid Bermuda	Lo-Med	Ryegrass	Med
St. Augustine	Lo	Tall Fescue	Hi
Tall Fescue	Hi		
Zoysia	Hi		

Table 7. Heat Tolerance

Warm-Season		Cool-Season	
Buffalo	Hi	Bentgrass	Hi
Centipede	Hi	Bluegrass	Med
Common Bermuda	Hi	Fine Fescue	Lo-Med
Hybrid Bermuda	Hi	Ryegrass	Lo-Med
St. Augustine	Hi	Tall Fescue	Hi
Tall Fescue	Med		
Zoysia	Hi		

Table 8. Drought Tolerance

Warm-Season		Cool-Season	
Buffalo	Hi	Bentgrass	Lo
Centipede	Lo-Med	Bluegrass	Med
Common Bermuda	Med-Hi	Fine Fescue	Hi
Hybrid Bermuda	Lo-Med	Ryegrass	Lo-Med
St. Augustine	Med	Tall Fescue	Hi
Tall Fescue	Lo		
Zoysia	Med-Hi		

Table 9. Thatching Tendency

Warm-Season		Cool-Season	
Buffalo	Lo	Bentgrass	Hi
Centipede	Med	Bluegrass	Lo-Med
Common Bermuda	Lo	Fine Fescue	Lo-Med
Hybrid Bermuda	Hi	Ryegrass	Lo
St. Augustine	Med-Hi	Tall Fescue	Lo
Tall Fescue	Lo		
Zoysia	Med-Hi		

This has proven to be an impossible task. If you are clearly located in the cool- or in the warm-season zones, the selection process will be fairly easy. An exception—the the reason that it is difficult to draw an accurate zone map for the western United States—is elevation. There are some locations in the East, as well as the West, that are clearly in the warm-season zone that, because of elevation, are better suited for cool-season grasses. Consider the optimum temperature ranges for the grass groups when making your choice.

Environment

All turfgrasses grow well in the sun, but not all do well in the shade (Table 3). Since most residential environments have some degree of shade, turfgrass selection can be critical. The term "shade" has no set definition. It can describe an area that is shaded by tree leaves for a brief period or areas that never receive any sunlight. Shade can be heavy enough so there aren't any turfgrasses that can survive.

All turfgrasses can live for a brief period in the shade. Those turfgrass stands that are not tolerant of shade quickly lose density. It takes about six hours of full sun to satisfy the needs of most turfgrasses. Any area receiving less than six hours of full sun should be established with one or more of the more shade-tolerant grasses.

Temperature extremes, both hot and cold, can be a problem for many turfgrasses and should be considered in the selection process (Tables 6 and 7). Water may be limited in many parts of the country (Table 8).

Soil

Most turfgrasses grow better in soils that are slightly acidic (pH 6.5). Some will tolerate soils that have a higher or lower pH (Table 10). There are parts of the country that have salt problems. If a soil test identifies a potential salt problem, select a turfgrass that has the highest tolerance (Table 11).

Other Considerations

THATCH—Some turfgrasses are capable of producing thatch. Thatch-producing turfgrasses may be more costly to maintain than those listed as having a "low" thatch tendency (Table 9).

FERTILITY—Some turfgrasses require relatively higher levels of nutrients to perform at optimum levels than others. In low maintenance situations, use turfgrasses that have low fertility requirements (Table 1).

TEXTURE—The width of the turfgrass plant's leaf may play a role in determining a turf's aesthetic appeal. Generally, turf made up of the finer-bladed grasses is considered to be of higher aesthetic value than lawns made up of course-bladed turfgrass (Table 2).

TRAFFIC—Turfgrasses are used for many sports fields and other highly-trafficked areas. Turfgrasses used for home lawns that occasionally support games should be established with some of the more wear-resistant varieties (Table 4).

HEIGHT-OF-CUT—Some activities require that the turf be cut as low as possible. If low mowing is necessary, select a turfgrass that performs best at the lower heights (Table 5).

MAINTENANCE LEVEL—In areas designed to receive low levels of maintenance, select turfgrasses that have low fertility needs (Table 1) and are as drought tolerant as possible (Table 8).

STEP TWO
Turfgrass Selection

There are four basic environmental or use situations that may be used to help select the best turfgrasses for turf areas. These are sun, shade, athletic and low maintenance. Suggestions are listed for each of these in all three turfgrass zones.

The North
(Cool-Season Turfgrasses)

SUN
Basic cultivar suggestions for completely sunny areas are:

1. Kentucky Bluegrass (single variety).
2. Kentucky Bluegrass (blend of varieties).
   NOTE: It is generally more advisable to use a blend of 3 or 4 different varieties than a single variety.
3. *Tall Fescue (single or blend of varieties).
   Kentucky Bluegrass (single variety).
   NOTE: Use in areas where tall fescue might perform better than Kentucky bluegrass.
   *Final mixture should be over 50 percent.

SHADE
There are two basic suggestions for shaded areas:

1. *Kentucky Bluegrass (single or blend of varieties).
   Creeping Red Fescue.
   Chewings Fescue.
2. *Tall Fescue (single or blend of varieties).
   Kentucky Bluegrass.
   NOTE: Use in drier or hotter shaded areas.
   *Final mixture should be over 50 percent.

ATHLETIC
Athletic and other high-traffic areas may be established using one of the following two suggestions:

1. *Kentucky bluegrass (blend of varieties).
   Perennial Ryegrass.
   NOTE: Use for lower use, but high aesthetic value fields.
   *Final mixture should be over 50 percent.

Table 10. Tolerance to Acid Soils

Warm-Season		Cool-Season	
Buffalo	Lo	Bentgrass	Med-Hi
Centipede	Hi	Bluegrass	Med
Common Bermuda	Med	Fine Fescue	Med-Hi
Hybrid Bermuda	Med	Ryegrass	Med
St. Augustine	Lo	Tall Fescue	Hi
Tall Fescue	Hi		
Zoysia	Lo-Med		

Table 11. Salinity Tolerance

Warm-Season		Cool-Season	
Buffalo	Hi	Bentgrass	Hi
Centipede	Lo-Med	Bluegrass	Med
Common Bermuda	Hi	Fine Fescue	Med
Hybrid Bermuda	Hi	Ryegrass	Med-Hi
St. Augustine	Hi	Tall Fescue	Hi
Tall Fescue	Hi		
Zoysia	Hi		

2. *Tall Fescue (blend of varieties).
   Perennial Ryegrass.
   Kentucky Bluegrass (at least 10 percent).
   NOTE: Use for the higher use fields.
   *Final mixture should be over 50 percent.

LOW MAINTENANCE

There are many turf areas that will receive minimum care. These areas should be established using the following:
   1. *Tall Fescue (blend of varieties).
   Creeping Red Fescue.
   Chewings Fescue.
   *Final mixture should be over 50 percent.

The South
(Warm-Season Turfgrasses)

SUN

There are several different turfgrasses that can be used in sunny locations:
1. Tall Fescue (single or blend of varieties in the upper South.
2. Common Bermuda (single variety).
3. Hybrid Bermuda (single variety).
4. St. Augustine (single variety in mid- to lower-south).
5. Centipede (single variety—better on acidic soil).
6. Buffalograss (single or blend of varieties—dry environments).
7. Zoysia (single variety—upper South).

SHADE
1. St. Augustine (single variety—mid to lower South).
2. Tall Fescue (blend of varieties—upper South).
3. Centipede (single variety).
4. Zoysia (single variety).

ATHLETIC
1. Common Bermuda (single variety).
2. Hybrid Bermuda (single variety).

LOW MAINTENANCE
1. Buffalograss (areas of lower humidity).
2. Common Bermuda (single variety).

OVERSEEDING DORMANT TURF
1. Perennial Ryegrass (blend of several varieties).
2. Poa Trivialis (rough bluegrass).

The Transition Zone
(Cool- and Warm-Season Turfgrasses)

SUN
1. Kentucky Bluegrass (blend of varieties).
   NOTE: Use in northern parts of zone or in higher elevations.
2. *Tall Fescue (blend of varieties).
   Kentucky Bluegrass.
3. Zoysia (single variety).
4. Common Bermuda (single variety).
   NOTE: Use in southern parts of zone.

SHADE
1. *Tall Fescue (blend of several varieties).
   Kentucky Bluegrass.
2. Kentucky Bluegrass (blend of several varieties).
   Creeping Red Fescue.
   Chewings Fescue.
   NOTE: Use in northern part of zone or in higher elevation.
3. Zoysia (single variety).
   *Should make up over 50 percent of mixture.

ATHLETIC
1. *Tall Fescue (blend of varieties).
   Kentucky Bluegrass.
   NOTE: Use in northern part of zone or in higher elevations.
2. *Kentucky Bluegrass (blend of several varieties).
   Perennial Ryegrass (blend of several varieties).
3. Common Bermuda (single variety).
   NOTE: Use in southern part of zone.
   *Should make up 50 percent of mixture by weight.

LOW MAINTENANCE
1. Buffalograss (single variety—in areas of low humidity).
2. Common Bermuda (single variety).
   NOTE: Use in southern part of zone.
3. *Tall Fescue.
   Hard Fescue.
   Chewings Fescue.
   NOTE: Use in northern part of zone or in higher elevations.
   *Should make up at least 50 percent of mixture by weight.

Step Three
Select Specific Varieties
This is the final process in selecting the best turfgrass or turfgrasses for a given situation. Each turfgrass has from a few to a few dozen different commercially-available cultivars or varieties. Even though specific varieties are of the same species, they may perform very differently. Evaluate the characteristics of each variety before making a final choice. Check the **Seed Pocket Guide** published every July in *Landscape Management* magazine for a complete up-to-date listing of all commercially available varieties.

Summary Of Suggested Selection Process

Step One
Determine the geographic location by turfgrass adaptation zone.
The North
The South
The Transition Zone

Step Two
Determine specific environment from:
a. Sunny
b. Shade
c. Athletic
d. Low Maintenance

Step Three
Select specific varieties or cultivars identified in STEP TWO.

Table 12. Optimum Germination Termperature Comparison	
Tall Fescue	Highest
Creeping Bentgrass	
Rough Bluegrass	
Perennial Ryegrass	
Chewings Fescue	
Annual Ryegrass	
Cereal Rye	Lowest

Seed Timing/Temporary Lawns

The cool-season turfgrasses do best when seeded in late summer to early fall. Second-best is early to mid-spring.

Newly-established warm-season turfgrasses need the warm days of late spring and early summer to get a good start. After mid-summer, the young, warm-season turfgrasses may have a hard time surviving their first winter, depending on how cold it gets, how fast it gets cold and how long it stays cold.

Many turf areas are completed outside the ideal seeding periods and need erosion protection. The weather window for sodding is much larger. Sod can be laid almost any time of the year, although it is not ideal to place sod on frozen soil or one freezing at night and thawing in the day.

Turfgrasses have different optimum germination temperatures, but the temperature at which most seed is stored is 40 degrees F. When temperatures get that low, seed won't germinate. The lowest optimum germination temperatures apply to the cereal grasses (Table 12). This means that as the days get cooler before freezing temperatures, grasses lower on the list (Table 12) should be used. The bottom line is that if it is too cool for cereal rye to germinate, nothing else will, either. There are many temporary cereal rye lawns each winter. In the spring, when it is time to seed the permanent turfgrasses, the rye is killed chemically or culturally by very low mowing.

Mixtures

It is unusual that any one turfgrass variety can be a perfect fit for any particular environment or use. More than likely, it will be desirable to select several different turfgrasses or several different varieties to meet wide environmental and use requirements.

The best approach is to develop a mixture of grasses based on desirable characteristics. Chances are, at least one of the grasses will be able to perform well under any condition. For example, if the turf will have shaded areas, including a turfgrass or two that tolerate shade makes sense. If the new turf will receive traffic, include a turfgrass with high wear resistance.

Another advantage of using mixtures is that turfgrasses vary in resistance to disease and insects. When several different turfgrasses are present in a turf, the chance that they all will be infected with a particular disease is reduced.

Any turfgrass that spreads by rhizomes or by tillers can be used in a mixture. Those that spread by stolons, regardless if they are established from seed, can not be a part of a mixture. Stoloniferous grasses do not mix well. They tend to segregate. That is, each will tend to form a solid patch and the turf will exhibit a patchwork pattern rather than forming a homogeneous surface. ❦

CHAPTER 5

Turfgrass Establishment

Turfgrass Establishment

Four basic methods are commonly used to establish turf: seed; plugs; sod; or sprigs or stolons.

Regardless of the establishment method, seedbed, sodbed or sprigbed preparation is the same. Plugs are planted individually and extensive soil preparation is not necessary. A soil test should be used to determine the rate and analysis of fertilizer to be worked into the seedbed. A fine firm soil surface is necessary for successful establishment.

Turfgrass Establishment Steps

SOIL TEST—Get a soil test kit at the local county extension office and follow the directions. Use this information to determine the proper fertilizer and rate. The test also will determine if the soil pH needs adjusting.

WEED CONTROL—Most annual weeds will be controlled when the soil is tilled. Any perennial weeds should be controlled with a post-emergence herbicide.

REMOVE ROCKS AND OTHER DEBRIS—Any material more than 1/2 inch in size can become a problem. Large concentrations of buried organic material can support fungal growth such as "fairy ring."

APPLY FERTILIZER—Apply the fertilizer indicated by the soil test. In the absence of a soil test, a high phosphorus fertilizer should be applied at a rate of two to three pounds of P2O5 per 1,000 square feet. Also apply any materials indicated for soil pH adjustment.

TILL—Tilling does several things. It works the fertilizer and pH control materials into the soil; it helps new roots grow; the loose surface also makes it easier to smooth and level.

RAKE—Rake the tilled soil to remove debris brought to the surface during tilling.

APPLY SEED, SPRIGS, SOD OR PLUGS—The least expensive way to establish turf is by seeding. The best germination temperature for cool-season turfgrasses is from 60 degrees to 85 degrees (F). The best time to seed cool-season turfgrasses is in late summer to early fall. The next best is mid-to-late spring, but it's better to seed in early fall as the soils are cooling down. New roots of cool-season grasses do not grow well in warm soil.

Warm-season turfgrasses are opposite of the cool-season grasses in reaction to temperature. The best temperature range for warm-season grass germination is from 70 degrees to 95 degrees (F). Early summer is the best time to seed common bermudagrass and to sprig or sod other warm-season turfgrasses, although it is possible to sod nearly anytime of the year.

Seed quality can be evaluated by reading the seed test information that every seed container must have. The seed test date should be current. Germination and purity should be as high as possible with a low weed and inert matter content. Buying certified seed insures the specified is being bought. Using seed treated with a fungicide or applying a fungicide shortly after seed application will help prevent loss from one of the damping-off diseases. Use a fungicide labeled for control of damping off. The most common disease is Pythium.

RAKE AND ROLL—Raking the newly-seeded area helps move the seed into the soil. Seed, sod or sprigs need good soil contact for best germination, and using a light roller will help. Rolling sod also helps eliminate air pockets.

WATER—A new seeding or sprigging must be kept moist by fairly frequent, light waterings until the new root system has developed. This may take several weeks. Do not continue this frequent watering any longer than necessary. Sod and plugs must be heavily soaked so that the soil underneath is completely wet. New roots will not grow in dry soil.

MOWING—Mow as soon as the grass gets high enough to cut at its optimum height. Generally, the more often it's cut, the faster the turf forms a dense surface.

WEED CONTROL—Any new annual weeds should be controlled by mowing. Hopefully, any perennial weeds were controlled earlier. Chemical weed control during the first year is discouraged.

Soil Fumigation

Soil fumigation is usually recommended to control and eliminate weeds, weed seed, soil insects, nematodes and soil-borne diseases. Methyl bromide is the most versatile fumigant available. Dosage will vary depending on target organisms, soil type and method of application. Methyl bromide must be confined to the soil after application and is covered with polyethylene film before or during application–again, depending on the method of application used.

Methyl bromide can be a dangerous compound, so care must be taken in handling. It is a restricted-use chemical and must be applied by experienced personnel, licensed and certified in turf fumigation.

Methyl bromide will kill almost all organisms it contacts. Providing the proper dosage is applied and the time of exposure is sufficient, most weed seeds, plant pathogenic fungi and bacteria, and parasitic nematodes will be killed.

Fumigation is the last step prior to seeding, sprigging or sodding. Proper soil preparation is important. The soil must be loose and porous for the gas to diffuse laterally and vertically. On golf course greens and tees, all shaping should be done prior to fumigation to reduce the chance of recontamination; care should be taken to prevent transporting non-fumigated materials into fumigated areas.

One important, very beneficial side effect from methyl bromide use is increased growth response. Test plots have shown significant results in a shorter grow-in period of fumigated areas opposed to areas not fumigated. This, in addition to the other benefits of fumigation, make it one of the most important steps in establishment of new turf.

Methods of Fumigation

Companies specializing in soil fumigation should be knowledgeable about and equipped to apply methyl bromide using either injection or hot gas application.

It is important that the proper method be used for the treatment to be successful and yet not damage the area to be fumigated or the areas surrounding it. Both methods are equally effective if the application is done correctly, the equipment is up to date and well maintained, and the personnel is experienced in both methods.

For golf course greens and tees and small landscaping sites, the applicator must be sure the area to be treated is adequately fumigated without damage to surrounding areas. If plastic liners are in place on a green, fumigate all areas of the green without damaging the liner. If the area surrounding the green has existing sod or has recently been planted, take care not to damage this area. Access to a green might restrict use of the injection method, which involves bringing a tractor onto the finished green. In many cases, the hot gas method is recommended and preferred on greens, tees or small areas.

Injection is performed with a specially designed, tractor-mounted machine. The methyl bromide is injected into the soil through shanks which are lowered into the soil. The machine also applies the tarp at the same time the gas is injected. Injection works well on large areas or where access is easy.

The hot gas method is performed by placing plastic hoses evenly spaced across the area to be fumigated. A trench is dug around the perimeter of the area. The tarping material is placed across the area and is sealed. Methyl bromide is introduced into a heat exchanger through a five pound calibrated "Shore" measuring device which insures a precise level of chemical is applied. Hot gas works well on small, confined areas and does not damage areas prepared for planting, since it does not require any equipment on the area.

Pre-Treating/Pre-Germinating Seed

Some turfgrass seeds take a fairly long time to germinate. There are times when it's desirable to speed up the process. Overseeding the thin turf of an athletic field between events or needing to get a stand of grass to prevent erosion are a couple of examples.

For a seed to germinate, water must get in through the seed coat. Pre-germinating seed is simply soaking the seed in water before it's applied to the soil.

One technique involves soaking the seed only until it begins to swell. Before the root and the shoot emerge, the seed is dried just long enough to apply it.

The fastest way to get a stand of grass is to carry the soaking process one step further. Continue to soak until the shoot and the root are seen coming through the seed coat. This pre-germinated seed must be handled very carefully and must not be allowed to get too dry. It has to be dry enough to spread but not dry enough to kill it.

The water used in the soaking process should be changed at least every 8 hours. The seed coat contains a chemical that inhibits germination. This chemical is soluble in water, and slowly the chemical soaks out of the seed coat. Changing the water gets rid of the chemical completely. The temperature of the water should be in the 75-80 degree range. Seeds need oxygen in the germination process, so some kind of aerifier in the soaking tank will help.

The two most commonly-used materials that are used as a carrier for pre-germinated seed are sand or an organic fertilizer.

Many seeds and young plants may be lost to disease. The seed bed must be kept moist to support germination, but this high level of moisture may also support one of the damping-off diseases caused by fungi. By pre-treating seed with a fungicide, disease chances are greatly reduced.

Coating each seed with a fertilizer is also a treatment option. Research has shown that the germinating seed needs to have an optimum supply of phosphorus available. The other nutrients are important, but the presence of phosphorus is especially critical. Phosphorus is nearly immobile in the soil and may be a fraction of an inch away from the seed and never be available. Very high rates of phosphorus fertilizer are usually recommended for seed or sod beds. The high rates help assure that the seed and phosphorus will be in close contact. A seed coated with phosphorus has a better chance for successful germination.

Treated seed is more expensive, but, considering the risks of losing a stand, treatment may be well worth the cost.

Seed Quality and Seeding Rate Calculations

The goal of seeding is to establish 1,000 turfgrass plants per square foot.

The first factor to consider is the seed label (Figure 1). Each state has laws regulating the sale of turfgrass seeds. In general, each state requires that certain information be listed on the seed container. It may be printed on the box or on a tag attached to the container. The information usually includes the following:

- The name of the seed producer or seller.
- The seed lot number.
- The seed variety (sometimes including the scientific name).
- The percent purity.
- The percent germination
- The percentage of any weed or crop seed present.
- The percentage of any non-seed material present, expressed as inert matter.
- A list by variety of any noxious weeds present and their rate of occurrence (usually number of seeds per pound).
- The date when the seed was last tested for germination.

All the above information is important when evaluating the purity of any seed. The purity and germination number should be as high as possible and the other numbers (weed, crop seed present, etc.) should be as low as possible. These are physical measurements of quality, but there is one other quality question. Since all bluegrass seed looks the same and all tall fescue seed looks nearly the same, how does the buyer know the seed is the variety stated on the label? Usually, there is really nothing to worry about, but there is a way to make sure to get the desired variety—certification (Figure 2).

Sample Calculations

How much Kentucky bluegrass seed is required to seed an area of 20,000 square feet, if the goal is to establish 1000 plants per square feet?

a. The first step is to determine the purity and germination (from the seed label) of the seed intended for use. The sample seed label indicates a purity of 95% and a germination of 80%. Purity X germination equals the percent of pure live seed (PLS) present in that seed lot.

95 percent X 80 percent = 76 percent PLS

This means that 76 percent of the seed in that lot is capable of germinating.

b. Next, determine from Table 1 the approximate number of seeds per pound of Kentucky bluegrass (2,200,000). Multiply the number of seeds per pound (2,200,000) by the PLS percentage.

0.76 (76 percent) X 2,200,000 = 1,672,000 PLS/lb

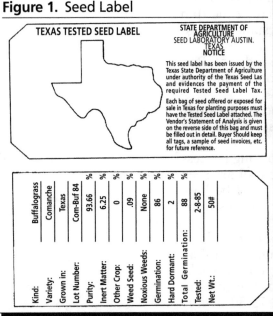

Figure 1. Seed Label

TEXAS TESTED SEED LABEL

STATE DEPARTMENT OF AGRICULTURE
SEED LABORATORY AUSTIN. TEXAS.
NOTICE

This seed label has been issued by the Texas State Department of Agriculture under authority of the Texas Seed Las and evidences the payment of the required Tested Seed Label Tax.

Each bag of seed offered or exposed for sale in Texas for planting purposes must have the Tested Seed Label attached. The Vendor's Statement of Analysis is given on the reverse side of this bag and must be filled out in detail. Buyer Should keep all tags, a sample of seed invoices, etc. for future reference.

Kind:	Buffalograss
Variety:	Comanche
Grown in:	Texas
Lot Number:	Com-Buf 84
Purity:	93.66 %
Inert Matter:	6.25 %
Other Crop:	0 %
Weed Seed:	.09 %
Noxious Weeds:	None %
Germination:	86 %
Hard Dormant:	2 %
Total Germination:	88 %
Tested:	2-8-85
Net Wt.:	50#

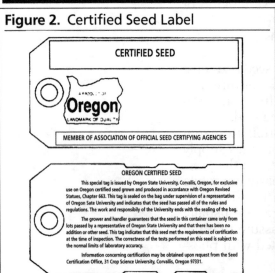

Figure 2. Certified Seed Label

CERTIFIED SEED

Oregon
LANDMARK OF QUALITY

MEMBER OF ASSOCIATION OF OFFICIAL SEED CERTIFYING AGENCIES

OREGON CERTIFIED SEED

This special tag is issued by Oregon State University, Corvallis, Oregon, for exclusive use on Oregon certified seed grown and produced in accordance with Oregon Revised Statues, Chapter 663. This tag is sealed on the bag under supervision of a representative of Oregon Sate University and indicates that the seed has passed all of the rules and regulations. The work and responsibly of the University ends with the sealing of the bag.

The grower and handler guarantees that the seed in this container came only from lots passed by a representative of Oregon State University and that there has been no addition or other seed. This tag indicates that this seed met the requirements of certification at the time of inspection. The correctness of the tests performed on this seed is subject to the normal limits of laboratory accuracy.

Information concerning certification may be obtained upon request from the Seed Certification Office, 31 Crop Science University, Corvallis, Oregon 97331.

c. The next step is to estimate how much of the planted seed will grow to mature plants. Seeds and young plants may be lost for a variety of reasons including, disease, planting too deeply or even to birds. Even with the best planting techniques, a loss of 25 percent is not unusual. Multiply the number of pure live seeds determined in step B by 0.75 (since 0.25 or 25 percent will be lost then 0.75 or 75 percent will survive).
0.75 X 1,672,000 PLS/lb. = 1,254,000 seeds per lb. should grow into mature grass plants

d. Assume that the goal is to establish 1,000 plants per square feet. To seed an area of 20,000 square feet, 20,000 X 1,000 total plants will be needed.
20,000 sq. ft. X 1,000 plants/sq.ft.—20,000,000 plants required

e. Since 1 pound of seed from step C will provide 1,254,000 plants, we need to divide that into the 20,000,000 plants required.
20,000,000 plants ÷ 1,254,000 plants/pound = 16 lbs. of seed
This means that 16 pounds of a Kentucky bluegrass seed having a 95 percent purity and 80 percent germination should establish 1,000 plants per square feet over a 20,000 square foot area, assuming a loss of no more than 25 percent in the seed bed.
NOTE: The same procedure may be used to calculate the seeding rate for any other turfgrass species. Use the purity and germination from the seed tag. Use the appropriate number of seeds per pound of the species you are seeding (from Table 1).
It may be desirable to establish a higher seedling density than 1,000 plants per square feet when seeding smaller-seeded species, such as bentgrass. If so, use a higher number in step C of the procedure.

Summary of Procedure for Determining Seeding Rate
a. Purity X germination = percent PLS
b. PLS X number of seeds per lb. = PLS per lb.
c. PLS X estimated seed loss during germination = number of plants that should grow
d. Area to be seeded (in sq. ft.) X desired number of plants per sq. ft. = total number of plants required
e. Number of seeds or plants that should survive (from step c) divided into the total number of plants required (from step d) = pounds of seed

Seeding Rate for Mixtures
There are two ways to determine the seeding rate when mixtures of several different turfgrasses are used.

The most commonly-used method is by weight. A box containing 10 pounds of a 50 percent Kentucky bluegrass, 25 percent creeping red fescue and 25 percent perennial ryegrass simply has 5 pounds of Kentucky bluegrass, 2.5 pounds of creeping red fescue and 2.5 pounds of perennial ryegrass. If we wanted to seed a 10,000 square foot lawn, we would end up with turfgrass population in Example A. The final population percentage is very different from the percentage on the seed label because the turfgrasses donít all have the same number of seeds per pound (Table 1). This method of calculating seed rates is by weight.

If we want to establish a lawn that will have a plant population of 50 percent Kentucky bluegrass, 25 percent creeping red fescue and 25 percent perennial ryegrass, then follow the method of Example B. This method considers the difference in seed weight to determine the final amounts of seed.

Table 1. Approximate Number of Seeds per Pound	
Turfgrass	**Seeds/Pound**
WARM-SEASON	
Buffalograss	50,000
Centipedegrass	400,000
Common Bermudagrass	1,800,000
COOL-SEASON	
Bentgrass	8,000,000
Bluegrass	2,200,000
Fine Fescue	500,000
Ryegrass	225,000
Tall Fescue	225,000

Sod

Any turfgrass that spreads by a rhizome or a stolon can be grown and harvested as sod. The best time to sod is when the turfgrass is actively growing. This means the sod will root or knit down as quickly as possible. As with seed, certified sod is available and is the only certainty that the buyer is getting the stated variety.

A potential problem associated with sod is the possible effect of a different soil type in the sod field and at the new site, especially if the sod is grown on a soil that contains a higher amount of clay and silt. A thin layer of soil different physically from the underlying soil could interfere with water drainage. A good core aerification program can help reduce the problem.

Different soil types can be especially troublesome when sodding a high-sand golf green or athletic field. Sod selected for these areas must be grown on soil as close as possible, physically, to the soil mixture used for construction. This is why greens are usually seeded. It's also very hard to lay sod so the surface is absolutely smooth. A number of top-dressings are necessary over the new sod to produce a puttable surface. Soils on most other turf areas usually have enough clay that the sod layer problem is not an issue.

Sprigs

Some turfgrasses spread by stolons, which may be harvested and used to establish a new turf. The cost of sprigging falls between the cost of seeding and the cost of sodding.

Sprigs are sold by the bushel. A bushel of sprigs is one square yard of sod, shredded. The rate used to establish both bentgrass and bermudagrass greens is around 10 to 12 bushels per 1,000 square feet. Tees would use the same rate, and for large areas—fairways and athletic fields—about 200 bushels per acre should be used.

Example A: Seed Rate By Weight

How much of the following mixture is needed to seed a 10,000 square foot lawn?
  50% Kentucky bluegrass
  25% Creeping red fescue
  25% Perennial ryegrass

10,000 feet^2 x 1,000 plant/ft^2 = 10,000,000 plants
1 lb KBG = 2,200,000 seeds x 95% purity x 75% germ. = 1,567,500 PLS
1 lb CRF = 500,000 seeds x 95% purity x 85% germ. =
  403,750 PLS

  1 lb PR = 225,000 seeds x 97% purity x 85% germ. =
    185,551 PLS
  1,567,500 Pure live KBG seeds/lb
  403,750 Pure live CRF seeds/lb
  185,551 Pure live PR seeds/lb
  2,156,801/3 = 718,933 PLS/lb

718,933 PLS/lb x 75% (25% seedling loss) = 539,200
potential plants/lb

  10,000,000 plants ÷ 539,200 plants/lb = 18.5 lbs of mixture

You will end up with a lawn that has:
  72.6% Kentucky bluegrass plants
  18.8% Creeping red fescue plants
  8.6% Perennial ryegrass plants

Example B: Seed Rate By Plant Population

How much of the following mixture is needed to seed a 10,000 square foot lawn to get the following distribution of grasses?
    50% Kentucky bluegrass
    25% Creeping red fescue
    25% Perennial ryegrass

10,000 feet^2 x 1,000 plant/ft^2 = 10,000,000
    Need: 5,000,000 Kentrucky bluegrass plants
        2,500,000 Creeping red fescue plants
        2,500,000 Perennial ryegrass plants

Kentucky bluegrass: 2,200,000 seeds/lb x 95% purity x 75%
    germination = 1,567,500 pure live plants/lb
    1,567,500 PLP/lb x 75% (25% seedling loss) = 1,175,625 potential plants/lb seed
    Need: 5,000,000 Kentucky bluegrass plants
        1,175,625 plants/lb of seed   or **4.25 lbs of seed**

Creeping red fescue: 500,000 seeds/lb x 95% purity x 85%
    germination = 403,750 pure live plants/lb
    403,750 PLP/lb x 75% (25% seedling loss) = 302,812 potential plants/lb seed
    Need: 2,500,000 Creeping red fescue plants
        302,812 plants/lb of seed   or **8.25 lbs of seed**

Perennial ryegrass: 225,000 seed/lb x 97% purity x 85%
    germination = 185,512 pure live plants/lb
    185,512 PLP/lb x 75% (25% seedling loss) = 139,134 potential plants/lb seed
    Need: 2,500,000 perennial ryegrass plants
        139,134 plants/lb of seed   or **18 lbs of seed,**

So: 4.25 lbs KBG seed, 8.25 lbs CRF seed and 18 lbs PR seed is needed to establish a 10,000 ft^2 lawn, with 1/2 of the grass plants Kentucky bluegrass, 1/4 Creeping red fescue & 1/4 Perennial ryegrass.

The higher the sprigging rate, the faster the establishment. A good rate for small areas such as home lawns is four or five bushels per 1,000 square feet.

Sprigging is the most common way that non-seeded bermudagrasses are established. Also, some of the older bentgrass varieties do not produce seed and must be sprigged. In certain situations, turfgrasses may not produce enough seed to be profitable, or the seed may not "come true" (the plant produced from the seed will not necessarily look or act like the plant that produced the seed). Sprigging buffalograss has not been satisfactory.

Overseeding

The technique of overseeding may be used for several reasons. It may be necessary to increase the density of a turf. Overseeding can be used to change the composition of a turf. It may be advantageous to introduce a more pest-resistant variety or a new variety that has demonstrated superior wear tolerance. In some high salt areas, overseeding with varieties with high salt tolerance makes sense.

There are three basic methods of overseeding. One is the use of a drop seeder. Care must be given when using a drop spreader to avoid skips. A cyclone or rotary type spreader helps to avoid skips. So far, the best type to use is the slit seeder. This machine makes a slit in the soil. It meters seed into the slit. This places the seed in the best contact with the soil.

The slit seeder can be used to overseed on turf—green or brown. It can cut through a modest thatch layer and get the seed down to the soil.

Overseeding Bermudagrass

Overseeding bermudagrass putting greens and athletic fields for late fall, winter and early spring play is becoming more and more common. The green playing surface not only has aesthetic appeal but also serves to protect the dormant bermudagrass from wear and tear.

More and more home lawns and business properties are being overseeded for aesthetic reasons.

Golf greens may be seeded with one or a blend of several different perennial ryegrass at rates around 15 pounds per 1,000 sq. ft. If *Poa trivialis* is used, it's rate is around 2 pounds per 1,000 sq. ft.

Athletic fields may be seeded with perennial ryegrass from 200 lbs./acre to 350 lbs./acre. Most home lawns are seeded with perennial ryegrass at about 5 lbs./1,000 sq. ft.

Bermudagrass turf should be overseeded about 2 months before the average first killing frost date. A late seeding may end up being damaged by cold temperatures.

Ideally, as the warm weather returns in the spring, the overseeded grasses will die out on their own. As they die, the bermuda begins to green up and the change back to bermuda is uneventful. A potential problem may occur when the weather in the spring tends to stay too wet and cool. The cool-season grass may not die but, in fact, may grow more vigorously and retard the bermudagrass.

If the overseeding remains too long, it is possible to lose the bermudagrass. If an overseeding hangs around too long, it might be necessary to take steps to kill it out. There are chemicals that can do this. Very low mowing and the use of a vertical mower may help thin out the overseeding and tip the balance toward the bermudagrass.

Hydraulic Planting

Hydroseeding and hydro-mulching are often used interchangeably to describe a planting technique that employs a wet slurry or seed, mulch fibers, fertilizer and water, resulting in rapid establishment of the intended plant varieties.

The two terms are slightly different, however, but refer to similar processes. Hydroseeding is the application of seed (and perhaps fertilizer or other ingredients) with a hydraulic planting machine. Hydro-mulching, on the other hand, refers to the same process, but with inclusion of a mulch to cover and protect the planted seeds. Of the two, hydro-mulching is considered by some to be more effective in establishing turfgrasses. Generically, the process is called hydraulic planting, a technique that came of age during construction of the nation's interstate highway system.

Large, relatively inaccessible areas could be quickly and effectively planted using long extension spray hoses or a powerful spray cannon. The technique is flexible enough to allow for virtually any seed mix and permits the inclusion of various liquid, powder, and granular additives, such as lime, gypsum and fertilizers. Hydraulic planting is an accepted method for establishing plants for erosion and dust control.

Hydro-mulching has some advantages over drill seeding, broadcast seeding and traditional hand seeding.

The mulch is mixed in the tank, along with water, seed and fertilizer. When sprayed on the ground, it forms a continuous blanket that protects the seeds by holding them in place and by retaining soil moisture. The mulch resists erosion caused by irrigation. By the time the grass begins to grow, the mulch has begun to deteriorate and disappear. The inclusion of mulch in the process often improves establishment on sloped or rolling terrain, in rainy weather, or when the homeowner may forget to water.

Drill seeding can be limited by the soil type and moisture conditions. Rocky soils do not plant well, and heavy, wet or gummy soils interfere with the drill. Rolling terrain presents another set of difficulties for the drill seeder or culti-packer.

Typical mulch rates range from 1,500 to 2,500 pounds per acre. A rate of 2,000 pounds produces full coverage of the ground and is standard for high-quality turf establishment. Small seeds (common bermuda or aggressive, quickgrowing varieties such as an annual ryegrass) are sometimes applied with only 1,500 pounds of mulch. As a general rule, the more expensive the seed, the higher the mulch rate. More severe sites (slope, rain, wind, heat) may need heavier applications. Rates beyond 2,500 pounds may interfere with germination and are not recommended for turf establishment.

Each machine holds a finite amount of mulch in the tank. A decision must be made before loading as to how much area one tank will cover. Coverage area will depend on how heavy the mulch is to be applied. Divide the number of pounds of mulch in the tank by the intended application rate per acre. The result is the fraction of an acre that will be covered by this tank load at the specified rate. The contractor should add just enough seed and fertilizer to cover that amount of area and should apply all of the material in the tank evenly to that size area.

In severe situations, organic glues called tackifiers are added to the slurry. They make the mixture slippery in the hose, but they dry to form a durable crust throughout the mulch blanket. A tackifier is especially useful on steep slopes, in high wind areas, or when there is a high potential for rain or heavy irrigation. Tackifiers may come separately in a powdered form, or may arrive mixed in the mulch by the manufacturer.

Like any seedbed, the site should be kept moist, not wet, through the first few weeks or until the grass is established.

How heavily you apply the mulch determines how much area you can cover with one tank load. Here are some examples:

The basic equation is:
Number pounds of mulch in tank ÷
Desired application rate per acre = area covered

EXAMPLES:
At a 2,000 pound rate (full coverage of the ground surface)
200 pounds in tank = .10 acres = 4,356 sq. ft. 2,000 pound rate

The same 200 pounds, applied at a lighter rate, goes farther.
200 pounds in tank = .117 acres = 5,096 sq. ft. 1700 pound rate

Per-acre rates expressed as pounds of mulch per 1,000 square feet:
2,000 Lbs. = 46 Lbs./1,000
1,700 Lbs. = 39 Lbs./1,000
1,500 Lbs. = 34 Lbs./1,000
1,350 Lbs. = 31 Lbs./1,000

Seed and fertilizer for hydraulic planting are added according to manufacturer/supplier-recommended rates, based on the amount of area covered by the tankload: i.e. if the seed rate is 7 pounds per 1,000 and the project is .15 acres, calculate as:

Change acres to square feet
.15 X 43,560 = 6,534 square feet

Seed rate is per 1,000, so find the number of 1,000s...
6,534 divided by 1,000 = 6.5 "thousands"

The seed for this tankload is then....
6.5 X 7 pound seed rate = 45.5 pounds of seed

The calculation for fertilizer or any other ingredient expressed in pounds per 1,000 is the same.

Manufacturers add tackifier at 3 percent concentration. The actual amount applied to the job site will depend on how heavily the mulch is applied.

3% at a 2,000 Lb. rate = 60 Ibs. per acre (.03 X 2,000)
3% at a 1,500 Lb. rate = 45 lbs. per acre (.03 X 1,500)

Lastly, here's an "after the fact" check equation to see at what rate the completed project was sprayed:

400 pounds of mulch were evenly applied on 8,000 square feet.

First, convert the 8,000 square feet back to acres.
8,000 divided by 43,560 = .183 acres

Plug these numbers into the coverage equation solve for x.

400 lbs. in tank = .183 acres

Multiply both sides by "x" to get 400 = .183x Divide both sides by .183 to get 2,185 = x

The effective coverage rate was 2,185 pounds per acre.

Specifications for Turfgrass Establishment & Maintenance

From time to time, it may be necessary to solicit bids for the establishment and/or the maintenance of turfgrass. The purpose of this section is to present sample wording for the preparation of bidding materials. The better written the bidding document, the better the chances of getting the desired materials or services. These paragraphs are suggestions and changes may be necessary to fit specific needs.

I. MOWING

A. General: All mowing equipment shall be approved prior to use and shall be maintained in good mechanical working order. All cutting surfaces shall be kept sharp so the mower produces a clean cut.

B. Height-of-Cut: The mower shall be adjusted to cut the grass at a height of _____ inches. This distance shall be the distance between a flat surface and the cutting edge of the rotary mower's blade. The cutting height of a reel type mower shall be the distance between a flat surface and the cutting edge of the bed knife.

C. Mowing Frequency: The frequency of mowing shall be a function of the turf growth rate. Each time the turf reaches a height approximately 1/3 higher than the Height-of-Cut, or inches, the turf shall be mowed inches.

In the event environmental conditions do not permit mowing at the specified interval, the turf shall he mowed as soon as conditions permit. If grass clippings remain on the turf surface after mowing they will be allowed to dry and then the turf shall be mowed again.

II. FERTILIZATION

A. General: All fertilizing materials shall conform to all applicable state laws. No unlabeled materials will he acceptable.

B. Analysis: Unless otherwise indicated by a soil test, the fertilizer used will have a nitrogen-phosphorus-potassium (N-P-K) ratio of either 3-1-2 or 4-1-2.

C. Nitrogen Source: At least 1/2 of the nitrogen source will be of a slowly available or slowly soluble material.

D. Application Rate: The rate of fertilizer application shall he no more than one pound (I) of nitrogen per 1,000 square feet.

E. Application Dates: Fertilizer shall he applied on the following dates:

———————   ———————

———————   ———————

If environmental conditions prevent the application on any of the specified dates the application shall be made as soon as conditions permit.

F. Application Techniques: Equipment used for the application of fertilizer shall be approved prior to use and shall be maintained in good working order. Equipment shall be operated so the specified rate of fertilizer is uniformly spread over the designated area. No ballast separation of blended or mixed fertilizer materials will be permitted. Equipment that may damage any coated fertilizer material will not be permitted.

III. IRRIGATION

A. General: Equipment used for the application of water shall he approved prior to use and maintained in good working order. The source of water shall be approved prior to its use.

B. Application Rates: Water shall be applied at a rate so the soil is completely wetted to at least a depth of from 4 to 6 inches. If run off occurs before the desirable wetting depth is reached, application shall stop. After the water has been allowed to soak into the soil for a brief period, irrigation shall continue until the desired wetting depth is reached.

C. Application Timing: The soil shall be allowed to dry completely before the next irrigation cycle. Irrigation will not be repeated until the grass begins to show drought stress symptoms. Under no circumstances will the grass be allowed to enter a drought induced dormancy. Irrigation will only be permitted during early morning hours when evaporation and possible wind distortion of the irrigation pattern are low, unless approval for other periods is granted.

IV. ESTABLISHMENT

1. Prior to the tilling operation, all debris, including stones inch in diameter or larger, logs, stumps or any other objectional material that could interfere with soil preparation shall be removed from the site.

2. An approved systemic herbicide shall be applied to all undesirable vegetation according to the manufacturer's label directions. A total of days shall elapse between the herbicide application and the tilling operation to assure a complete kill.

3. Mechanical rotary tillage equipment shall be used for the preparation of the soil to a depth of not less than inches. Areas that are inaccessible to mechanical rotary tillage equipment shall be prepared by hand to a depth of not less than inches.

4. After seedbed preparation has been completed, any additional debris brought to the surface as a result of the tillage operation shall be removed (see spec. 1).

5. Fertilizer as specified by a soil test shall be uniformly spread at the recommended rate over all areas. The fertilizer shall be mechanically incorporated into the top _ inches of soil.

6. Use 6a for seeding or 6b for sodding or 6c for sprigging.

6a. The following seed mixture shall be spread uniformly over all areas at a rate of pounds per 1,000 square feet. Each turfgrass should be certified by the State Department of Agriculture in the state in which it was grown. The seed test date to determine the purity and

Seed Mixture	Minimum Purity	Germination
Seed A	_____ %	_____ %
Seed B	_____ %	_____ %
Seed C	_____ %	_____ %

Suggested minimums Turfgrass	Purity	Germination
Kentucky bluegrass	85%	80%
Tall fescue	98%	85%
Chewings fescue	98%	90%
Creeping red fescue	98%	85%
Sheeps fescue	98%	85%
Perennial ryegrass	95%	90%
Buffalograss	60% P.L.S.	
(Purity x Germination = P.L.S.)		

germination shall be within the past nine months.

(In order to assure seed quality a minimum acceptable purity and germination should be specified as below.)

6b. Sod shall be cut into strips of uniform width and thickness with square ends. Sod shall be free of all debris or weeds and shall have been regularly maintained prior to cutting. Within one hour after being cut, the sod shall be rolled or stacked. Precautions shall be taken to prevent drying or heating. Sod damaged by heat or dry conditions, or sod cut more than 18 hours shall not be used.

Sod shall be placed in rows or strips. On slopes, the strips shall run at right angles to the flow of water. Sod pieces shall be placed tightly against each other. Joints at the end of sod strips shall be staggered at least one foot.

Sod shall be cut from fields that have been certified to variety by the State Department of Agriculture or another acceptable agency in the state in which the sod is grown.

6c. Sprigs shall be produced by shredding sod. One square yard of sod shall be used to produce one bushel of sprigs. Cut sod, processed into sprigs, shall be planted within 24 hours. Sprigs shall be planted at a rate of bushels per 1,000 square feet using equipment designed for that purpose or shall be uniformly spread over the designated area at a rate of bushels per 1,000 square feet.

7. Immediately after (seeding) (sodding) (sprigging) the area shall be rolled with equipment designed for that purpose. (Note: If the area was broadcast planted to sprigs after rolling, it could be top dressed with 1/4 to 1/2 inch of soil. That's just enough to bury the sprigs. It could then be rolled again.)

8a. After rolling the seeded area, it shall be irrigated with enough water to completely wet the seedbed. The seedbed shall be kept wet and not allowed to dry out until germination occurs. As the young grass begins to grow, the frequency of irrigation shall be reduced.

8b. After the sod has been rolled it shall be irrigated with enough water to completely wet the sod and the soil under the sod. The sod will be re-irrigated at infrequent intervals. As soon as the sod has rooted down, the regular maintenance irrigation schedule will be followed.

8c. After the sprigging area has been rolled, the areas shall be completely wetted. The sprigbed shall be kept wet and not allowed to dry out until the sprigs begin to grow. As the grass begins to grow, the irrigation frequency shall be reduced.

9. Mowing shall begin and shall be repeated when the grass reaches a height of approximately inches and shall be cut at inches. 🌿

CHAPTER 6

Woody Ornamental Establishment

Landscape designers use a number of criteria—mature plant size, plant shape, season of bloom, bloom color and foliage texture—in choosing plants. If plants selected for the project are not of the highest quality, are not planted properly and do not receive adequate post-planting care, success of the whole project may be diminished.

Plant Quality

Depending on species, woody ornamental plants may be purchased as bare root, container grown, or balled and burlapped. The quality of a tree or shrub is just as important, if not more, than any other selection criteria. Several plant characteristics can be used to help determine quality and should be used when selecting plant material.

Root System

The condition of the root system is perhaps the most important quality consideration. Basically, plants grown in containers or balled and burlapped should have a well-developed fibrous root system that retains its shape and holds together when removed from the container or when the ball is unwrapped. A broken earth ball is a sure sign of potentially serious root damage. A defective or underdeveloped root system may lead to poor growth or death of the plant.

No matter if the plant is bare root, container grown or balled and burlapped, the root system should never be allowed to dry out. The root system only has to dry out once to cause serious damage.

Consider two basic root defects—kinked roots, in which the taproot or major branched roots have become sharply bent, and roots that begin to circle the container. It may be possible to straighten out some defective roots when transplanting, but it may be necessary to remove the defects by pruning, and root pruning may retard early growth of the plant. The plant certainly would be retarded if the defects remained, however.

Any damaged roots should be removed. Plants grown in containers may develop roots that tend to circle or coil around the inside of the container. If left alone, these roots could girdle the normal roots and the plant might be lost. If this condition exists, split the lower ½ of the root system before planting. Spread both halves in the planting hole. This should encourage new roots that will grow normally.

Bare Root

Some woody ornamental species can be dug while dormant and replanted in a bare root form. The soil is removed from the root system and replaced with a lightweight material, such as sphagnum, that holds moisture. Plants are then packaged in paper or plastic containers and should be replanted before they begin to bud out.

Table 1. Suggested Container Sizes and Plant Heights			
Plants	1 Gal.	2 Gal.	5 Gal.
Shade Trees	15-18 in.	24-30 in.	3-4 ft.
Ornamental Trees	15-18 in.	18-24 In.	3-4 ft.
Deciduous Shrubs	9-12 in.	15-18 in.	2-3 ft.
Coniferous Evergreens	6-9 in.	12-15 in.	18-24 in.
Coniferous Evergreens Dwf.	5-8 in.	10-12 in.	15-18 in.
Broadleaf Evergreens	6-9 in.	12-15 in.	18-24 in.
Broadleaf Evergreens Dwf.	5-8 in.	10-12 in.	15-18 in.

Figure 1.

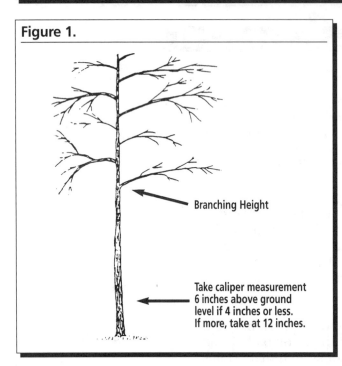

Branching Height

Take caliper measurement 6 inches above ground level if 4 inches or less. If more, take at 12 inches.

Figure 2.

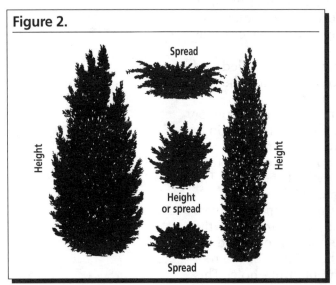

Spread

Height

Height
or spread

Height

Spread

Container Grown

These plants are usually grown in the containers in which they are sold. As they grow too large for a container they are moved to the next largest size. Container grown plants can be planted anytime, but during times when environmental conditions cause high plant stress, establishment may be difficult.

Container grown plants are sold by container size. The most commonly used containers are:

1 gallon—Minimum of 5 inches across top and height of 6 inches or equivalent volume.

2 gallons—Minimum of 7 inches across top and height of 7½ inches or equivalent volume.

5 gallons—Minimum of 9 inches across top and height of 10 inches or equivalent volume.

The container should be of a material strong enough to hold the root mass without being disturbed. The plant material should have been grown in a container large enough so that when it is removed the whole root mass, including the planting media, retains its shape and holds together.

Size of plant to container guidelines (Table 1) are not absolute but may be considered as suggestions. Some plant materials have unusual growth habits that may not fit these guidelines.

Be especially aware of plant material that seems too small for the container. It may have been just recently moved up to get a higher price.

Overly large plant material may have serious root problems. Inspect the root system carefully.

Balled and Burlapped

Balled and burlapped trees and shrubs are dug during the dormant season. They may be planted during the same dormant season or "heeled in" in the nursery and planted at any time. As with any other plant, planting during a stress period makes establishment more difficult.

A strong relationship exists between the size of the plant and the size of the ball. The bigger the ball, the more roots it contains and the better the chance it will survive the moving process. However, since soil is very heavy, consider a reasonable ball size that will contain enough roots.

Tree size is usually expressed as "caliper," a measurement in inches of the tree's trunk thickness or diameter. The caliper measurement should be taken at a point 6 inches above ground level if the tree is less than 4 inches in diameter. For larger trees, the measurement is taken at 12 inches above ground level (Figure 1).

If trees or shrubs are sold by height or spread, a simple measurement from the ground level to the top branch or from the center of the plant to the outermost branch is adequate (Figure 2).

Trees with a single trunk should be trimmed free of branches in balance with their overall height. For example, a 5-6 foot tree should be free

Table 2. Plant Size vs. Ball Size
Group Classification

Group I		Group II		Group III		Group IV	
Plant* Size	Ball** Size	Plant* Size	Ball** Size	Plant* Size	Ball** Size	Plant* Size	Ball** Size
10-12 in.	7"	10-12 in.	7"	¾-1" cal.	12"	12-15 in.	7"
12-15 in.	8"	12-15 in.	8"	1-1¼" cal.	13"	15-18 in.	8"
15-18 in.	9"	15-18 in.	9"	1¼-1½" cal.	14"	18-24 in.	8"
18-24 in.	10"	18-24 in.	10"	1½-1¾" cal.	16"	2-3 ft.	9"
24-30 in.	12"	24-30 in.	11"	1¾-2" cal.	18"	3-4 ft.	9"
30-36 in.	14"	30-36 in.	12"	2" cal.	20"	4-5 ft.	10"
3-4 ft.	16"	3-4 ft.	13"	2½" cal.	23"	5-6 ft.	11"
4-5 ft.	18"	4-5 ft.	14"	3" cal.	27"	6-7 ft.	12"
5-6 ft.	22"	5-6 ft.	15"	3½" cal.	32"	7-8 ft.	12"
6-7 ft.	26"	6-7 ft.	16"	4" cal.	36"	6-8 ft.	12"
7-8 ft.	30"	7-8 ft.	18"	4½" cal.	40"	1-1¼" cal.	12"
8-9 ft.	32"	8-9 ft.	20"	5" cal.	45"	1¼-1½" cal.	13"
9-10 ft.	34"	9-10 ft.	24"	5½" cal.	50"	1½-1¾" cal.	14"
10-12 ft.	36"	10-12 ft.	26"	6" cal.	54"	1¾-2" cal.	15"
12-14 ft.	40"	12-14 ft.	28"			2" cal.	16"
14-16 ft.	44"	14-16 ft.	30"			2½" cal.	18"
16-18 ft.	48"	16-18 ft.	32"			3" cal.	21"
18-20 ft.	52"	18-20 ft.	35"			3½" cal.	24"
						4" cal.	27"
						4½" cal.	30"
						5" cal.	35"
						5½" cal.	40"
						6" cal.	44"

*height
**diameter

of branches up to 4, feet and a tree that's 1½ inches in caliper should be free of branches up to 5 or 6 feet of its height (Figure 1).

Plants are also sold in a "clump" or "multi-trunk" form (Figure 3). A "clump" plant means that its natural growth habit of branching near the ground precludes removal of low branches. Multi-trunked trees are treated like single trunk trees.

In order that the ball contains an adequate mass of roots for successful transplanting, a certain ratio between ball diameter and the depth of the ball should be followed (Table 2).

Minimum ball size may vary according to the tree or shrub species being moved. These plants may be divided into several different groups (Table 3).

Table 3. Examples of Ball Size Group

	Ball Size Group		
I	II	III	IV
Spreading Juniper Dwarf Euonymous	Ligustrum Eleagnus	Oak	Forsythia Maple Redbud Dogwood

Planting

Before planting, trees must he kept moist enough so they don't dry out and they must not be allowed to get too hot or too cold. Bare root plants can be temporarily "heeled-in" out-of-doors. Cover root systems with a moist material, mulch or sawdust, and keep in the shade.

Container-grown and balled and burlap may also be "heeled-in" using sawdust, mulch or a similar material to keep their root systems cool and moist.

Planting Hole

The planting hole should be deep enough so the new plant is no deeper than it was in the nursery or container. In heavy soils, it might help to

Figure 3.

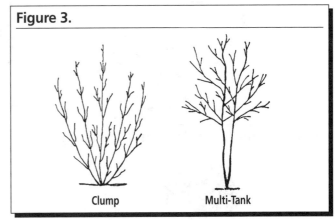

Clump   Multi-Tank

Figure 4. Large Tree Planting and Guying

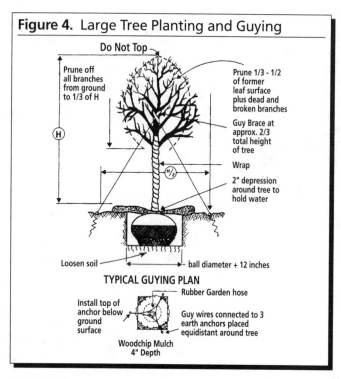

Do Not Top

Prune off all branches from ground to 1/3 of H

Prune 1/3 - 1/2 of former leaf surface plus dead and broken branches

Guy Brace at approx. 2/3 total height of tree

Wrap

2" depression around tree to hold water

Loosen soil

ball diameter + 12 inches

TYPICAL GUYING PLAN

Install top of anchor below ground surface

Rubber Garden hose

Guy wires connected to 3 earth anchors placed equidistant around tree

Woodchip Mulch 4" Depth

Figure 5. Small Tree Planting and Bracing

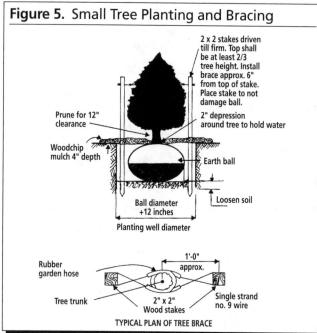

2 x 2 stakes driven till firm. Top shall be at least 2/3 tree height. Install brace approx. 6" from top of stake. Place stake to not damage ball.

Prune for 12" clearance

2" depression around tree to hold water

Woodchip mulch 4" depth

Earth ball

Ball diameter +12 inches

Loosen soil

Planting well diameter

Rubber garden hose

1'-0" approx.

Tree trunk

2" x 2" Wood stakes

Single strand no. 9 wire

TYPICAL PLAN OF TREE BRACE

Figure 6. Small Tree Planting and Bracing

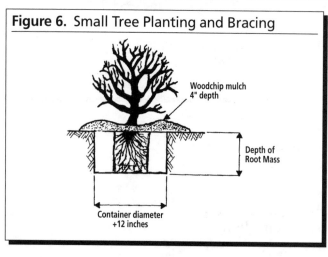

Woodchip mulch 4" depth

Depth of Root Mass

Container diameter +12 inches

---

set the new plant slightly higher than it grew before. Do not plant it deeper.

Generally, the planting hole should be about one foot larger (6 inches on each side) than the size of the ball or container or the spread of the bare root system

Soil in the bottom of the hole for balled plants and container grown plants should be loose enough to prevent air pockets when the plant is placed in the hole. Because the soil in the bottom of the hole has been loosened, the plant may settle. Remember, the plant can't be deeper than it grew in the field or container. (Figures 4, 5, 6, & 7).

Many planting holes are dug with machines and some tend to compact or glaze the sides of the hole as they dig. If so, the sides should be scarified. Roots have a hard time growing into or through a layer of compacted soil.

Soil used for backfill should be the soil taken out of the planting hole. There doesn't seem to be any advantage to amending backfill soil. The plant, sooner or later, must grow in the native soil and it seems better for the plant to be planted in the soil it will grow in forever.

Planting

Remove packing material from bare root plants. Carefully inspect the root system and prune off damaged or dead roots. Soak the root system in water from one to 24 hours.

Place the plant in the planting hole and allow the root system to assume its natural pattern. Slowly work the soil around the root system. It may help to use water as an aid to insure the soil gets around all the roots and to get rid of air pockets. If the soil is firmed by hand, avoid excessive force that may injure the root system. Make sure the plant is straight before finishing the backfill process.

Container grown plants should be removed from containers before planting. Handle the plant by the container rather than by the stem. Do not break the soil ball apart. Remove damaged or dead roots. If there are circling roots, cut the outer roots in two to three places to encourage growth of new, normal roots.

Place the plant in the hole. Make sure that, after some soil settlement, it's not too deep and is at the same height it was in the container. Begin backfill using the soil that came out of the planting hole. Water will help settle the backfill and prevent air pockets. Make sure the plant is set straight.

Place balled and burlap plants in their planting hole using the soil ball. Since these plants are usually very heavy, be careful not to break the soil ball. Ease the plant into the hole. You need not remove the burlap or any similar decomposable material completely. Make sure the material is completely buried in the backfill. Any ball material remaining exposed to the surface may act as a wick and cause the whole ball to dry out. If possible, cut twine or string used to hold the material around the ball. Make sure no twine or string is left around the stem of the plant. Many transplanted plants have been girdled by materials left around the bottom of the plant.

As with any other transplant, make sure it is not too low and backfill with the soil that came out of the hole. Water will help settle the soil and prevent air pockets. Make sure the plant is straight.

Usually, no fertilizer is added to the soil used to backfill the plant. It is possible that newly developing roots could be damaged by fertilizer. If a soil test has indicated a need for fertilizer, add it in its soluble form as a part of the final watering operation after planting. The regular fertility program should begin after the first growing season.

Post-Planting Care

After the plant is completely backfilled and is settling at its proper height, create a ring of soil a few inches deep at the outer edge of the planting hole to serve as a basin to hold water. Watering is critical for the new plant and it is very important that the water soak deep into the soil. The basin should hold water long enough so it will soak in. Fill this basin with a good mulch. Bark, wood chips or pine needles are ideal.

Bare root, as well as balled and burlapped plants, need to be pruned just before or just after planting. In both cases, the plants have lost a fairly high percentage of their original root system through the digging process. The smaller root system can't supply water and nutrients the top of the plant needs.

The rule-of-thumb is to reduce the top of the plant by about ⅓. There are several ways to do this (Figures 4, 7, & 8). Do not ruin the natural growth form of the plant, but prune by using a thinning technique. The center leader of any tree should not be pruned.

Balled and burlapped plants that have been dug and heeled-in for several months may have adjusted for the loss of roots and may not need to be pruned when planted. Container grown plants have their whole root system and may not require pruning.

Staking

Generally, bare-root trees over six feet should be supported (Figure 7). A single stake (2"x2") should be driven in so that it is about ¾ the height of the tree, before the tree is planted. The stake should be two to four inches from the center of the hole and located on the side of the prevailing

Figure 7. Planting and Staking Bare Root Tree

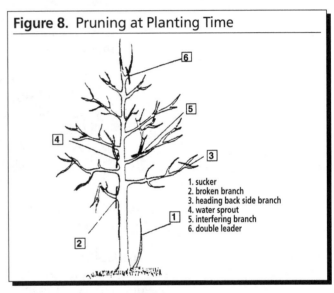

Figure 8. Pruning at Planting Time

1. sucker
2. broken branch
3. heading back side branch
4. water sprout
5. interfering branch
6. double leader

Figure 9. Method of Root Pruning a Tree Before it is Moved

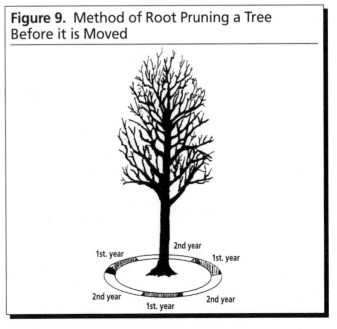

wind, usually the southwest side, but it may vary in different parts of the country. Plant the tree as described above. Fasten the tree to the stake using a wire to form a loose loop. Slip a piece of rubber hose on the wire to protect the area wire comes in contact with the trunk. Do not use this method for container grown or balled and burlapped plants. The stake placed so close to the trunk could damage the ball or root system.

Small trees or large shrubs grown in containers or planted as balled and burlapped may be supported using a two-stake method (Figure 5). After planting, drive two stakes into opposite sides, just outside the planting hole. The height of the stakes after being driven should be about ⅔ the plant. The plant is supported by wires attached to both the stakes and looped loosely around the tree or shrub. Use a piece of rubber hose to protect the plant.

To support very large trees, use stakes and guy wires (Figure 4). The stakes or soil anchors should be placed an equal distance from the tree and from each other. They should be driven 18 to 30 inches deep at a 45-degree angle away from the tree trunk. The wire is attached to the stakes and is fastened to the trunk of the tree about ⅔ up. A rubber hose loop contacts the tree. Each wire should be equally tight, but loose enough to allow slight movement of the tree.

Support may be removed from shrubs and small trees after one growing season. Leave supports on larger trees for at least two seasons.

Shrubs usually do not need to be supported after planting unless large specimens have been used.

COMMON MISTAKES

The most common mistakes in planting trees and shrubs are:
- Planting too deeply
- Planting too shallow
- Airpockets in the backfill
- Planting plants with circling root systems
- Not removing or burying non-decomposable materials from balled and burlapped plants

Transplanting Native Plants

Trees and shrubs grown in nurseries are periodically root pruned to develop as compact a root system as possible, to save as much of the root system as possible when they are dug. Container grown plants have their whole root system.

Plants in the wild have a normal root system with feeder roots a significant distance from the base of the plant. These plants can be transplanted, but it takes time. The idea is to divide the root system of the plant into six equal parts (Figure 9). During the dormant season, root prune ½ of the plant's root system. The next dormant season, root prune the remaining ½ of the root system. The plant can be moved to the new site the third dormant season. This should give the plant the best possible chance to survive a move.

Root pruning alone does not assure success in moving wild plant material. Some plants are very sensitive to changes in soil moisture levels, to differences in soil pH and differences in light levels. Moving wild or native plant material is not easy. They may die from a completely undetermined or an unexplainable reason. The larger the plant, the greater the risk of failure.

Fill Around Trees

When building in a woody area, sometimes it's necessary to change the grade around the existing native trees. Some trees can survive more fill than others. Also, the sandier the soil, the deeper this fill may be without any damage to the root system.

Tree roots like all other plants take in oxygen and give off carbon dioxide. When a new tree grows its root system, the roots grow at a soil depth that allows for the proper air exchange between the soil and the atmosphere. When soil is added, the rate of air exchange is reduced. The available amount of oxygen is reduced and carbon dioxide levels may increase.

The best answer to this problem is to establish a tree well. (Figure 10).

Before adding the fill, install the tile field and build the tree well. Note that the tile system opens to the surface through the well itself and the vertical pipes. The more open tiles under the fill, the better the chance the tree has to survive the change in grade.

Transplanting Large Trees

Larger trees are harder to move. There are two basic reasons. The first is the root system. As a tree gets larger, the feeder root system gets larger and is further and further away from the trunk of the tree. This means that to move enough of the feeder root system to keep the tree alive, the root ball or size of the ball or size of the tree spade must be larger and larger. At some point, it is just physically impossible to move enough of the root system. Experts recommend at least a 10- to 12 inch root ball for each 1 inch of tree diameter.

Large trees that have been root pruned (Figure 9), stand a better chance of being moved, as do trees that have been dug and grown in large containers for a brief period. Any technique that helps restrict or compact the root system will help the move.

Another factor is the age of the tree. Younger trees can recover from a move much easier than an older tree can. If the tree has not been growing at a normal rate, the chances are the tree can't be moved. It is possible that a transplanted, young tree growing at an optimum rate will pass the size of a transplanted older tree in a few years.

The older, large tree will have a better chance if it is moved to a site which closely resembles the site it grew in. If the tree grew in the shade, full sun may cause a problem. A big difference in soil pH or soil drainage pattern can also be a problem. Older large trees just can't take environmental changes very well.

Also, be aware that the newly transplanted older tree will be in severe stress and it may be more susceptible to insect and disease problems. ❦

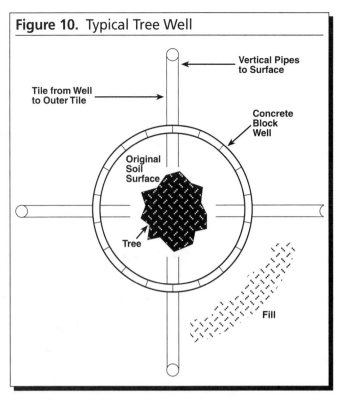

Figure 10. Typical Tree Well

Plant Nutrition

A well-planned, reasonable fertility program is a basic part of landscape maintenance. Under-fertilized plants tend to be thin, with poor growth. But where over-fertilized, especially with high levels of a soluble nitrogen fertilizer, turf may have thatch problems and excessive leaf growth and all plants may be prone to more insect and disease damage.

Required Nutrients

All plants require some 15 or 16 nutrients for best growth (Table 1). In most cases, the soil serves as a reservoir of some plant nutrients. But soils vary in the amounts and in the ability to supply those nutrients to plants.

Plants may survive in some soils without added nutrients, but it is highly unlikely the turf will be dense or thick enough to resist weed invasion.

When a plant requires more of a nutrient than the soil can supply or a nutrient that isn't there, a fertilizer must be used. A soil test can measure a soil's current plant nutrient status.

Of all the nutrients required by the turfgrass plant, nitrogen (N), phosphorus (P) and potassium (K) are usually not available in the soil in high enough quantities for good turf growth and must be added periodically as a fertilizer. Other nutrients, such as iron (Fe) or magnesium (Mn) , may also be required.

Table 1. Primary Plant Nutrients and Their Source

Macro-Nutrients	Primary Source
(N) Nitrogen	Fertilizer & Soil
(K) Potassium	Fertilizer & Soil
(P) Phosphorus	Fertilizer & Soil
(S) Sulfur	Soil
(Mg) Magnesium	Soil
(Ca) Calcium	Soil
Micro Nutrients	**Source**
(Fe) Iron	Soil
(Mn) Manganese	Soil
(Zn) Sinc	Soil
(Cu) Copper	Soil
(Mo) Molybdenum	Soil
(B) Boron	Soil
(Cl) Chlorine	Soild
Others	**Sources**
(O) Oxygen	Water & Carbon Dioxide
(H) Hydrogen	Water
(C) Carbon	Carbon Dioxide

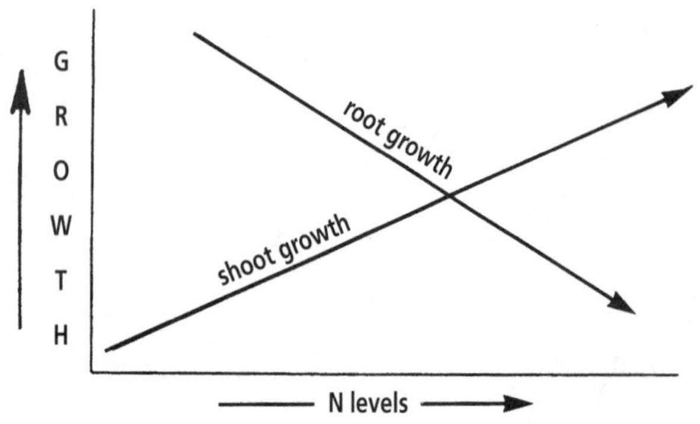

Nitrogen (N)

Most plants require nitrogen in the highest quantity of any plant nutrients. It's not uncommon for nitrogen levels in the plant to be as much as 4 percent or 5 percent by dry leaf weight. Nitrogen is part of chlorophyll and has a great deal to do with nearly all the growth and development processes in the plant.

As the amount of nitrogen supplied to the plant increases, the rate of shoot or leaf growth increases. This increase comes generally at the expense of root growth (Figure 1).

Rapid leaf growth tends to use all the food produced by the plant and leaves very little for the roots and other organs, such as stolons or rhizomes. Since it is possible to produce a turf with very high leaf growth and good color, but with a very restricted root system, reasonable levels of nitrogen are usually desirable.

Figure 1. Effect of N on Shoot & Root Growth

High levels of nitrogen tend to produce a plant with thin cell walls and a high percentage of water in its tissues. Cell wall thickness becomes important when a fungus or insect tries to invade the plant. Also, a plant containing a high percentage of water requires more irrigation and is more susceptible to heat and drought stress.

The amount of nitrogen supplied to the plant has a great deal to do with the amount of food reserve the plant is able to store for periods of unfavorable weather, such as winter dormancy or summer dormancy.

The plant manufactures food material (carbohydrates) in the leaf tissue. Leaves take priority over other plant parts for growth. Since nitrogen stimulates leaf growth, the over-supply of nitrogen—especially during the period just before normal dormancy—may promote leaf growth to the point of using all the food the plant can supply.

If this happens, little food is available for storage, and the plant may not live through the dormant period. The goal of a good fertility program should be to produce a reasonable amount of top growth, but not at the expense of root growth or carbohydrate storage.

Table 2. N-P-K

Plant Function	Nitrogen	Phosphorus	Potassium
Leaf Growth	X		
Root Growth	X	X	X
Seed Germination	X	X	
Wear Resistance	X		X
Disease Resistance	X		X
Insect Resistance	X	X	
Drought Resistance	X		X
Cold & Heat Stress	X		X
Flower Growth	X	X	X

Table 3. Typical Nutrient Sources

Nutrient	Fertilizer Source
Nitrogen-Soluble	Urea Ammonium Nitrate *Ammonium Sulfate
Nitrogen-Slowly Soluble	*Sulfur-Coated Urea Ureaformaldehyde Methylene Urea Isobutylidene *Natural Organics Resin-Coated Urea
Phosphorus	Super Phosphate *Monoammonium Phosphate *Diammonium phosphate
Potassium	*Potassium Chloride *Potassium Sulfate *Potassium Nitrate

*Supplies more than one nutrient.

Phosphorus (P)

For years, many textbooks have suggested that phosphorus was necessary for good root growth. This is true, but only in the sense that all plant nutrients are necessary for the optimum growth of all parts of the plant.

Phosphorus has a great deal to do with the process of energy transfer and storage within the plant. The roots are a primary organ for energy storage and thus depend on phosphorus.

The formation and germination of the seed is a process that creates a high demand for phosphorus. A high level of energy must be stored in the seed for it to survive until it can germinate. Also, the rapid growth processes associated with germination require high amounts of energy.

Under most conditions the turf plant is not maintained for its seed production. Its need for phosphorus is rather low, and most turf fertilizers reflect that. However, when turf is to be established from seed, sod or sprigs, a fertilizer containing higher levels of phosphorus is suggested. Plants grown for their flowers have a higher phosphorus need.

Phosphorus moves very slowly in the soil. It may take years to move down just a few inches, with the speed of movement depending on the amount of clay in the soil. The higher the clay content, the slower it moves.

The slow movement of phosphorus in the soil and the relatively high demand of phosphorus for turf establishment makes it highly desirable to incorporate a fertilizer with an N-P-K ratio of 1-1-1 or 1-2-1 into the soil before seeding, sodding or sprigging.

Potassium (K)

Potassium has not been given sufficient credit for its role in plant growth, many experts believe. The way potassium functions in the plant has not been well understood, while the functions of other nutrients, such as nitrogen and phosphorus, have been more clearly defined.

Potassium is involved in many growth processes, but one of its most important roles relates to water within the plant.

Table 4. Average Plant Food Content of Fertilizer Material

Materials	N	P₂O₅	K₂O	Oxides	Availability
		Percent Plant Food			
Ammonium Nitrate	33.5	—	—	—	Rapidly
Ammonium Sulfate	21	—	—	24 S	Rapidly
Ammo-Phos A	11	48	—	—	Moderately
Ammo-Phos B	16	20	—	—	Moderately
Ammoniated Superphosphate	6	17	—	—	Moderately
Anhydrous Ammonia	82	—	—	—	Rapidly
Aqua Ammonia	25	—	—	—	Rapidly
Calcium Nitrate	15.5	—	—	19 Ca	Rapidly
Cal Nitro	20.5	—	—	—	Rapidly
Nitrate Soda	16	—	—	26 Na	Rapidly
Nitrate Soda Potash	15	—	14	18 Na	Rapidly
Potassium Nitrate	13	00	44	—	Rapidly
Urea	45	—	—	—	Rapidly
Calcium Cyanamide	21	—	—	28.5 Ca	Rapidly
Castor Pomace	6	1.2	.5	—	Slowly
Cocoa Shell Meal	2.5	1.5	2.5	—	Slowly
Cottonseed Meal	6	2.5	1.5	—	Slowly
Dried Blood	12	1.5	.8	—	Mod. Slowly
Fish Scrap	5	3	0	8.5 Ca	Slowly
Guano, Peru	13	8	2	—	Moderately
Humus	2.4	—	—	—	Slowly
Sewage Sludge	6	2.5	—	—	Slowly
Soybean Meal	7	1.2	1.5	—	Slowly
Tankage, Animal	6-9	10	15.5	—	Slowly
Tankage, Garbage	2.5	1.5	1.5	4.5 Ca	Very Slow
Tankage, Process	6-9	—	—	—	Slowly
Tobacco Stems	1.5	0.5	5	—	Slowly
Steamed Bone Meal	2.5	25	0	33 Ca	Mod. Rapidly
Raw Bone Meal	3.5	22	0	31.5 Ca	Slowly
Basic Slag	—	8	—	30 Ca 15 Fe	Rapidly
Ground Rock Phosphate	—	33	—	—	Very Slowly
Superphosphate	—	18-20	—	20 Ca 12 S	Rapidly
Concentrated Superphosphate	—	42-48	—	14 Ca 1.6 S	Rapidly
Manure Salts	—	—	22	54 Cl	Rapidly
Muriate Potash	—	—	60	50 Cl	Rapidly
Sulfate Potash	—	—	50	17 S	Rapidly
Sulfate Potash Magnesia	—	—	22	18 Mg 23 S	Rapidly
Dolomite	—	—	—	30 Ca 20Mg	Very Slowly
Calcitic Limestone	—	—	—	40 Ca	Slowly
Borax	—	—	—	36	Rapidly
Copper Sulfate	—	—	—	33	Rapidly
Iron Sulfate	—	—	—	27.75	Rapidly
Manganese Sulfate	—	—	—	31	Rapidly
Zinc Sulfate	—	—	—	44	Rapidly
Magnesium Sulfate	—	—	—	26.5	Rapidly
Aluminum Sulfate	—	—	—	10	—

Just as high levels of nitrogen tend to produce a plant with thin cell walls and high water content, inadequate potassium has the same effect. As the amount of potassium supplied to the plant increases in relation to the level of nitrogen, cell walls are thicker and the water content of the plant drops. This makes the plant less susceptible to the potential invasion of a disease, an insect attack or stress.

Potassium affects the balance between leaf and root growth. As the level of potassium is increased in relation to the level of nitrogen, the rate of leaf growth reduces. As the demand for food by the leaves drops, more food becomes available for stolon, rhizome and root growth.

Potassium is considered to be the most leachable of the plant nutrients and must be supplied at a near constant rate. It may even be lost from the plant through leaves during rain or irrigation.

Fertilizers with relatively high levels of potassium have been hard to "sell." Unlike other nutrients, its application to turf does not necessarily result in a change that is easy to see or measure. But research has shown that when potassium is supplied at optimum levels, the plant is less susceptible to drought, heat, cold and disease (Table 2).

Other Nutrients

From time to time, depending on the local soil and its pH, nutrients such as sulfur, magnesium or iron may be required. A soil test and/or a tissue test will serve to identify nutrient problems.

Most minor nutrient problems are a result of soil pH that is too high or too low. When a minor nutrient problem is identified by soil or tissue testing, the missing minor nutrient must be made available to the plant as efficiently as possible. The best way is to use a "chelated" form of that nutrient. The chelation process helps move the nutrient through the soil solution to the plant without the nutrient becoming tied up with other chemicals in the soil.

Fertilizers

When the environment cannot supply to the turfgrass plants the nutrients in the amounts needed, the nutrients are supplied as a fertilizer. (Tables 3, 4).

Turf fertilizers typically contain only (N) nitrogen, (P) phosphorus and (K) potassium. But other macro- and some micro-nutrients may be included, depending on local soil conditions.

The three numbers on the bag represent the percentages of N, P and K. On the back of most bags is the guaranteed analysis (Table 5). In this example, the fertilizer is 15 percent nitrogen.

It is important to note that 7.5 percent (half) of the nitrogen is in a soluble form and the other half is in one of the slowly soluble nitrogen forms (Table 3). Soluble nitrogen materials result in a very fast increase in growth rates, especially leaf growth rates, and very fast greenup. This rapid increase is fairly short lived.

Slowly soluble nitrogen materials result in a relatively slow increase in growth rates and color, but their effects last longer. Depending on the material and the environment, some may supply nitrogen from three to four months up to a whole growing season (Figure 2).

The method by which nitrogen is made available to the plant from the controlled or slow-release nitrogen materials can be important in managing a fertility program (Table 6). Some materials are released by water action (hydrolysis), others through the action of soil-borne bacteria.

As an example, microbial activity is low in cold, wet soils. A nitrogen material that relies on that type of release will not be as effective as one that is released by hydrolysis. Soils very high or very low in pH also have reduced microbial activity.

Fast growth tends to require higher amounts of water. The plant has thinner cell walls, which make insect or disease invasion easier. These plants may also be more susceptible to heat and cold damage.

Table 5. Typical Fertilizer Analysis

Total nitrogen	15%
Water-soluble nitrogen	7.5%
Water-insoluble nitrogen	7.5%
Total P_2O_5	5%
Total K_2O	10%
Total Sulfur	6%
Total Iron	3%

Table 6. Nitrogen Release Characteristics

N Source	Hydrolysis	Microbial Decomposition
IBDU	X	
Natural Organic		X
Ureaformaldehyde		X
Resin-Coated Urea	X	
Methylene Urea		X
Sulfur-Coated Urea	X	X

Figure 2. Nitrogen Release

GROWTH (vertical axis) — TIME (horizontal axis)

Fertilizer Applied

—— Soluble Nitrogen
------ Slowly-Soluble Nitrogen

Organic Fertilizers

Nitrogen is available in a fertilizer either in an organic form or in an inorganic form. The inorganic forms are water soluble and quickly available to the plant. The organic forms may be a synthetic product such as urea or one of the many forms of natural organics including sewage sludge and animal manures. Even though urea is an organic source of nitrogen, it is still water soluble and quickly available to the plant. All the forms of organic nitrogen listed in Table 6 are slowly soluble and typically release nitrogen over a 6- to 8-week period.

All organic forms of nitrogen are converted first to the ammonical form (NH_4 of nitrogen and then to the nitrate (NO_3) form in the soil by microbial action. Plants prefer and only take up the nitrate form of nitrogen.

The basic disadvantage of organic fertilizers, especially the slow-release ones and the natural organics, is that they tend to have a very low nutrient content (Table 4).

Salt Index

Fertilizing materials are salts, just like table or rock salt. If fertilizers are over-applied they can cause the death of a plant, known as "fertilizer burn."

When a fertilizer is applied and enters the soil solution, the osmotic pressure of that solution is increased. Water moves from areas of low

Table 7. Salt Index	
Nitrogen Sources	**Salt Index per Unit of N**
Ammonium Nitrate	3.2
Ammonium Sulfate	3.3
IBDU	0.1
Methylene Urea	0.7
Natural Organic	0.8
UF	0.8
Urea	1.7
Sulfur-Coated Urea	0.7
Others	**Salt Index per Unit of Nutrient**
Super Phosphate	8
Potassium Chloride	114
Potassium Sulfate	46
Gypsum	8
Dolomite	1
Diammonium Phosphate	1.7
Monoammonium Phosphate	2.7
Potassium Nitrate	73

osmotic pressure to areas of high pressure. Normally, the solutions inside the plant are higher than the soil solution, so water runs into the plant. If a fertilizer is over-applied, water can be pulled out of the plant, though, and the plant would then die from lack of water (Figure 3).

The possibility of fertilizer burn is countered by watering the fertilizer into the soil. Any salt effect is thus diluted. The possibility of fertilizer burn is greater on hot days than on cool days because plants use more water on hot days.

Fertilizing materials vary in their ability to produce a burn (Table 7). The salt-index number has no units and is just used to compare materials. For example, if a fertilizer has urea as its nitrogen source, there would only be one-half the chance of fertilizer burn than if ammonium nitrate was used.

Note that all slowly soluble nitrogen materials have a low salt index and thus a low burn potential. If a soil or water test indicates the presence of a potential salt problem, then it makes sense to use low salt index fertilizer materials.

Fertilizer Application

Three basic questions should be asked when a landscape manager develops a turf fertility program:
- What fertilizer analysis is best?
- How much of that fertilizer should be applied?
- When should it be applied?

Analysis: The best way to determine the correct analysis is to soil test. In this age of environmental concern, it is more important than ever to apply only those nutrients absolutely needed by the turf. Nutrients not used by the plant may end up as sources of groundwater pollution. Only a soil test can help evaluate a given soil's capacity to supply plant nutrients.

Most state land grant universities, through their local extension services, offer soil testing. Follow the directions and make sure the sample represents the whole area to be fertilized. Testing the soil every two to three years can be beneficial.

The best time for this procedure is in the winter, during the dormant season.

Use the same lab each time, as labs may vary in the techniques they use.

The real value to soil testing, aside from the current information it provides, is evaluating the soil's status over a long period. For example, if the soil test reports the soil salt level, it's important to know if the salt level is decreasing or increasing over the years. If salt levels are going up, it would become necessary to find out where the salt is coming from and to develop a program to reverse the trend. If the soil levels of phosphorous, potassium or any other nutrient are going up over several testing periods, less of that nutrient should be used.

When properly evaluated, soil tests are important in any landscape management program. Testing is the only way to determine the best fertilizer analysis to use.

Turfgrass Application Rate

Fertilizer is a growth regulator. The more you apply, the more the plant grows. Of course, this is only true up to a point, since too much fertilizer may increase the risk of fertilizer burn.

A rule of thumb for fertilizer application holds that no more than 1 pound of nitrogen should be applied for each 1,000 square feet of turf, especially if the nitrogen source is soluble. A slowly soluble or controlled-release source is usually applied at slightly higher rates. All turf fertilization rates are based on pounds of nitrogen per 1,000 square feet.

Application Frequency: Frequency of fertilizer application depends on the form of nitrogen in the fertilizer. The goal of any fertilizer program is to provide the turf with a slow, steady supply of the plant nutrients it needs, as it needs them. The turfgrass plant needs this steady supply of all plant nutrients during its favorable growth periods.

Under most circumstances, a pound of nitrogen from a soluble source will effectively last from four to six weeks, depending on environmental conditions, soil sandiness and clay content. Fertilizers do not last as long when the soil is sandy because of increased leaching. Fertilizer containing nitrogen in a slowly soluble or insoluble form may last from six to eight weeks and even longer.

Application Dates: Fertilizer timing should be a function of turf growth and not the calendar. In spring, both North and South, the fertilizer program should begin when the turf begins to grow.

In the North, fertilizer programs begin in early spring. Fertilizing should stop if and when growth begins to slow down as summer temperatures increase. Fertilizer is again applied as the cool fall temperatures encourage renewed growth. Researchers have found that a final fertilizer application, after turf has stopped growing in the fall and before it freezes, improves turf quality.

In the South, the fertilizer program begins with spring greenup and continues through the summer. The last fertilizer application should be about six or eight weeks before the average killing frost date.

A good turf fertilization program is a result of soil testing, careful observation and experience.

Woody Plants

There is a fairly good chance that the soil in which the new plant is placed will not contain optimum amounts of all the nutrients it needs for good growth. A soil test is critical. Soil test results should reflect the analysis of the fertilizer selected to be added at the end of the planting process.

Woody plant fertilization can keep the plant growing at an optimum rate and help reduce pest problems. Well-established plants may not need a fertilization at all. In fact, the over-application of soluble nitrogen may cause a very weak growth form that is susceptible to insect and disease problems.

There are five common fertilizer application methods used for woody plants. They are broadcast, drill holes, liquid soil injection, foliar spraying and implants.

Liquid Soil Injection—In this system, the amount of nutrient getting to the plant depends on the release rate of the fertilizer material, the spacing of the injection holes, the amount of liquid injected and the depth at which the material is placed. Generally the whole area under the tree to several feet beyond the canopy is fertilized. Injection holes about 8 to 12 inches deep are spaced about 3 feet apart.

Drill Holes—This method is based on 250 holes per 1,000 square feet. This means that the 8- to 12-inch deep holes are 2 feet apart. Instead of a

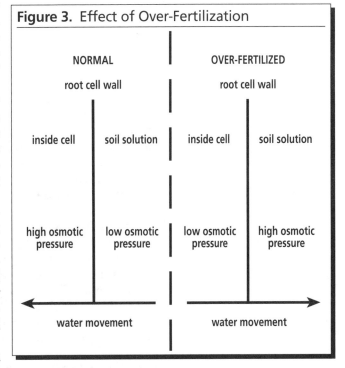

Figure 3. Effect of Over-Fertilization

NORMAL — root cell wall — inside cell | soil solution — high osmotic pressure | low osmotic pressure — water movement

OVER-FERTILIZED — root cell wall — inside cell | soil solution — low osmotic pressure | high osmotic pressure — water movement liquid being injected into each hole, dry fertilizer is used. A suggested fertilizer rate is ¼ cup of a 10 percent nitrogen fertilizer per hole. It is suggested that no holes be dug within 3 feet of the tree trunk.

Broadcast—This is the basic method of fertilizer application for lawns and shrub beds. The same fertilizers used on lawns can be used at the same rate on shrubs.

Foliar Spraying—This technique is usually used to correct many micro-nutrient deficiencies, such as iron, zinc, boron and manganese. This is a very effective, fast way to overcome these deficiencies.

Trunk Implants or Injections—Used to correct many micro-nutrient deficiencies, but should be used only if other methods fail. The wood and bark around the hole may be killed and could lead to decay.

Time of Application

Generally, the fertilizer should be available in the rootzone when the tree or shrub begins growth in the spring. The worst time to fertilize is in late summer, when the fertilizer can stimulate an excessive amount of new growth. This new growth may be highly susceptible to winter damage and even winter kill.

Foliar sprays containing one or more micro-nutrients can be applied in early spring after the first new lawns are full size.

Fertilizer Application Calculations

The percentages of most fertilizer nutrients, including nitrogen (N), are expressed on an elemental basis. The percentages of phosphorus (P) and potassium (K), however, are expressed as the compounds phosphoric acid (P_2O_5) and potash (K_2O).

The standard method of measurement of fertilizers is by "percentage of weight." This is true whether the fertilizer is in liquid or solid form. If it is a liquid, the weight of the liquid must be determined before the amount of nutrients it contains can be known. Typically, turfgrass fertilizer application rates are expressed as pounds of N per 1,000 square feet or per acre.

EXAMPLE 1. A 100-pound bag of 12-4-8 fertilizer contains how many pounds of N, P and K?

The number 12 indicates that the fertilizer is 12 percent N. Multiply the weight of the bag (100 pounds) by the percent N (12) in decimal form (0.12).

100 x 0.12 = 12 pounds N

The number 4 indicates that the fertilizer is 4 percent P_2O_5. Multiply the weight of the bag (100 pounds) by the percent P_2O_5 (4) in decimal form (0.04)

100 x 0.04 = 4 pounds P_2O_5

The final step is to determine the amount of potash (K_2O) in the 100-pound bag of 12-4-8. The final number, 8, indicates the fertilizer is 8 percent K_2O. Multiply the weight of the bag (100 pounds) by the percent K_2O (8) in decimal form (0.08).

100 x 0.08 = 8 pounds K_2O

In summary,100 pounds of a 12-4-8 fertilizer contains:

12 pounds N

4 pounds P_2O_5 4 pounds x .43* = 1.7 pound P

8 pounds K_2O 8 pounds x .83** = 6.6 pounds K

* P_2O_5 is 43 percent or .43 actual P.

** K_2O is 83 percent or .83 actual K.

EXAMPLE 2: How many pounds of an 18-6-12 fertilizer are required to fertilize a 7,500 square foot green at the rate of 2 pounds N per 1,000 square feet?

The first step is to determine how many pounds of the 18-6-12 are needed to get 1 pound N. Since the 18 is a percentage (0.18) it is divided into 1.

$$\frac{1}{0.18} = 5.6$$

This means that 5.6 pounds of 18-6-12 contain 1 pound N.

Your answer may be rechecked by multiplying the answer, 5.6 by the percent N (0.18).

5.6x0.18 = 1.01b.N

Since 5.6 pounds of 18-6-12 will provide 1 pound N, then 2 x 5.6 pounds (11.2 pounds) will provide 2 pounds N.

There are 7.5 1,000s (M) in 7,500 square feet = 7.5 M (M abbreviation for 1,000).

7.5 x 11.2 lbs. = 84 lbs. of 18-6-12/green, so 84 pounds of 18-6-12 will provide 2 pounds N on 7500 square feet.

EXAMPLE 3: How many pounds of a 20-2-8 fertilizer are needed to apply 1 pound N per 1,000 square feet on a 2.3 acre fairway?

In a 2.3 acre fairway there are 100,188 square feet.
(43,560 sq. ft./A. x 2.3 A. = 100,188 sq. ft.)

Since the rate is 1 pound N per 1,000 sq. ft. and there are approximately 100 M square feet in the fairway, about 100 pounds N are needed.

The fertilizer is 20 percent N.

$$\frac{1}{0.20} = 5 \text{ lbs. of 20-2-8 will provide 1 lb. N}$$

(Check: 0.20 (20 percent N) x 5 lb. (20-2-8) = 1.0 lb. N)

If 5 pounds of 20-2-8 contains 1 pound N and 100 pounds of N is needed, then 5 x 100 or 500 pounds of 20-2-8 will provide 1 pound N per 1,000 square feet on the 2.3 acre fairway.

EXAMPLE 4: How much of a 15-6-9 liquid fertilizer is required to apply 1 pound N per 1,000 square feet on a 6000 square foot green?

The following information is needed in order to solve this problem: 1 gallon of liquid fertilizer weighs 10 pounds (always check container to get this weight). If 1 gallon of fertilizer weighs 10 pounds and is 15 percent N, then 1 gallon contains 1.5 pounds N.

0.15 (15 percent) N x 10 lbs. = 1.5 lbs. N.

Since 1 gallon contains 1.5 pounds N, then 0.67 gallon contains 1.0 pound N.

$$\frac{1}{1.5} = 0.67 \text{ gal.}$$

Since the green is 6000 (6 x 1,000) square feet, the total amount of liquid fertilizer required is 6 x 0.67 gallon or about 4 gallons.

NOTE: First determine the weight per gallon of a liquid fertilizer before determining the application rate on a liquid basis.

EXAMPLE 5: If all other factors are equal, which of the following is a better buy?

	Fertilizer A	Fertilizer B	Fertilizer C
Analysis:	12-4-8	24-8-16	9-3-6
			(Liq. 10.5 lb./gal.)
Cost/ton:	$120	$216	$27.00/5 5 gal.

In order to compare the costs, first determine the cost of a unit of N for each fertilizer.

Fertilizer A is 12 percent (0.12) N fertilizer. In 1 ton (2,000 lbs.) there are 0.12 (12 percent) x 2,000 or 240 pounds N.

If 240 pounds cost $ 120, then 1 pound costs:

$$\frac{\$120}{240 \text{ lbs}} = \$0.50/\text{lb. N}$$

Fertilizer B is a 24 percent (0.24) N fertilizer. In 1 ton there are 0.24 (24 percent) x 2,000 or 480 pounds N.

If 480 pounds cost $216, then 1 pound costs:

$$\frac{\$216}{480} = \$0.45/\text{lb N}$$

Fertilizer C is 9 percent (0.09) N fertilizer and weighs 10.5 pounds per gallon. In 1 ton there are 0.36 (36 percent) x 2,000 or 720 pounds N. If the weight per gallon is 10.5 pounds, then 55 gallons will weigh 577.5 pounds.

577.5 lbs. x 0.09 (9 percent N) = 52 lbs. N if - 52 pounds cost $27, then 1 pound costs:

$$\frac{\$27}{52} = \$0.52/\text{lb. N}$$

Therefore, in this example, Fertilizer B at $0.45 per pound N is the better buy.

NOTE: The per-pound prices of N determined in this problem do not reflect the true cost of a unit of N. This is only a method which may be used to compare fertilizer prices. All three fertilizers in this example have the same ratio of nutrients (3-1-2) .

Water insoluble N sources tend to be more expensive than water soluble N sources per unit of N. The amount of water insoluble N contained in a fertilizer, as well as the percentages of the other nutrients it contains, must be considered when comparing fertilizer prices.

EXAMPLE 6: How much of the following fertilizer materials will be required to apply a 3-1-2 ratio of nutrients (N-P205-K20) at a rate of 1 pound N per 1,000 square feet on a 7,000 square foot green?

Fertilizer Materials:
A. 38-0-0 *(ureaformaldehyde)*
B. 0-20-0 *(superphosphate)*
C. 0-0-50 *(potassium sulfate)*

A. Since ureaformaldehyde (UF) is 38 percent (0.38) N, then $\frac{1}{0.38}$ or 2.6 pounds of UF contain 1 pound N.

2.6 lbs. (UF) x 7 (7,000 sq. ft.) = 18.2 total lbs.
UF required to apply 1 pound N per 1,000 sq. ft. on the green.

B. The ratio of nutrients in this problem is 3-1-2. This means for every 3 units of N there is 1 unit of P_2O_5, or for every 1 unit of N there is one-third unit of P_2O_5.

Since the rate of N application is 1 pound per 1,000 sq. ft., then the rate of P_2O_5 application is one-third pound per 1,000 sq. ft.

Superphosphate is 20 percent (0.20) P_2O_5.

$\frac{1}{0.20}$ = 5 lbs. of 0-20-0 will contain 1 lb P_2O_5

We need one-third pound P_2O_5 per 1,000 sq. ft, so 1/3(0.33) x 5 = 1.65 lbs. of 0-20-0 will provide one-third lb. P_2O_5/1,000 sq. ft.

1.65 lbs. x 7 (7,000 sq. ft.) = 11.5 total lbs. 0-20-0 required to apply one-third pound P_2O_5/1,000 sq. ft. on the green.

C. The ratio of nutrients in this problem is 3-1-2. This means for every 3 units of N there is 2 units of K_2O, or for every 1 unit of N there is two-thirds unit of K_2O.

Since the rate of N application is 1 pound per 1,000 sq. ft., then the rate of K_2O application is two-thirds pound per 1000 sq. ft.

Potassium sulfate is 50 percent (0.50) K_2O.

$\dfrac{1}{0.50}$ = 2 lbs. of 0-0-50 contain 1 lb K_2O.

We need 2/3 pound of K_2O per 1000 sq. ft., so 2/3 (0.67) x 2 = 1.34 lbs. 0-0-50 will provide 2/3 pound K_2O/1,000 sq. ft.

1.34 lbs. x 7 (7,000 sq. ft.) = 9.4 total lbs. 0-0-50 required to apply 2/3 pound K_2O/1,000 square feet on the green.

The answer to this problem is therefore:
18.2 pounds 38-0-0
11.5 pounds 0-20-0
 9.4 pounds 0-0-50
NOTE: In the above problem, the rates of both P and K were determined on the basis of P_2O_5 and K_2O. If the problem had asked for the material rates based on an elemental (N-P-K) ratio instead of a oxide ratio, the results would be different. Because N is always expressed on an elemental basis, there would not be any difference in the amount of UF needed.

Superphosphate (0-20-0) is expressed as P_2O_5 which is 43 percent (0.43) P. To convert from P_2O_5 to P use the formula P = percent P_2O_5 x (0.43), and to find out how many pounds of 0-20-0 are needed to provide 11.5 pounds of P, divide 1 by 0.43

$\dfrac{1}{0.43}$ = 2 3

Then multiply 11.5 x 2.3 = 26.5 lbs. 0-20-0 provides 11.5 pounds P.

Potassium sulfate (0-0-50) is expressed as K_2O which is 83 percent (0.83) K. To convert from K_2O to K, use the formula K = percent K_2O x (0.83), and to find out how many pounds of 0-0-50 are needed to provide 9.4 pounds K, divide 1 by 0.83.

$\dfrac{1}{0.83}$ = 1.2 lbs.

Then multiply 9.4 x 1.2 = 11.3 lbs. 0-0-50 contain 9.4 pounds K.

The answer to the problem on an elemental basis is: 18.2 pounds 38-0-0
26.5 pounds 0-20-0
11.3 pounds 0-0-50.

Spreader Selection, Use, and Calibration
Spreader Types and Selection

Turf managers can now choose from three basic types of fertilizer spreaders—the broadcast type and the drop type which have been around for years, and a recent addition, the air carrier spreader. Each type has advantages and disadvantages.

The pattern width of a drop spreader is limited to the width of the hopper. Better quality spreaders of this type generally provide very uniform patterns and they require no pattern adjustment. Drop spreaders work very well in small turf areas, or areas such as golf greens where uniformity of application is critical. Application with a drop spreader, however, will usually take longer than with broadcast spreaders, since comparably-priced broadcast spreaders usually have a considerably wider effective pattern width. Drop spreaders have two other potential limitations. Some of them have low ground clearance, and thus the ports may tend to plug from dew on the turf. Also, some drop spreaders will not handle larger particles of fertilizer without plugging. Some high-quality drop spreaders avoid both of these problems, but they are more expensive.

Drop spreaders tend to have more aggresive agitation than broadcast spreaders, and thus may crack or damage coated fertilizer materials, negating such fertilizers' slow-release characteristics.

Broadcast spreaders fall into two subcategories: rotary and pendulum. Rotary broadcast spreaders use one (or two) spinning impellers to sling the granules out in an arc around the spreader. Pendulum broadcast spreaders use a tube oscillating back and forth in a horizontal plane to sling the granules out in an arc behind the spreader. The primary advantage of pendulum spreaders over rotary spreaders is that pendulum spreaders provide a pattern that is fairly uniform from side to side without any pattern adjustment, while rotary spreaders require a pattern adjustment to center the pattern when choosing products. The pattern adjustment on rotary spreaders may be accomplished by moving the drop point of the granules on the impeller radially or angularly, changing the angle of the impeller fins, or restricting flow from some of the metering ports.

Broadcast spreaders will generally deliver a pattern that is less uniform than that delivered by a drop spreader, but broadcast spreaders are more forgiving: an overlap error of 2-3 inches will probably cause a stripe with a drop spreader, while most broadcast spreader patterns are more tolerant of overlap errors since the patterns taper at the sides. This tapering characteristic of broadcast spreaders becomes a negative, however, when trying to apply product uniformly along the edge of a sidewalk or driveway. A major concern with broadcast spreaders is that an effective swath width must be determined for each product in all broadcast spreaders—even pendulum spreaders. In contrast, the swath width remains constant for drop spreaders.

Striping of turf can also occur when a broadcast spreader is used to spread a blended fertilizer whose particles sizes are not uniform. If, for instance, the nitrogen granules are larger than the potash granules, the outer fringes of the pattern will have a higher ratio of nitrogen to potash than the center of the pattern, causing striping. This is not a problem with homogenous fertilizers, and the problem is minimal if all of the components of a blend are the same particle *size* (note that particle size uniformity is much more important than having the same particle *density*).

Air carrier spreaders use streams of air in tubes to convey the granules out to distribution points along a boom. As the air and granules exit the tubes, the granules strike a scatter plate to provide a more uniform pattern that should not stripe the turf. Pattern width is consistent and predictable. A critical concern with air carrier spreaders is the uniform splitting of the metered granual into the individual distribution tubes. Better air carrier spreaders do this well and thus achieve good uniformity. Particle damage with air carrier spreaders is usually not a major problem, but could be a concern with delicate product granules.

Drop and air carrier spreaders can usually be used in moderate wind with minimal pattern disturbance; broadcast spreader patterns are very susceptible to wind disturbance.

Spreader Use

No matter how good the spreader or product, uniform application at the correct rate depends on the operator. Spreaders should be calibrated and then used according to the manufacturer's instructions.

To deliver uniform rates, most spreaders must be operated at consistent travel speeds. Although some large spreaders used by commercial applicators are speed-compensating, virtually all turf spreaders are speed-sensitive. Some sources have claimed that drop spreaders are not sensitive to speed changes, but research has proven that they are. Broadcast spreaders are even more sensitive to speed, in terms of both rate and pattern changes. Walk-behind push spreaders are generally calibrated for 3 mph. Tractor-drawn or mounted spreaders may be operated over a wide range of speeds, but must be calibrated for the speed to be used.

It is usually desirable to lay out headlands across both ends of rectangular turf areas or around the edges of an irregular area, then operate the spreader back and forth between the headlands, *being certain to shut the spreader off as you enter the headland*. Do not leave the spreader open while turning, since this will result in a heavy, uneven pattern.

If the proper calibration procedure is followed and the spreader pattern is acceptable, the normal swath width can be used. If the spreader cannot be adjusted enough to provide an acceptable pattern at the normal swath width or if excellent uniformity is required, the operator can improve uniformity by using half the normal swath width and a rate setting that delivers half the desired rate (see Figure 4). This method is far more effective than making two trips over the turf area at right angles. The right angle method just changes the potential for a striped pattern into the potential for a checkerboard pattern; it does not eliminate the pattern extremes.

Spreader Calibration

Many spreaders and/or granular products come with tables of spreader settings. These published settings should be used only as a starting point for individual calibration since spreader performance rate and pattern can be affected by many factors including operating speed, spreader angle, humidity, changes in granule size from batch to batch, and condition of the spreader. All spreaders should be calibrated for rate by the operator who will be using the spreader, and all broadcast spreaders should be tested in addition so that an effective swath pattern width and pattern settings, where applicable, can be determined. Pattern testIng must be done first, since the width must be known prior to rate calibration.

The easiest way to conduct a pattern test is to operate the spreader past a perpendicular line of collection trays, (as shown in Figure 5). The trays can be shallow cardboard boxes, cake pans, or commercial pattern trays. The trays should have interior subdivision to prevent granules from bouncing out. After operating the spreader past the line of trays, the material in each tray is poured up and either weighed or volumetrically measured. It is often desirable to make more than one pass over the trays to get enough material to measure (note that multiple passes must all be in the same direction). After observing the measured amount of material from each try, it should be possible to determine if the pattern is acceptable, and if so, the effective swath width. If the observed

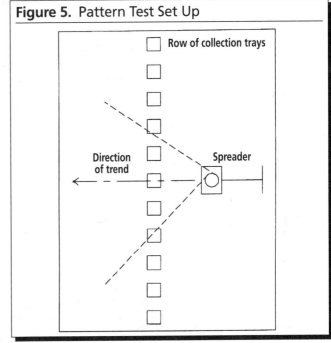

Figure 4. Spreading Operating Patterns

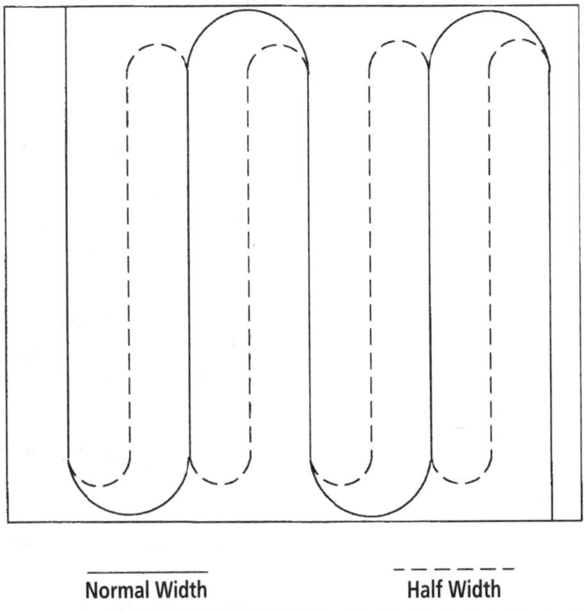

Normal Width   Half Width

Figure 5. Pattern Test Set Up

Row of collection trays

Direction of trend   Spreader

pattern is not acceptable, the spreader should be adjusted and the test repeated. If the pattern appears acceptable, the effective swath width can be determined by noting the points on each side of the pattern.

When the rate has dropped to approximately half the average rate in the center pans. The sum of the distance left and right to this point is the effective swath width.

Computer programs are available to help determine pattern uniformity and effective swath width once the data has been collected, but the approximate method detailed above will generally give satisfactory results. In fact, measuring the granules in the trays can be eliminated (with some loss in precision) if the granules are merely poured into slim vials or test tubes. The vials can then be arranged side by side for a graphic portrayal of the pattern. The swath width can be visually determined from the vials.

Once the swath width is known, the operator can proceed with rate calibration. In order to perform a rate calibration, two things must be determined: a test area and the amount of material applied to that area. The easiest way for an operator to calibrate any spreader is to catch the material discharged by the spreader while traversing the known area.

For drop spreaders, a long, narrow collection pan can be suspended under the hopper. A simple way to make such a pan is to cut a piece of metal gutter material to length and close off the ends with wood, paper, etc. This pan should hang from the spreader axle or from the top edge of the hopper. It should *never* be attached to the shut-off plate that controls the spreader rate.

For rotary broadcast spreaders, a box that fits around the impeller and collects material while the spreader operates seems to work best. These boxes are commercially available and a good investment for turf managers, but a simple box could also be fabricated in-house.

EXAMPLE 1: Suppose you measure the material in the collection trays and get the following result:

10' left	8' left	6' left	4' left	2' left	center	2' right	4' right	6' right	8' right	10' right
1 g	2 g	8 g	9 g	8 g	5 g	4 g	4 g	2 g	2 g	0 g

In this case, it is obvious that the pattern is skewed heavily to the right and needs to be adjusted.

EXAMPLE 2: The spreader is adjusted and retested with the following result:

10' left	8' left	6' left	4' left	2' left	center	2' right	4' right	6' right	8' right	10' right
1 g	2 g	4 g	6 g	8 g	9 g	8 g	7 g	4 g	3 g	1 g

This pattern is not perfect, but is typical for broadcast spreaders. The center of the pattern averaged about 8 g, thus the overlap points should occur where the rate is about half that amount or 4. This occurs at 6 feet left and 6 feet right. The effective swath width is thus 12 feet. This means that the operator should make the centerline of each pass 12 feet from the centerline of the preceding pass.

For air carrier spreaders, it is simplest to attach paper or plastic bags to each tube to catch the output.

For all of the above situations, the spreader is operated over a known distance, say 100 or 200 feet. This distance multiplied by the effective swath width becomes the application area. Dividing this area into the weight of material collected gives the application rate

EXAMPLE 3: A drop spreader with a width of 2 feet is pushed 100 feet while a collection pan catches the granules. The weight of material caught is 1.2 pounds.

The effective area is thus 2 feet x 100 feet or 200 square feet. This can be converted to acres (A) or thousand square feet (M).

$$200 \text{ ft}^2 \times \frac{1 \text{ A}}{43{,}560 \text{ ft}^2} = 0.0046 \text{ A}$$

or

$$200 \text{ ft}^2 \times \frac{1 \text{ A}}{1{,}000 \text{ ft}^2} \quad 0.2 \text{ M}$$

The delivery rate is thus 1.2 lb/0.0046 A = 261 lb/A

or

1.2 lb/0.2 M = 6.0 lb/M.

The rate calibration for a pendulum spreader is slightly different. The operator should drive the known distance in the appropriate gear and throttle setting and measure the time to traverse the distance. Next, the spout should be removed and a bucket or bag used to collect the material discharged by the spreader while operating at the same throttle setting with the vehicle stationary and the PTO engaged. The calculations are the same as above. The area is the effective swath width multiplied by the test distance.

Once a delivery rate has been determined for any spreader, the rate is compared to the desired or label rate. If the actual rate does not match the desired rate, the spreader rate setting must be changed and the test repeated until the desired rate is obtained. ❧

Spreader information provided by
Dr. Richard L. Parish
Louisiana State University

Notes

8 CHAPTER

Landscape Irrigation

One of the goals in landscape management is to produce plants that grow at a steady rate during the growing season. This means water must be available to the plant at regular intervals. Few parts of the country can depend on natural rainfall to completely supply water at the desirable intervals. Irrigation then becomes necessary.

Some plants survive even extended dry periods without water, but none stay green and growing without irrigation. There is a great difference in the relative need for water between turfgrass types and varieties (Table 1). Water availability and cost should be a consideration when selecting a turfgrass.

Plants vary in the expression of drought stress. The leaves of some plants begin to droop. Others, such as turfgrasses, dry up, with the leaves rolling and turning a dull purple color. This process is called dry wilt.

Too much water also has a harmful effect on plants. The root system must take in oxygen and give off carbon dioxide to live. When water is applied too frequently, the soil becomes saturated and oxygen movement into the soil and carbon dioxide movement out of the soil is stopped. The result is a condition in the plant termed "wet wilt." If not corrected, plant death may soon follow.

New Turf

Newly seeded or sprigged areas should be watered lightly at frequent intervals. The seed or sprigs must be kept moist, not saturated, during this initial growth period. This means that during hot, windy days, four or five applications of water per day might be necessary.

The first 10 days to two weeks is especially critical. If young plants are allowed to dry out, they may die. After about two weeks, root development should be adequate to slowly reduce watering frequency. About one month after seeding or sprigging, water the same as an established turf.

Newly sodded or plugged areas should be watered much like established turf, except more frequently. After planting, the sod or plugs should be soaked so that soil under the sod is wet to a depth of two or three inches.

Each time the sod or plugs begin to dry, resoak. Roots develop fairly rapidly, and within about two weeks the area should be treated like established turf.

Established Turf

WHEN TO WATER—Ideally, any turf should be watered just before it begins to wilt. Most grasses take on a dull purple cast and leaf blades begin to fold or roll. Turf under drought stress also shows evidence of tracks after someone walks on it. These are some of the first signs of

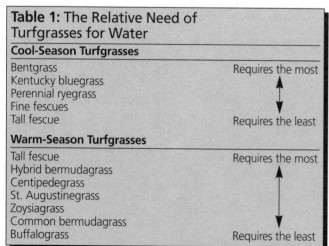

Table 1: The Relative Need of Turfgrasses for Water	
Cool-Season Turfgrasses	
Bentgrass	Requires the most
Kentucky bluegrass	
Perennial ryegrass	
Fine fescues	
Tall fescue	Requires the least
Warm-Season Turfgrasses	
Tall fescue	Requires the most
Hybrid bermudagrass	
Centipedegrass	
St. Augustinegrass	
Zoysiagrass	
Common bermudagrass	
Buffalograss	Requires the least

wilt. With careful observation and experience, it isn't hard to determine just how many days turf can go between waterings.

Early morning is the best time to water. The wind is usually calm and the temperature is low, so less water is lost to evaporation. The worst time to water is late evening because the grass may stay wet all night, making it more susceptible to disease. During the hot afternoon, evaporation rates are highest.

HOW MUCH WATER?—When a landscape needs water, enough should be applied to wet the soil to a depth of four to six inches, but the type of soil has a great deal to do with how much water is needed. In Figure 1, note the depth of wetting resulting from the application of one inch of water. It should take about 1/2 inch of water to achieve the desired wetting depth if the soil is high in sand content, and about 3/4 inch of water if the soil is a loam. For soils high in clay, an inch of water is usually necessary to wet the soil to the desired depth. It takes about 27,000 gallons for each one inch of water over one acre of surface.

If water application rates are too light or frequent, plants may become weak and shallow rooted, making them more susceptible to stress injury (Figure 2).

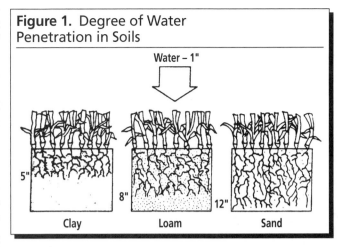

Figure 1. Degree of Water Penetration in Soils

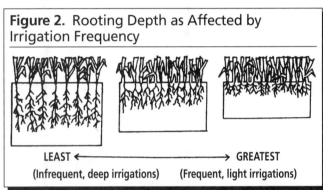

Figure 2. Rooting Depth as Affected by Irrigation Frequency

LEAST ← → GREATEST
(Infrequent, deep irrigations) (Frequent, light irrigations)

Factors To Consider

SOIL TYPE—Water penetrates a sandy soil much faster than a clay soil, so plants grown on sandy soils require more frequent watering than those grown on soils high in clay. Because water moves fairly slowly into a clay soil, application rate should be as slow as possible (See Chapter 1-Table 2).

SLOPE—Landscaped areas with a high degree of slope present a particular problem. Water may run down the slope without penetrating the soil and must be applied at very slow rates from sprinklers near the top of the slope. Sprinklers on the slope or near the bottom may prove ineffective. Core aerification and/or use of a wetting agent may aid water penetration.

FERTILIZER—The faster a plant grows, especially turfgrass, the more water it requires. Slow- release fertilizers containing materials such as sulfur-coated urea or ureaformaldehyde as nitrogen sources do not tend to produce high growth rates. Heavy applications of fertilizers high in soluble nitrogen should be avoided.

MANAGEMENT FACTORS—Use of an aerifier or coring device aids in increasing movement of water into the soil. A surfactant or wetting agent may also aid the movement of water into high clay soils.

WATER QUALITY—Landscaped areas use a variety of sources for irrigation water. Treated city water may have the highest quality, but may be the most expensive. Rivers, ponds and wells usually supply less expensive water, but there could be water quality problems with these sources.

There are many materials that cause damage by polluting water supplies. Surface water supplies are especially open to pollution. Chemicals such as pesticides as well as fine soil particles like silt and clay may cause problems. Dirty irrigation water can slowly seal the surface of a soil and create serious drainage problems.

Presence of high levels of soluble salts may also cause poor water quality.

Water testing by a competent lab is a recommended, especially if there is any reason to suspect trouble.

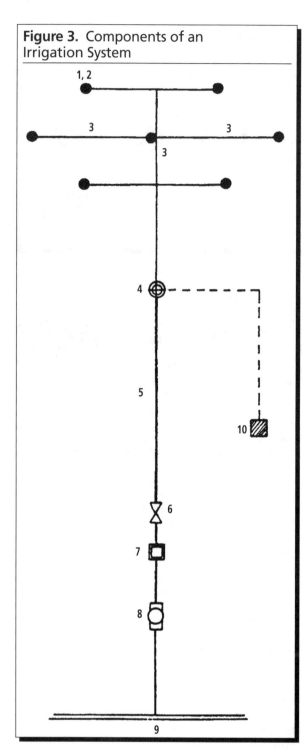

Figure 3. Components of an Irrigation System

Irrigation systems should be designed to fit the topography of the landscape, soil type (infiltration rates) and direction of the prevailing winds. Sprinkler pattern distortion caused by wind can be a problem.

Sprinkler System Terminology

Many elements comprise good irrigation design. Essential to good design is knowledge of terminology and function of irrigation system components (Figure 3).

Starting from the point where the water is discharged and working back to the point of connection with the water supply are the following components:

1. Nozzle/emitter from which water is directed to the plants.
2. Head—holds the nozzle and is usually buried in the ground with the top flush with the soil surface.
3. Lateral lines connect all the heads in one zone to the mainline.
4. Zone valve controls operation of a zone of heads.
5. Mainline—the major waterline that services all the zones.
6. Main shut-off valve (gate valve) separates the irrigation system from the other water service (diagram shows typical alignment for a residential irrigation system). When in conjunction with a dedicated meter for the irrigation system, the main shut-off valve is often placed between the meter and the check valve.
7. Check valve/backflow-preventer is required by most building codes to prevent irrigation system water from flowing back into the water supply.
8. Meter—measures the amount of water flowing from the water supply to the user, usually for billing purposes.
9. Water main—water supply for the water service.
10. Controller—electric "brains" of an irrigation system, controls when the system operates and for how long it waters.

Sprinkler Heads, Micro-Sprinklers and Drip Emitters

In most irrigation systems, not all sprinkler heads can operate at one time because of pressure constraints. The task of developing zones of sprinkler heads requires separating different precipitation-rate heads, plants with different water needs (such as turf versus shrubs), sunny areas from shady areas and slopes from flat ground.

Each of these separate zones has its own valve, which allows it to operate independently of other zones. An irrigation system with many zones allows the greatest flexibility in managing the system. This flexibility is highly desirable as restrictions on outdoor water-use become more commonplace, especially during droughts.

The function of a well-designed irrigation system is to apply water to the plant's rootzone. It does not spray water high in the air; it does not create mist that is blown away or evaporated; and it does not water sidewalks, buildings, streets or other non-living surfaces.

The key to preventing these water wastes is using the proper watering equipment at the appropriate water pressure. Unfortunately, there is not just one irrigation method appropriate for watering every plant in the landscape. A well-designed irrigation system is a hybrid of several different methods that may include pop-up sprays, bubblers and drip and/or other low-flow irrigation.

Pop-up sprayers are ideal for watering turf areas and low-growing ground covers. Use bubblers for deep watering trees and large shrubs and to flood-irrigate planters and below-grade parkway strips (i.e., area between sidewalk and street) or parking lot medians.

Drip and other low-flow irrigation systems are good for watering rows of shrubs, flower beds and vegetable gardens. These also can be used to water taller ground covers, over 12 inches in height.

Sprinkler head or emitter layout is primarily determined by coverage of the nozzle and by recommendations provided by the manufacturer for the specific equipment. Of equal importance is keeping water off non-plant areas.

Specifications are part of the irrigation design package, including recommended brand of equipment, installation guidelines and a management schedule.

Other Irrigation System Components

Several pieces of irrigation equipment allow systems to be as effective and efficient as possible. These include: controller, rain shut-off device and a soil moisture measuring device.

An irrigation system can be only as flexible as the controller that operates it. At minimum, the controller should offer multiple programs so that different zones can operate on varying days of the week with at least three cycles per program for repeat watering during one operation. Repeat-cycle watering prevents run-off from slopes and tight clay soils.

A rain shut-off device keeps an irrigation system from turning on during rainfall or immediately after a significant rain event. This is a useful public relations tool for public and commercial landscapes, as well as a water and money saver for all types of landscapes, including residential.

A soil-moisture sensing device takes readings at the plant rootzone and allows the irrigation system to operate only at a pre-set moisture level. This keeps the system from operating too frequently, including following sufficient rainfall.

Irrigation Application Calculations

Knowing the amounts of water put out by a sprinkler will tell two things: 1) how much total water is being used with a certain number of sprinklers running; and 2) how many inches of water per hour are being put out.

a. What will the rate of water application in inches per hour (i.p.h.) be from a sprinkler that has a discharge rate of 30 gallons per minute (g.p.m.) and covers an area with a diameter of 90 feet?
   The formula is: $\dfrac{122 \times \text{g.p.m.}}{\text{diameter}^2}$

Using the information provided:
   $\dfrac{122 \times 30}{90^2} = \dfrac{3660}{8100} = 0.45$ i.p.h.

b. What must be the capacity of an irrigation system be in g.p.m. considering the following information?
   irrigated area = 125 acres
   system water factor* = 2
   peak need per week** = 1.6 in.
   hrs. per day available for irrigation = 10

Note: *The system water factor reflects the amount of water that must pass through the system to effectively apply one inch of water. It considers run-off evaporation, and assumes an "average" design of the irrigation system. This formula assumes an efficiency of 50 percent which will be low for some irrigation users.

**The peak need period is the amount of water in inches needed during the hottest and driest period of the year.

The first step is to multiply the number of acres (125) by the system water factor (2) and the peak need per week (1.6 in.).

125 A. x 2 x 1.6 in. = 400 A. in./week

The problem assumes 10 hours per day available for irrigation.

10 hrs./day x 7 days/wk. = 70 hrs./wk.

The system must have the capacity to apply 400 acre inches in 70 hours.

$$\frac{400 \text{ A. in.}}{70 \text{ hrs.}} = 57 \text{ A in./hr.}$$

If one A. in. = 27,000 gals., then 5.7 A. in./hr. = 153,900 gal./hr.

Divide by 60 to convert from gals./hr. to gals./min.

153,900 gals./hr. = 2,565 gals./min. capacity 60 min./hr.

Evapotranspiration (ET)

Landscape managers no longer rely on appearance alone to gauge water requirements. Instruments can measure moisture loss from the soil and in many states sophisticated, computerized weather stations gather meteorological data and translate it into information readily usable by landscape managers. Some larger expanses, such as golf courses or parks, have their own weather stations which collect site-specific data and feed it directly into a computerized irrigation system.

Plants lose water from both leaf and soil surfaces, and this water loss is called evapotranspiration. By measuring maximum and minimum air temperatures, solar radiation, wind speed, relative humidity and precipitation, meteorologists can come up with an evapotranspiration (ET) rate based on the location of the weather station or stations and specific to the datagathering site.

In California, a state agency maintains more than 70 CIMIS (California Irrigation Management Information System) stations throughout the state which approximate the water use of an irrigated pasture grass for a reference ET. The University of Arizona maintains a similar weather station network called the Arizona Meteorological Weather Network (AZMET). Landscape managers in many other western states rely on ET information generated by private weather stations or the National Weather Service. Actual daily reference ETs can be taken on a daily basis from these stations using computer modems. Or irrigators can use historical yet highly accurate ETs, gained from many years of weather records, to estimate plant water use.

Coefficients have been given for most agricultural crops, including landscapes, using evapotranspiration to measure water needs. By multiplying the reference ET by the crop coefficient, the exact water use of landscapes can be determined for any given day, week or month.

Crop coefficient (Kc) values for cool- or warm-seasons turf are then multiplied by the reference ET for a 24-hour period to get the exact ET for a certain period of time. For example, the AZMET crop coefficient for bermudagrass (0.80) multiplied by a 24-hour ET rate (0.30) would give a turfgrass manager the amount of soil water used by turf the previous day (0.30 x 0.80 = 0.24 inches). That's the amount of water that should be replaced to bring the turfgrass water availability back to 100 percent.

In most states, monthly crop coefficients are provided for both warm- and cool-season turfgrasses. The annual California crop coefficients are 0.8 for cool-season turfgrasses and 0.6 for warm-season turfgrasses.

A note of warning: crop coefficients may need to be decreased under shady conditions or increased slightly when turf is surrounded by heat-storing asphalt or cement.

Applying the correct amount of water is not only a conservation practice, but also not over- or under-irrigating lessens the chances of diseases, prevents fertilizer loss and encourages deeper turfgrass rooting, making the turfgrass more drought tolerant and less expensive to maintain.

An irrigation schedule can be determined with the water budget method, matching grass ET with the re-application of water to replace water used.

A water budget accounts for the water available to the plant based on its rooting depth and soil moisture capacity. It also accounts for the ET of turfgrass.

All soils contain two water fractions. The first, unavailable water, is tightly held by mineral and organic particles and is unavailable for plant use. The second, available water, is the amount the plant can absorb for transpiration and metabolism.

Generally, for turfgrass irrigation, a 50 percent depletion of soil water is suggested. This, along with root depth, gives an indication of the amount of water available to the turfgrass in the soil profile.

Turf species differ in rooting ability. In addition to species difference, root depths are influenced by seasonal fluctuations, management practices such as mowing and fertilization, and by on-site soil compaction. The best method to determine root depth in a particular location is by physical inspection. Since it is the objective of irrigation to supply water to the root system, root depths and soil texture play an important role in both water application and irrigation frequency.

Using soil depth, the effective root system depth and the evapotranspiration data, a water budget can be constructed. For example, a cool-season grass with a one-foot root system, growing on a loam soil, would have the following soil water reservoir:

Water available per foot (in inches) x root depth (in feet) = soil water reservoir (0.75 inch available/ft. x 1 foot = 0.75 inch water available). If the daily water use is 0.15 inch per day, then soil water reservoir divided by ET = days of sufficient supply (0.75 inch/foot divided by 0.15 inch per day = 5 day water supply).

Catch Can Test

The distribution uniformity (DU) and the average application rate of a sprinkler irrigation system can be measured by a catch can test. A catch can test involves placing cans on the surface of the irrigated area, operating the irrigation system for the irrigation time typical of the system operation, collecting and recording the water collected in each of the catch containers and evaluating the data to determine application uniformity and average application rate of the system.

The following equipment is necessary for performing a field catch can test:
1. 100 catch cans.
2. Plastic graduated cylinders (100 ml 250 ml. and 500 ml).
3. Measuring tape.
4. Stop watch.
5. Wire flags to mark sprinkler head locations.
6. Pitot tube and pressure gauge.
7. 4-foot length of hose and 5-gallon pail.

The opening diameter of the cans should be at least 2 inches. A vertically sided container is recommended to allow for easy measuring with a thin ruler. However, these containers cannot be stacked as easily as cans with sloping sides. An unbreakable, plastic container is preferable to glass or metal containers, which may break or rust. The base of the container should be large enough that the container will not easily tip over during the field test. It may be necessary to use stakes to support the catch cans in steep topography.

Where the audit is performed on a large site such as a golf course or park area, select a representative portion of the site. Sprinklers in large turf areas are frequently laid out in a repetitive pattern (triangular or square spacing). Unless significant pressure differences exist within the system, a typical subsection could be evaluated and the rest of the area assumed to have a similar application uniformity and average application rate. If such an assumption is made, the sprinkler heads throughout the system must be checked to insure that they are of the same type and have the same size nozzles.

The irrigation auditor may choose to perform a catch can test at a "problem" site, such as an area where the reason for poor turf performance needs to be identified. If the problem site is not typical of the rest of the system, additional, representative tests should be performed to typify the overall system.

It is difficult to provide detailed criteria on how many catch cans to use and where to place them during an evaluation because of the wide variety of irrigation systems in operation. The following recommendations, however, should provide some guidelines, but placement of the catch containers ultimately is left to the evaluator's judgment.

Catch cans should be placed in a grid spacing within the evaluation area. This allows easy recording of the test data and when data are evaluated it will identify areas being over- or under-irrigated, which then can be corrected.

Distance between catch cans should be limited to no more than 10 feet. Wider spacing may not provide the sensitivity necessary to discern inconsistencies in water application. Spacing closer than 10 feet is desirable, but halving the spacing requires more than twice as many catch containers. For a catch can grid covering an area 30 feet x 40 feet, a 10-foot spacing of containers requires 20 containers, while a 5-foot spacing would require 63 containers. The additional effort may not be worthwhile. The following example taken from an actual turfgrass audit illustrates this point:

Sprinkler spacing 30 x 40 feet;
Sprinkler diameter of coverage 70 feet.

The catch can test should match the normal operating time of the irrigation cycle to provide an accurate measure of the uniformity during a typical irrigation. If the irrigation system is automated, operating the system for the operation time already programmed into the controller is often simpler, and it also will provide an opportunity to time the controller with a stop watch to make sure it is operating properly.

It may be necessary to extend the operating test period if the normal cycle will not generate enough water for a meaningful test.

Measure the volume of water collected rather than the depth of water collected. Water depth can be measured only when using a vertical-sided container. Pouring the water collected in a can into a graduated cylinder allows rapid, precise measurement of the volume. Conical catch can containers with graduations marked on the sides are best because they can be read easily without pouring the water into a measuring device, but they are substantially more expensive than simple plastic tubs.

While volumes of collected water can be used directly to determine the application uniformity, it is more useful to convert the volume measurements to an application rate. The following formula is useful for making such a conversion for catch cans with circular openings:

$$\text{Application rate (in/hr)} = \frac{\text{Volume collected (ml) x 4.65}}{\text{Test duration (min) x}\atop\text{(can opening diam. in inches)}^2}$$

Converting from volume to application rate (in./hr.) allows easy comparison with irrigation scheduling information in inches of required water.

Monitoring the discharge or pressure of sprinklers can also yield information. The discharge (gpm) from a sprinkler can be measured by placing a short length of hose over the nozzle, directing the water into a container of known volume (a 5-gallon pail works well for this purpose). The time required to fill the container is measured with the stop watch, determining the discharge rate. For example, if it takes 45 seconds to fill a 5-gallon pail, the sprinkler discharge is:

$$\text{5 gallons x 60 sec/min} = \frac{\text{6.7 gallons per minute}}{\text{45 seconds.}}$$

Friction losses in the pipelines may vary the discharge rate. A rule-of-thumb is that discharge from similar sprinklers within the system should not vary by more than 10 percent.

Another way to measure variation between sprinklers is to monitor the pressure at the sprinklers. Using a pitot tube attached to a pressure gauge provides a rapid, accurate means of measuring pressure. The pitot tube is placed in the discharge stream, $\frac{1}{8}$ inch from the nozzle opening. The pressure is read on the gauge. The operating pressure, in conjunction with the diameter of the nozzle opening, can help determine the sprinkler discharge rate. Pressure at similar sprinklers within a system should not vary by more than 20 percent.

The average application rate is calculated by knowing the sprinkler discharge (gpm) and the sprinkler spacing. The following formula can be used to determine that rate:

$$\text{Application rate} = \frac{\text{96.3 x Sprinkler Discharge (gpm)}}{\text{Spacing between sprinkler heads (ft)}\atop\text{x Spacing between sprinkler lines (ft).}}$$

Frequently, there is variability in sprinkler head discharge and sprinkler spacing in turfgrass irrigation systems. Under such circumstances, the average application rate is best determined from the results of a catch can test.

The following example illustrates the step-by-step analysis of data collected during a catch can test:

A catch can test was performed on a turf area with rotary sprinklers in a 60-foot triangular spacing. The catch cans had an opening diameter of 3.45 inches and the test duration was one hour. A total of 42 catch cans with spacing between catch cans of 10 feet in a grid layout were used. The operating pressure, measured at the sprinkler head was 45 psi.

A sample calculation for a collected water volume of 24 ml is as follows:

Catch can opening diameter = 3.45 inches
Volume collected in catch can = 24 ml.

$$\text{Application rate (in/hr)} = \frac{\text{Volume collected (ml) x 4.65}}{\text{Test duration (min) x (can opening diameter in inches)}}$$

$$= \frac{24 \text{ ml x } 4.65}{60 \text{ minutes x } (3.45)} = .16 \text{ in./hr.}$$

Catch can test results also can be quickly and easily evaluated by computer using a spreadsheet or other software customized for evaluating sprinkler tests.

Assuming the catch can test was an actual irrigation in which the manager knew that the average application rate of the system was 0.16 in./hr. and that the desired depth of applied water was 0.16 inches, the irrigation system would be run for one hour if no consideration was given to application uniformity. However, the distribution uniformity of this test was 69 percent, meaning running the system for one hour would result in under-irrigated areas.

Use the following equation to determine the gross amount of irrigation required to compensate for the non-uniformity. For a required net application of 0.16 inches and distribution uniformity of 69 percent, the calculation of the gross irrigation application is:

$$\text{Gross Irrigation Application} = \frac{\text{Net Irrigation Application x 100}}{\text{DU(\%)}}$$

$$\text{Gross Irrigation Application} = \frac{0.16 \text{ inches x 100}}{69 \text{ percent}}$$

Gross Irrigation Application = 0.23 inches.

It would be necessary to operate the irrigation system for 87 minutes rather than for 60 minutes (0.23 inches/0.16 in./hr. = 1.44 hours = 87 minutes) to compensate for the non-uniformity.

Compensating for water application non-uniformity insures that most locations will be adequately watered, but requires that an additional 0.07 inch of water (a 44 percent increase) be applied. Increasing the distribution uniformity to 80 percent through irrigation system improvements would require that only an additional 0.04 inch (a 25 percent increase) of water be applied. This would save in water costs.

'Walk-Through' Irrigation System Evaluation and Checklist

A "walk-through" of an irrigation system identifies obvious problems affecting irrigation performance and efficiency. This must be done before a catch can test is performed.

It consists of an evaluation of the control system, zoning of stations, health of the plant material and physical condition of the system components. After the necessary repairs are performed, the application rate and uniformity of systems can be determined for use in irrigation scheduling.

An irrigation system evaluation check list (below) is used to record problems found during the "walk-through." For large systems, more than one form may be required.

Ideally, a system should be equipped with a controller that allows the irrigation manager to program each station or valve independently for day, start time, run time and number of repeat cycles. However, many controllers are designed with one or several programs which designate the start time and day of irrigation. The operator sets the program start time and irrigation days, and then selects which stations are to be run with that program and inputs the run time for each station.

Valves: Each should be operational and not leaking.

Wiring: It should be inspected for visible breaks, poor connections or broken insulation. If a valve is not functioning and wiring is suspected, the wiring voltages should be checked and repaired.

Backflow prevention: Backflow prevention devices are required to prevent the contamination of domestic water supplies. Either a check valve, anti-siphon valve, pressure vacuum breaker or reduced pressure backflow prevention device must be present.

Soil moisture sensor: Soil moisture sensors are becoming more popular for use in scheduling irrigation. Most read either soil moisture tension or electrical resistance. The sensors can be read manually or they can be wired into the controller to override irrigation programs and allow watering only when needed. Placement of the sensors is crucial for proper operation. They should be placed at a location in the plant's root-zone which is under the influence of the irrigation system. Sensor depth of 4 to 6 inches is adequate for turf and shrubs. Sensors may be placed deeper (up to 24 inches or more) for shrubs and trees, depending on the depth of rooting and water penetration.

Rainfall Sensor: A rain gauge or sensor is used to monitor rainfall and, if integrated into the controller, to inactivate programmed irrigations when rainfall is adequate.

Pressure Regulators: A pressure regulator is often needed to reduce water supply line pressure to that needed for proper irrigation system operation. Sprinkler systems are run at pressures ranging from 25 to 85 psi. For drip and low-volume systems, the pressure is usually reduced to 10 to 25 psi. Indications that the pressure is too high include: excessive atomization, fogging and misting from sprinkler nozzles, and component damage from high water pressure. Indications of low pressure include: inadequate breakup of sprinkler spray patterns and uneven discharge rates from sprinklers or emitters. More than one pressure regulator is needed if both sprinkler and drip systems are used. In addition, if topography varies greatly, pressure regulators can be installed on individual lines to assure equal pressure and even distribution of water at different elevations.

System Evaluation

A station-by-station evaluation is used to identify specific problems with each station or zone of the irrigation system. Problems can include mixing types of systems on the same station or line; mixing plant types with vastly different water requirements; both sunny and shady areas under one station; inappropriate type of system for the plant material present.

Plant health, disease problems, brown spots in turf areas, salt damage to leaves, as well as the presence of moss, salt, crust, or ponding of water can be indications of over- or under-watering.

Ponding water around plant trunks creates conditions favorable to root rot. Water should drain away from the trunk or crown area. Mulch is used to cool soil, add aesthetic value, and prevent excessive evaporation from soil surfaces. Mulch materials include organic material such as wood or bark chips, and inorganic materials such as plastic and rock. Mulch layers are usually 2 to 3 inches thick. Although mulches are beneficial, irrigation needs to penetrate mulch layers and into the soil to be effective. In addition, excessive mulch against plant trunks can be conducive to root rot.

Soil compaction and excessive turfgrass thatch can reduce the infiltration rate of water into the soil, resulting in runoff or ponding of water. Physical breaking up of the soil, organic or chemical soil amendments to

Irrigation System Evaluation Checklist

LOCATION:_____ EVALUATOR:_____ Page ____ of ____
ADDRESS:_____ TELEPHONE:_____
CONTACT PERSON:_____ DATE:_____
TELEPHONE:_____ TIME SPENT:_____

IRRIGATION CONTROL SYSTEM EVALUATION:

1.) Controller Type:_____ No. of Stations:_____ No. of Programs:_____
2.) Valve Conditions: (Circle) GOOD NOT WORKING LEAKING BAD SOLENOID REMARKS:_____
3.) Wiring Conditions: (Circle) GOOD BROKEN POOR CONNECTIONS REMARKS:_____
4.) Backflow Prevention: YES NO
5.) Soil Moisture Sensor: YES NO Station #_____   7.) Pressure Regulator: YES NO MULTI
6.) Rainfall Sensor: YES NO   8.) Manifold Pressure:_____ PSI

STATION BY STATION SYSTEM EVALUATION: (✓) indicates problem observed

Column headers (diagonal):
STATION #; SYSTEM TYPE: Sprinkler, Mini Sprinkler, Shrub Heads, Bubbler, Drip; PLANT TYPE: Warm Season Turf, Cool Season Turf, Trees, Shrubs, Bedding Plants, Drought Tolerant?; NOT ZONED FOR PLANT REQ.; NOT ZONED FOR EXPOSURE; OBVIOUS OVER-WATERING; OBVIOUS UNDER-WATERING; PONDING NEAR PLANT TRUNKS; MULCH NEEDED; SOIL COMPACTION; EXCESS TURFGRASS THATCH; BROKEN COMPONENTS; HEADS/NOZZLES NOT SIMILAR; SPACING UNEVEN; PRECIP. RATES NOT MATCHED; SPRAY PATTERN BLOCKED; SPRAY MISDIRECTED/OVERSPRAY; WRONG PATTERNS 1/4-1/2 FULL; SUNKEN HEADS; HEADS NOT VERTICAL; HEADS NOT TURNING; CLOGGED NOZZLES/EMITTERS; WORN NOZZLES/EMITTERS; UNEQUAL DISCHARGE RATES; UNEQUAL PRESSURES; LOW HEAD DRAINAGE

REMARKS:
_____

Prepared by the University of Calif. Cooperative Extension Service.

soil, aeration, dethatching or vertical mowing of turf and reduction of traffic are options to help eliminate or lessen soil compaction.

Broken components and dissimilar heads and uneven spacing are the most common problems with irrigation systems. These irregularities lead to uniformity problems (wet and dry spots).

Precipitation rates should be matched between sprinklers and between different sprinkler patterns (one-fourth, one-half, three-fourths, and full circle) to provide uniform water application. A one-fourth head should discharge 25 percent of the water that a full circle does, a 1/2 head 50 percent, etc. If the precipitation rates are not matched, different patterns should be on different valves with different run times.

Spray pattern blocked, spray misdirected, wrong spray pattern, sunken heads, heads not vertical, heads not turning, clogged heads or emitters, worn heads or emitters, and unequal pressures are other conditions that lead to poor water distribution or unequal discharge rates.

Low head drainage occurs when water drains out of the lines (at the lowest heads) after the system is turned off. In-line check valves or the use of sprinklers with internal anti-drainage features will prevent low head drainage.

Use of Effluent

The concept of using effluent for landscape irrigation water is not new. But an increasing number of managers, in the face of dwindling drinkable water resources, are turning to effluent. As water shortages become more common and the expense of potable water increases, effluent will become a more viable source for turfgrass irrigation water.

Fortunately, limitations in using effluent are rather minimal if water is properly applied.

Technology is turning out better quality reclaimed water. However, the idea of using treated effluent water to irrigate plants, even non-food crops such as turf, is still relatively new.

In California, for instance, most of the state's population lives close to the coastline and more than two-thirds of all treated water goes unused, flowing directly into the ocean or estuaries. Once mixed with salt water, it becomes useless. Much of the remaining one-third is returned to fresh water streams or spread on land. Most of this water is used for groundwater recharge, control of salt water intrusion, or industrial or agricultural use.

The general public is unwilling now to accept the return of reclaimed effluent to municipal water systems for drinking, cooking and bathing, despite the fact that technological advances in sewage reclamation now produce reclaimed water comparable to and, in some cases, better than many existing water supplies.

Competition for use of effluent is still minimal. However, this likely will change. Reclaimed water is invariably less expensive for plant managers than potable supplies. Depending on the proximity to a golf course or other turfgrass facility, it's cost is often onethird that of delivered drinkable water. Municipalities are eager to dispose of effluent through turfgrass and landscape irrigation because it reduces the amount that has to be discharged into the ocean or other areas. In many cases, municipalities will subsidize its use in landscape in return for relinquishing use of or rights to potable water, especially if a potential effluent user is relatively close to a treatment plant.

Parks, golf courses and other areas of non-food agriculture will be in a better position to compete for reclaimed water than for fresh water. The ultimate users of effluent water will no doubt be restricted by state and local laws and regulations; however, several arguments favor use of this water on golf courses, parks, cemeteries and other non-food plantings, over food-related agriculture.

First, turfgrasses absorb relatively large amounts of nitrogen and other nutrients often found in reclaimed water. This characteristic greatly decreases the chances of groundwater contamination. Second, reclaimed water is produced continuously, and any use, therefore, also needs to be continuous.

Turfgrass fits this criteria much better than agricultural crops where irrigation is interrupted by cultivation, planting, harvesting and other cultural practices. Third, large turfgrass areas are located in close proximity to where effluent water is generated, minimizing transportation costs. Fourth, potential health problems from reclaimed water use on turf would be less likely compared to use on food crops. And finally, soil-related problems that might develop from use of reclaimed water will have less social and economic impact in turf than in food crop production.

Turfgrass may be the best plants for effluent irrigation. However, some species are better adapted than others. If salinity is likely to become a problem, salt-tolerant grasses such as Fults alkaligrass, Adalayd or Excalibre seashore paspalum, bermudagrass, St. Augustinegrass, tall fescues and seaside creeping bentgrass are good selections.

Treatment Processes

Reclaimed water may be primary, secondary or advanced (tertiary) treated municipal or industrial waste water. Primary treatment is generally a screening or settling process that removes organic and inorganic solids from the waste water. As sewage enters the treatment plant, it flows through screens to remove floating objects. These vary from coarse to fine and are usually placed in a slanted receptacle so that debris can be scraped off and disposed of. Some treatment plants grind this debris, leaving it in the sewage flow, removing it later in a settling tank.

After screening, the water passes into a grit chamber where materials such as sand, cinders and small stones settle to the bottom. This material is normally washed and used as landfill.

At this point, sewage still contains undissolved suspended matter which can be removed in either a second settling tank or a primary clarifier. In either case, this material gradually settles out of the liquid and forms a mass of raw sludge that is drawn off into a digestor which concentrates it for use as landfill.

Liquid remaining in the settling tank is called primary effluent, and, if only primary treatment is intended, it may be treated with chlorine to destroy disease-causing bacteria and reduce odor, and then discharged.

Secondary treatment is a biological process in which complex organic matter is broken down to less complex organic material, then metabolized by simple organisms which are later removed from the waste water. Secondary treatment can remove up to 90 percent of the organic matter in incoming sewage. The secondary liquid effluent may also be chlorinated before release. Reclaimed water used for agriculture is principally secondary effluent waste.

Advanced waste water treatment is similar to potable water treatments such as chemical coagulation and flocculation, sedimentation, filtration or adsorption of compounds by a bed of activated charcoal. Advanced treatment usually follows high-rate secondary treatments and is referred to as tertiary treatment. These processes can provide highly purified waters, especially if followed by chlorination for disinfection.

The biological composition of effluent water is a matter of concern because of potential pathogenic bacteria and viruses. Properly operated secondary and advanced treatment plants can reduce pathogen concentrations significantly. However, it is difficult to insure complete, continuous elimination of pathogens, and the potential for disease transmission through treated effluent water reuse is a concern.

Although some risk of human exposure to pathogens exists in almost every waste water reclamation operation, the health concern in each situation is proportional to the degree of human contact with the water, and the adequacy and reliability of the waste water treatment. Effluent waters are not generally released for irrigation without prior approval of federal, state, county and city public health authorities.

Use standards include water-quality criteria, treatment process requirements, sampling and analysis requirements, operational requirements and treatment reliability requirements. The degree of treatment required increases with the likelihood of human exposure to the waste water and where the effluent will be used. These criteria are intended to insure an adequate degree of health protection from disease transmission. However, they do not address potential effects of reclaimed water on either crops or soil.

Generally, effluent water released for turf and landscape irrigation is secondary effluent, and may contain some harmful chemicals and biological substances. Therefore, irrigation practices should avoid both direct human contact with the water and pollution of surface or groundwaters. In addition, an entirely separate delivery system must be constructed to carry the effluent to eliminate the possibility of accidental contamination of a domestic water system.

Seasonal variation in reclaimed water quality can be a factor in using effluent. For example, the amount of a specific mineral contained in effluent may vary based on the seasonal operation of processing plant served by a sewage treatment plant.

Annual variation in water quality is as important, if not more so, than seasonal variation. For example, disposal of detergent could increase the levels of boron or phosphorus in the sewage system of a city experiencing population growth.

Most contracts for waste water require that a specific amount be accepted each day, regardless of weather conditions. Therefore, storage capability is a common feature of effluent water irrigation systems. In most cases, this storage is a critical link between the treatment plant and the irrigation system to equalize daily variations in flow from the treatment plant to the user. Usually, waste water flow exceeds irrigation demands in winter, but in the summer storage is needed because flow is less than needed for peak irrigation demands. Storage also insures against the possibility of unsuitable reclaimed waste water entering the irrigation system and provides additional time to resolve temporary water quality problems. Suspended solids, nitrogen and micro-organisms may also be reduced during storage.

Soil Factors

Physical and chemical properties of soil are relevant to successful effluent irrigation of turfgrass. Cation exchange capacity, infiltration and percolation rates and water-holding capacity of the soil are among the more important factors in using reclaimed water.

Coarse-textured soils are best for use of reclaimed water. However, reclaimed water may be used on heavier soils as long as changes in soil chemical properties are evaluated regularly.

A soil's water-holding capacity is important in determining its suitability for reclaimed water irrigation. Frequent application of reclaimed water on soils with high water-holding capacity will create salt and heavy metals buildup.

Shallow soils atop rock, hard pans or clay pans often have poor water percolation and drainage. These perched-water-table situations will create unwanted accumulations of salts and heavy metals.

Soil factors usually should not preclude use of effluent water, but they must be considered in any reclaimed water irrigation management program.

Algae clogging sprinkler nozzles is a problem with reclaimed water, and necessitates a good filtration process. Irrigation uniformity also is more critical with effluent because both harmful and beneficial substances may be applied with irrigation water.

Water Properties

Composition of untreated and treated waste waters—the actual amounts of physical, chemical and biological constituents present—depends upon the composition of the municipal water supply, the number and type of commercial and industrial establishments being serviced by a waste water treatment plant and the nature of the residential communities contributing to the supply.

As long as the waste water has gone through a secondary and/or advanced treatment process, in most cases it is suitable for turfgrass irrigation. There may be only a few instances where treated municipal waste water quality is too poor for use on turfgrass. Nevertheless, because effluent waters do contain impurities, careful consideration must be given to each situation to evaluate possible long-term effects on soils and turfgrasses from the treatment. The following are the most common water quality problems associated with use of low-quality effluent water:

Salinity

Salinity problems occur when the soluble salts in the grass rootzone are too high. Most effluent waters have excessive salts which could be harmful to most turfgrasses, especially in heavy soils.

In general, water picks up approximately 300 parts per million (ppm) inorganic salts in one cycle of use. Depending on the initial salt content of the water, this level could make the resulting water unsuitable for turf-grass irrigation. For example, if the original water contained 600 ppm salts, the effluent water would contain 900 ppm, an amount considered potentially hazardous to turf, especially on heavy clay soils.

Permeability

Permeability problems may occur if effluent water contains high levels of sodium. Permeability hazard is often expressed as SAR (Sodium Adsorption Ratio), the ratio of sodium to calcium and magnesium. A high ratio—above 9—indicates potential permeability problems.

Reduced soil permeability also can occur when the salt content reduces permeability by dissolving calcium and other soluble salts from the soil. Removal of salts causes the final soil particles to disperse and fill the soil pore space. The result is impermeability.

Carbonate and bicarbonate content can also affect permeability and must be evaluated along with the calcium, magnesium and sodium content of both soil and effluent water.

Typical symptoms of reduced permeability include water-logging, slow infiltration, crusting or compaction, poor aeration, weed invasion and disease infestation.

Toxic Elements

Effluent waters usually contain a wide variety of elements in small concentrations. Problems can occur when certain elements accumulate in the soil to toxic levels. Toxicities can occur from accumulations of boron, chloride, copper, nickel, zinc or cadmium. Boron is added to the water through soaps and detergents, and concentration can vary from 0.5 to 1 ppm. Although this range by itself is not toxic to most plants, levels may increase on heavy soils and present problems, especially for trees and shrubs. Turfgrasses are usually much more tolerant of boron than are other plants, if mowed frequently with clippings removed.

Chloride is not particularly toxic to turf, but most trees and shrubs are quite sensitive to a chloride content of 355 ppm. Copper, nickel, zinc and cadmium are heavy metals that, in some instances, build to high levels in reclaimed water. High concentrations of zinc and copper are usually beneficial to turf; nickel and cadmium are of concern only if the land will be used for other agricultural purposes (crop production). The National Academy of Sciences has recommended that effluent contain no more than 0.005 ppm of cadmium, 0.2 ppm of copper, 0.5 ppm of nickel and 5.0 ppm of zinc for continuous use as irrigation water. Most secondary reclaimed waters meet these standards, but frequent monitoring is essential.

Effluent Water Benefits

Effluent provides an additional water source where the fresh supply of water is limited. This factor is of particular importance in the West and South and in all highly populated locations of the United States where water is becoming a more limited natural resource.

Reclaimed water is often much less expensive. In some cases, effluent water-users pay only the pumping costs necessary to get it to their property. In cases where effluent water is available at prices close to those of fresh water, the actual value of treated water is that it will be available even during drought, when fresh water may not be available at any price.

Nutrient value of reclaimed water may be an important economic consideration. Reclaimed water can be high in nutrients. Nitrogen, phosphorus and potassium, all of which are beneficial in turfgrass management programs, are primary nutrients present in most reclaimed waters and represent significant economic value.

Even if nutrient quantities in reclaimed water are low, they are efficiently used by the turfgrass because nutrients are applied on a frequent, regular basis. In most cases, turf and other landscape plants will obtain all the phosphorus and potassium they need, and a large part of their nitrogen requirement, from reclaimed water. Sufficient micro-nutrients are also supplied by most reclaimed waters.

Managing Drought

Plants require water for survival, provided by rainfall or supplemental irrigation, or a combination of both.

Regardless of the source, there will be times when water is inadequate for optimum growth and appearance. When rainfall is less than needed, managers rely on supplemental irrigation, using groundwater or surface water. However, these supplemental supplies are not infinite. A declining water table, combined with increasing pumping costs, can limit the supply of groundwater. A lack of rainfall and/or snowmelt to fill reservoirs can drastically limit supplemental water supplies from surface sources. Municipally-supplied water sources can also be drastically curtailed or shut off altogether in times of drought.

Drought cycles are inevitable, and it is during these times that landscape managers are challenged to stretch available water supplies. The challenge can range from maintaining acceptable green color to keeping plants alive, regardless of color.

Drought survival techniques extend far beyond irrigation. Fertilization, mowing, thatch removal and aerification play important roles for plants to survive a water shortage.

With a shortage of supplemental water, irrigation becomes more judicious. It no longer becomes standard operating procedure but one predicated on the survival of the plant. Wilting is a sure sign of water stress. Watch for spots in the grass that turn bluish; footprints that remain in the grass long after being made, and leaf blades folded in half lengthwise for all plants.

When water is in short supply, irrigate infrequently and deeply, but avoid runoff by matching application rates to soil infiltration. Apply water in several short repeat cycles instead of a single, long irrigation to prevent runoff.

Stretch intervals between irrigations and water late at night or the early morning to avoid losses from wind and evaporation.

Reduce irrigation of shaded areas relative to unshaded ones and repair leaky pipes, heads and valves immediately.

While modest use of nitrogen can produce beneficial, deeper roots and acceptable top growth, excessive fertilization can over-stimulate top growth, increasing demand for water. To minimize the negatives of turfgrass fertilization, do not apply excessive nitrogen during late spring, summer and early fall. Heavy, frequent spring and summer nitrogen use can actually stop root growth and increase water use. Avoid lush growth in a drought situation. If nitrogen is necessary for play or other special use, use very light, infrequent applications.

Potassium promotes increased root growth and thicker cell walls, enhancing drought tolerance. Sample for deficiency and apply potassium if necessary.

Increasing the allowable mowing height during a drought increases the turfgrass leaf area and increases photosynthesis, resulting in more carbohydrates for plant growth, especially root growth. The higher the cutting height, the deeper and more extensive the root system. Although transpiration (and therefore water loss through the plant) will also be slightly greater with higher mown turf, the advantages of a more expansive root system outweighs this drawback.

Do not allow grass to grow more than 1½ times its mowing height. For example, if the mower is set for a 2-inch cut, mow before the turfgrass reaches an overall height of 3 inches. Keep mower blades sharp and properly balanced. A leaf blade cut by a sharp mower blade will heal more quickly, losing less water, than a leaf shredded by a dull mower.

Soil compaction affects all plants. Thatch buildup also is detrimental to turfgrass. Coring or slicing aerification enhances water penetration, improves shoot and root growth and, overall, improves drought tolerance through improved water use and efficiency, especially in clay soils or compacted areas. Compaction reduces water entry into the soil, resulting in unwanted runoff or evaporation.

A deep thatch layer also can reduce or eliminate water infiltration into the soil profile, especially into hydrophobic soils. Water use efficiency increases when thatch is maintained at acceptable depths (about 0.5 inches) and not allowed to dry out.

Prioritizing water use can stretch available water supplies to critical areas. For example, golf greens should be given a higher water priority than fairways and rough areas. Under severe water restrictions, it may be possible to shut off irrigation on rough areas and fairway approaches and still provide normal amounts of water to the rest of the course. A similar approach may be employed in most turf areas.

If several turfgrasses are separately incorporated in a turf and landscape scheme, shut off water to a specific species according to the following ranking: kikuyugrass, bermudagrass, zoysiagrass, tall fescue, red fescue, Kentucky bluegrass, perennial ryegrass, highland bentgrass, creeping bentgrass, dichondra. This ranking is based on drought tolerance, root depth and recuperative potential. More drought tolerant and deeper rooted turfgrasses can withstand a longer drought period by going dormant and resuming growth once water is available. Less drought-tolerant species may actually die in a prolonged drought period.

Good weed control becomes even more important in a drought situation because of the water-robbing characteristics of unwanted species in turfgrass.

Regrading to remove mounds and other hard-to-irrigate topographic areas also can save water.

In some cases, a brown, dormant turf resulting from lack of irrigation may not be objectionable. There is always, however, the option of turning a brown lawn green by applying turf colorant (synthetic turf dyes) to dead or dormant grass. Some colorants may provide acceptable appearance for up to 10 weeks.

Wetting Agents

Wetting agents are basically surfactants—similar to spreaders and stickers used to improve plant coverage when applying pesticides. They reduce the surface tension of water, or the contact angle between water and a hydrophobic surface. This makes the surface wetter. Non-ionic (neutral) wetting agents are used mostly in turfgrass as opposed to cationic (positively charged) or anionic (negatively charged) agents.

Reductions in water applications of between 30 percent and 50 percent have been reported with use of wetting agents in turf by improving overall water infiltration and drainage.

Wetting agents have been praised for improving soil infiltration, drainage and rewetting of localized dry spots and hydrophobic (water-repelling) soils. Wetting agents also have been reported to help reduce evapotranspiration rates, soil compaction, thatch buildup, wilting, disease and dew formation while enhancing movement of pesticides through the rootzone and improving overall turf quality.

Some experts report that phytotoxicity is a concern with wetting agents, especially when applied under stress conditions. It is, therefore, very important that these materials be applied according to label recommendations.

Wetting agents may be sprayed on, alone or in tank mixes, spread on and watered in, or injected through irrigation systems which provide quick and uniform coverage with considerably less labor costs.

Research has shown that particles from hydrophobic sand have a non-wettable organic coating. Likewise, a fungus that can produce a wax-like material on thatch and soil particles, which causes them to become water repellent, may exist. These affected areas are called localized dry spots. Some wetting agents act like stripping agents, removing this waxy coating, and, in combination with other cultural practices, improve water absorption.

Golf course superintendents use wetting agents to prevent drought damage, applying them as soon as they see signs of wilt. This helps prevent hot spots. Wetting agents also have been reported beneficial in improving weed control by breaking down the waxy cuticle. ✿

Notes

9 CHAPTER

Turfgrass Cultural Management

Mowing

Perhaps the single most important cultural practice associated with turf maintenance is mowing. In many cases, most of the total maintenance effort is directly associated with the labor and equipment requirements of mowing.

When considering the possible effects mowing may have on the turfgrass plant, remember that the plant is designed by nature to grow and mature at a height far in excess of the selected mowing height. The plant is forced to live and perform at a much lower height. This is done so the plant will fit our intended use. Mowing, in a sense, is not natural because it upsets natural growth patterns in the plant.

To develop a good mowing program, one needs to understand how the turfgrass plant operates.

The most apparent effect of mowing is the reduction of the plant's leaf surface area. The leaf system manufactures and supplies the plant with carbohydrates. Carbohydrates to the plant are analogous to the food we eat. During the active growing months (spring and fall for cool-season grasses and summer and early fall for warm-season grasses), carbohydrate production is high and the plant is able to store food reserves. During periods of stress or dormancy, the plant draws on these reserves in order to survive.

Mowing at lower than optimum heights during periods favorable for carbohydrate storage may seriously impair the plant's ability to develop adequate food reserves for stress or dormancy periods. The resulting death of the plant may falsely be attributed to "heat or cold injury" when, in fact, the food reserves were not high enough to carry it through the period.

When part of the plant's leaves are removed by mowing, the first priority becomes the re-establishment or replacement of its former leaf surface area. This flush of leaf growth requires carbohydrates and may reduce the supply of carbohydrates available to the root system for a short period. In the carbohydrate "pecking order" of the plant, the leaf system has priority over roots, rhizomes or stolons. This demand for carbohydrates by the leaves after cutting may result in temporary reduction or stoppage of root growth. The larger the percentage of leaf tissue removed, the longer the period root growth may be reduced.

Just as the amount of leaf surface removed has an effect on root growth, so does the cutting height. There is a direct relationship between cutting height and the total volume of root system. The turfgrass plant, like all other plants, develops a balance between its top parts and root system. A certain size root system is needed to support a certain volume of top growth, and vice versa. If either the top parts or the root system is reduced, the plant reacts by reducing the other. This is analogous to transplanting a tree. The top is pruned to compensate for the root system lost in the digging operation. Mowing the turfgrass plant reduces its top parts. The plant no longer needs the same quantity of root system, so in order to achieve balance, it reduces its root system. The more top growth is removed (i.e. the lower the cutting height), the shallower the root system may become. (Figure 1)

A shallow root system can seriously impair the plant's ability to withstand stress, especially drought stress.

There is another important function of the leaf system—the function of insulation. The growing points or crowns of most turfgrass plants are at or near the surface of the soil and are very high in the chemical activities that control the growth processes. These areas of the plant are very temperature sensitive.

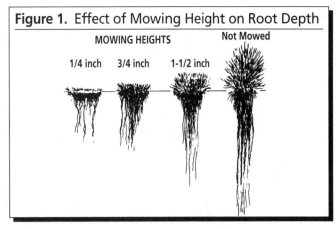

Figure 1. Effect of Mowing Height on Root Depth

The upper optimum temperature range for cool-season turfgrasses is from about 60 to 75 degrees, and warm-season turfgrasses from about 80 to 95 degrees. When the temperature of the growing point goes above these temperatures, the growth process slows down. If the temperature of the growing point is too high for a long enough period, especially with cool-season grass, the plant goes into summer or heat dormancy.

The leaf surface insulates the growing point from high temperatures. As leaf surface area is reduced, the amount of insulation available for the growing point is reduced. As the cutting height is reduced from the optimum assigned to the particular variety, the more susceptible the plant becomes to high temperature injury. This is very important when maintaining cool-season grasses.

Most of the turfgrasses are subjected to some degree of wear. Golf course putting greens, tees, fairways, and athletic fields receive some of the highest wear of any turf area. The leaf surface area protects the growing point of the plant from direct mechanical injury associated with traffic. As the leaf surface is reduced, the overall wearability of the turf is reduced. Turfs cut at low heights are subject to high wear damage and may tend to gradually thin out.

Mowing practices may have an effect on the incidence of disease. An increase in disease problems with turf maintained at below optimum cutting heights has been observed, and may be associated with weakness resulting from extremely low cutting heights.

Just as the proper selection of height-of-cut is important, so is the frequency at which the turf is cut. A turf should be cut at its assigned mowing height when it gets one-third higher (Table 1).

Ideally, the frequency between mowings should be long enough to allow the plant to recover from the last cutting. Leaf growth rate and the intended use of the turf will, to a large degree, dictate the mowing frequency.

Considering the desirability of not removing more than one-third of the leaf surface at any one mowing, the application of nitrogen at high rates may force an increase in the frequency of mowings. This is especially true when high rates of nitrogen are supplied in a soluble form. The golf course putting green, because of the demands of the sport, must be cut at fairly frequent intervals to provide a dense putting surface. If high growth rates result in too frequent mowing on other parts of the course or for other turfs, consider adjusting both the nitrogen rate and source. Slower-releasing nitrogen materials do not tend to produce the lush, fast growth associated with the soluble sources and should result in longer periods between mowings.

Mowing Equipment

The selection of mowing equipment is dependent on a number of factors. The intended use of the area should be the first consideration. For

Table 1. Suggested Mowing Heights and Intervals

Turfgrass	Suggested Height of Cut	Suggested* Mowing Height
Buffalograss	2	3
Centipedegrass	2	3
Colonial Bentgrass	1	1½
Creeping Bentgrass	¼	⅜
Fine Fescue	2	3
Hybrid Bermudagrass	¼ to 1	⅜ to 1½
Kentucky Bluegrass	2	3
Perennial Ryegrass	2	3
St. Augustinegrass	2	3
Tall Fescue	2	3
Zoysiagrass	1 to 2	1½ to 3

*This reflects the 1/3 mowing rule. Do not remove any more than one-third of the leaf blade at any one mowing.

Table 2. Number of Blades Needed for Intended Cutting Height

Intended Cutting Height	Number of Blades on Reel
below ½ inch	7 or 8
between 1 and ½ inch	6
above 1 inch	5

example, a reel mower does a better job than a rotary at relatively low mowing heights, therefore golf course greens are cut with reel-type mowers.

The cutting height used for a particular area can even affect the number of blades on a reel (Table 2).

A rotary mower may do a much better job than a reel mower in turf areas that have been assigned higher mowing heights. The upper height of cut limit for a reel-type mower is around 1½ to 2 inches while a rotary mower doesn't do as well much below 1½ inches.

With all equipment, maintenance is very important. An equipment replacement program should be developed based on a reasonable machine life expectancy. Many facilities end up with whole fleets of nearly worn out equipment at one time, and it becomes impossible to budget enough money to buy all new equipment. Some organizations, depending on their financial situation, have chosen to lease equipment. A financial advisor should be able to help with the "buy or lease" decision.

In most turfgrass situations, clippings are not removed. Removal may be required when they interfere with the intended use of the turf (i.e. the golf course putting green) or are too heavy and smother the turf. Generally, the shorter the clippings, the better they fall deep into the turf and the more rapid the decomposition. Double-cutting or running the mower over the same areas twice will help "chop" up long clippings.

Mulching mowers, designed to cut clippings into very small pieces, have become popular. Contrary to popular belief, clippings do not contribute to thatch. There is absolutely no need to pick up or remove grass clippings if a reasonable mowing program is followed.

Mowing practices are extremely important in any turfgrass management program. The proper selection of height-of-cut and mowing frequency, as well as the development of a reasonable growth rate, has a profound effect on the health and vigor of any turfgrass system.

Mower Blades

Proper sharpening of rotary mower blades has many benefits. Grass looks better when cut with a sharp blade. A clean cut heals over more quickly and with less stress than a ragged cut from a dull blade. The clean cut offers fewer places for disease to enter a plant.

When blades are sharp, a mower deck is less likely to develop a buildup of pulped and mangled grass, so more air passes through the deck. This lets the deck function as it was designed to, generating a vacuum that stands the grass blades up for a more uniform cut. Clippings disperse more cleanly (or are mulched more effectively), and the job is done quicker.

Many professionals in turf maintenance start each working day with a sharp blade, and some change blades more than once a day, especially when working on sandy soils or in grasses like zoysia that have a high mineral content that takes the edge off the blade.

If blades are sharpened frequently, each sharpening is more of a touch-up of the cutting edge, rather than a major grinding project. This makes it easier to retain the original cutting edge bevel. A light grinding reduces the amount of heat the blade must absorb, reducing the chance of taking the temper out of the blade through overheating.

Before sharpening, take precautions to insure safety, and put on eye protection. A full-face clear plastic shield (available from welding supply stores) provides better visibility, won't fog up like goggles, and is more comfortable for people who wear glasses. Make sure clothing won't catch in the grinder. Clear flammable materials or liquids from the area, so a fire doesn't start from a grinding spark.

Make sure the blade is worth sharpening by making a visual check. Scrape off built-up grass and mud and look for cracks. Set the blade on a flat table or against a door jamb and make sure it remains straight. If the blade is built with a "droop" shape, prop the center of the blade on a block, like a piece of 2-by-4 wood, and check that the blade is equal side-to-side.

If the blade looks good, check it with your ears. Slide a nail or similar thin object through the mounting hole, and tap the blade with a piece of metal, like a small hammer. It should produce a clear ringing sound that lasts several seconds, like a bell. If the sound is "flat" and doesn't last, a crack may be developing in the blade. Blades are cheaper than body parts. Don't risk injury from a blade that might come apart while mowing. Replace it.

The tip of a rotary mower blade travels at about 200 miles per hour. While a blade looks like a simple hunk of iron, it is actually a precisely-designed machine part, and should be treated with respect.

Adopt a light touch when grinding. If you hear the grinding wheel slow down as you press the blade into it, you're pressing too hard. Grinding produces heat, and excess heat can take the temper out of the blade metal, leaving blue spots on the freshly-ground surface. Keep a metal can of water nearby (a 3-pound coffee can works well) and dunk the blade frequently to cool it off.

While a blade may be 20 to 30 inches long, the actual cutting and wear takes place mostly on the outer inch or two. Unless it's a special blade, like on a mulching mower, it is usually not necessary to increase the length of the cutting edge beyond what was found on the original blade.

Try to duplicate the blade's original cutting edge bevel when sharpening. If you want to reshape the bevel, do it to satisfy your mowing needs. A blade bevel that is more upright (closer to a square, 90 degree edge) will provide the greatest resistance to physical damage from rocks, tough brush and the like. But it will also produce the most ragged cut. A blade with a long flat bevel gives the cleanest, most knifelike cut, but is the most vulnerable to damage.

Sharpen blades so that the outermost edge of the cutting tip retreats backward toward the wing tip each time you sharpen the blade. Grind off just enough to remove any nicks from the cutting edge. Stop sharpening and replace the blade when the cutting edge gets within a 1/4 inch of the root of the wing tip. Never grind on the wing tip.

Always apply the blade to the grinding stone at an angle. Avoid pushing the blade into the stone at a right angle and producing a sharp inside corner at the inner edge of the new cutting surface. If the blade tip strikes an object, a crack can easily develop in the sharp inside corner, possibly leading to the end of the blade fracturing.

After grinding the bevel on the top side of the blade, lightly apply the back side of the blade to the stone to remove the burr from the edge. This can also be done with a file. Some technicians like to run a file lightly across the cutting edge to give it a rounded profile, rather than a sharp point. The slightly rounded edge is more durable and stays sharper longer than the sharp edge.

The final step is to balance the blade. This can be done by hanging the blade from a nail driven squarely into a wall or clamped in a vise. Inexpensive cone-type balancers do the job well. For the ultimate in balance and checking for warpage, specialized blade balances are available.

Make sure the blade is free of clumps of grass, etc., before balancing. To lighten one side of the blade, grind its cutting edge back a bit, or nibble a bit off the end. Never grind the top off the wing tip—that will destabilize the blade's aerodynamics when it is in use and produce a ragged cut.

Chemical Mowing

Mowing typically represents one of the highest costs in turf maintenance. The faster turf is growing, the more often it should be cut, and the higher the overall maintenance cost. In an effort to reduce plant leaf growth without having any negative impact on turf quality, researchers are investigating the use of plant growth regulators (P.G.R.s). These chemicals offer the possibility of reducing the need to mow without harming the turf plant.

Early on, costs of these chemicals tended to be high in cost, and their use was limited. Some chemicals were erratic in performance and some were difficult to apply. New chemicals, however, are proving to be very effective and easier to use.

With the need to reduce mowing pressures, because of mowing costs and because of problems with grass clipping disposal, the use of plant growth regulators is on the rise. Increased acceptance will be tied to the continued development of better materials. And as use increases, costs should be reduced.

Growth Regulators and Enhancers

Until recently, controlling turfgrass growth has been a function of water and nitrogen applications. Growth stimulation has resulted from applying moisture and nitrogen within limits. Growth reduction has been realized by withholding moisture and nitrogen. As long as temperatures were favorable for growth of warm- season grasses, water and nitrogen could make a profound difference.

In addition, other essential mineral nutrients were applied, often as a result of soil test recommendations. These are all recognized as essential to maintain healthy turf and to prevent deficiency symptoms. Sulfur and iron, in addition to phosphorus and potassium, have received major attention. Also, calcium and magnesium, as well as manganese, molybdenum, copper, boron and zinc are required for normal growth.

Of course, once the desirable growth rate is achieved, the mowing machine is used to keep the foliar canopy at the proper upper limit for the most attractive and/or most functional condition for home lawns or sports turf.

Now, following years of research on growth retardants and stimulants, products that can fine tune turf growth responses to meet specific needs have become available. The specific needs include:
   —Growth reduction to reduce frequency of mowing;
   —Suppression of seedhead formation to reduce frequency of mowing;
   —Suppression of seedhead formation to enhance annual bluegrass control;
   —Regulation of growth during stress to enhance turf persistence;
   —Regulation of growth to favor root development;
   —Regulation of growth to improve resistance to disease;
   —Regulation of growth to improve water use efficiency.
The products are classified either as growth regulators or growth substances.

In order to have fine lawns and sports turf, foliage growth must be regulated. Common cultural practices, such as mowing, watering, fertilizing, liming, thinning, core cultivation and pest control do this. For the most part, these practices stimulate growth or re-growth of foliage. By withholding moisture or fertilizer, the growth rate can be slowed.

However, there is another method of growth suppression that is becoming increasingly important as we learn more about it. This involves use of plant growth regulators. Following are several that have been thoroughly evaluated, including:

Common Name	Trade Name
Amidochlor	Limit
Chlorflurenol	Maintain
Cyclohexadione	Primo
Flurprimidol	Cutless
Maleic hydrazide	Slo-Gro
Mefluidide	Embark
Paclobutrazol	Pro Turf

AMIDOCHLOR—root-absorbed; effective for suppressing vegetative growth and reducing seedhead production; inhibits both cell division and elongation; effective on cool-season turfgrasses; best used in medium maintenance turf.

CHLORFLURENOL—foliar-absorbed; used in combination with maleic hydracide; accumulates in the growing tips and inhibits cell division; considered a replacement for 2,4-D for broadleaf weed control.

CYCLOHEXADIONE—taken up through the foliage and translocates to the growing point, where the material inhibits the formation of gibberellic acid. This causes grass internodes to elongate less, reducing and compacting the growth of the turfgrass. The material is absorbed quickly and results are apparent in five to seven days.

FLURPRIMIDOL—foliar-absorbed; also absorbed by stems and roots; water in for most effective results; reduces vegetative growth of both cool season and warm season grasses; does not effectively control seedheads; inhibits growth by preventing plant elongation; used to control annual bluegrass with similar activity as paclobutrazol.

MALEIC HYDRACIDE—used on low maintenance turf; translocated through the plant and causes growth regulation by inhibiting cell division but not cell elongation; foliar-absorbed; causes shoot and seedhead suppression; may cause root and rhizome inhibition; may be phytotoxic.

MEFLUIDIDE—foliar-absorbed; suppresses both vegetative and seedhead growth on cool-season grasses; inhibits cell elongation used on annual bluegrass for control of seedheads in the spring; does not control annual bluegrass.

PACLOBUTRAZOL—foliar-absorbed; also absorbed by stems and roots; is transported in the xylem, thus root absorption for turf is important; inhibits growth by interfering with plant elongation; effective in vegetative suppression but poor in seedhead suppression; used primarily on fine turf for annual bluegrass control; differentially suppresses growth of annual bluegrass and creeping bentgrass.

Plant growth regulators are being used effectively on roadside turf. They reduce mowing costs and improve motorist and pedestrian safety. Removal of seedheads, at times 3 feet in height, is important in these locations.

Timing of application makes a difference.

Treatments must be made before seedheads appear (while they are still in the boot or sheath). Amidochlor, chlorflurenol, maleic hydrazide and mefluidide work best.

Care must be taken to make uniform applications as any overdose is likely to injure the grass.

Areas that are difficult to mow because of uneven terrain may be sprayed with plant growth regulators as long as the areas can be reached with a fixed-boom sprayer. Use of a handgun sprayer is not acceptable because of difficulty in avoiding overdoses.

Fine turf areas are treated at times with plant growth regulators to eliminate seedhead emergence and to manipulate plant competition. With proper timing of applications, more than 90 percent of seedhead development can be stopped with little discoloration to the turf. Mowing frequency can be reduced for two to three weeks following treatment.

Plant growth regulators also ease maintenance around trees, buildings, playground equipment, airport runways and taxiway markers, monuments in cemeteries and other areas that require trim mowing. They are not likely to become a routine substitute for mowing home lawns.

Growth of fine turf under ideal temperature and moisture conditions is not difficult. But when it's either too hot or too cold, or too wet or too dry, stress develops within grass plants and causes trouble. Add to this stress additional unfavorable soil aeration from turf use and resulting soil compaction and the net result is weakened grass plants. Careful fertilization and watering practices are necessary for turf to recover to a normal healthy condition. The fine tuning of growth by appropriate use of growth regulators and growth substances throughout the season is beneficial.

Aerification

Nearly every turf area experiences some amount of traffic from time to time. The traffic may only be occasional foot traffic or it may be the result of some daily activity, such as cart traffic on the golf course fairway or the high amount of foot traffic on athletic fields or golf course greens.

Areas that have high traffic are subject to some degree of soil compaction. Soils that are high in clay are more easily compacted than those high in sand. The more traffic, the more potential for compaction.

Compaction is a physical process which slowly reduces the amount of oxygen contained in a soil (Table 3). The mineral friction of the soil, which is sand, silt and clay, is not compactible, nor is the organic material. With traffic, the only part of the soil that can be compacted is the air space. As the air space is reduced, the percentage of water in the soil is increased.

Roots of the turfgrass plant need oxygen, and as a product of their growth process, give off carbon dioxide. Oxygen from the atmosphere moves into the soil through very small pore spaces to the roots of the plant. Carbon dioxide escapes up through the soil into the atmosphere. As the soil absorbs traffic, the soil particles in the top inch or two are compacted into a layer so that less and less oxygen can enter the soil and less and less carbon dioxide can escape. The net result is a gradually thinning turf until, ultimately, the soil can no longer support any turf growth. Only a few weeds can grow in oxygen deficient, compacted soils.

Since compaction is the result of a physical process, it takes another physical process to reduce or prevent its effects.

Aerification or cultivation is an important element in maintaining healthy turfgrass. It will prevent or alleviate a number of problems, including compaction and thatch buildup. It can also improve water infiltration, irrigation efficiency and air exchange. Its benefits are far- reaching and are limited only by the amount of time and money available and by the amount of disruption tolerated in modifying the soil profile under turfgrass.

A wide variety of mechanical devices are available to modify the soil profile at depths ranging from 1/4 inch to 16 inches. Some do more than simply puncture the soil beneath the turfgrass. Core aerifiers, for instance, have hollow metal tines, from about 3/8 inch to 1 inch in diameter. When the machine is operated, they penetrate the soil to a depth of two, three or even as deep as 12 inches (Figure 2) .

Other aerifiers vibrate, shatter or actually lift up the soil like a pitchfork, adding pore space to the soil profile for improved oxygen, water and nutrient movement.

The latest turfgrass aerification technology has perfected the use of highly pressurized water and air to break up the subsoil instead of using spikes, blades or tines, causing literally no disruption on the soil surface.

Table 3.		
	Normal Soil	**Compacted Soil**
Mineral	45%	45%
Air Space	25%	10%
Water	25%	40%
Organic Material	5%	5%

Environmental and turfgrass conditions are important in determining when and if to aerify. Aerification may injure stressed turf, increase weed establishment, decrease turf quality where a disruptive form of aerification is utilized, and can actually impede water filtration below the depth of cultivation by creating a compaction layer at the aerification depth.

However, the advantages of aerification far outweigh any disadvantages.

Identification of the problem will largely dictate the type of aerification to use. Some of the obvious signs of soil problems include a hard soil, low water infiltration rates, a black layer, poor turfgrass rooting, waterlogging or standing water, or isolated droughty areas. But it takes more than visual examination to find the problem. It requires soil sampling.

Take a soil profile to a depth of 2 feet, observing the different layers and identifying the problem areas. Observe root growth within the core sample, identifying any condition where soil conditions are limiting root development. Don't ignore small layers if they differ distinctly from surrounding layers. Identifying the problem is important because unless the cultivation method selected penetrates the problem zone, the problem will not be solved.

The degree of disruption desired is determined by spacing of the tines or blades and the depth of the penetration.

The most common aerifiers are hollow tine or solid tine devices. They can be either walk-behind or tractor-drawn units. Tine diameters can range from ¼ to 1 inch with spacings ranging from 1 to 8 inches.

Hollow-tine aerification will bring up more soil to the surface, requiring that the cores be removed or worked back into the soil. Either way, use of the turf is interrupted. This interference dictates the time of the year and frequency hollow-tine aerification can be done. However, it is considered generally the most effective form of aerification. Because of the disruption, hollow-tine aerification should be done only when the species is experiencing rapid growth and use of the turfgrass is relatively minimal and not during the time of the year when it is expected to receive its most use.

Solid-tine aerification acts much the same as hollow tine, except that no cores are pulled and disruption is minimal. Solid tines are often used during heavy use periods when the turf is damaged by heavy traffic and aerification is necessary without disturbing the surface. Many aerifiers are engineered for interchanging hollow and solid tines.

Shattering or vibrating motions often are associated with solid-tine aerification, enhancing the action of the penetrating tines. However, there is a hollow-tine aerifier which also features a lifting motion as it penetrates.

There are aerifiers which feature a slicing motion using straight line tines or blades. They can penetrate to depths of about 8 inches and like the solid-tine units, create minimal disturbance. Some of these also vibrate as they move through the soil.

Spiking units penetrate to a depth of about 2 inches and are generally pull types with the weight of the unit determining the depth.

One type of aerification system is water injection cultivation developed by the Toro Co. (HydroJect). It uses water pressurized to 5,000 psi released through small nozzle orifices, creating a high-velocity stream of water, cutting cleanly through the turf surface and creating a channel in the soil. Depending on the soil conditions, channel depth ranges from 3 to 8 inches with channel diameter from ½ to ¼ inch.

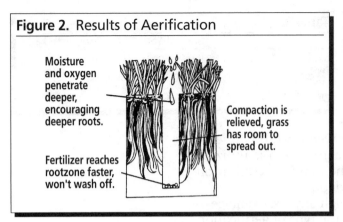

Figure 2. Results of Aerification

Moisture and oxygen penetrate deeper, encouraging deeper roots.

Compaction is relieved, grass has room to spread out.

Fertilizer reaches rootzone faster, won't wash off.

A unique feature of water injection aerification is the variable channel length created by the water. It minimizes the possibility of compaction at the same depth, which is the tendency of mechanical tines.

Compressed air, injected beneath the soil surface with probes, also has proven effective in breaking up compacted soil. A unique feature of this cultivation method is that it allows the turfgrass manager to inject nutrients and other materials like polymers into the soil structure while it opens it up through fissures, cracks and capillary tubes created by the compressed air.

Mechanical cultivation disturbs the turfgrass and quick recovery is an important consideration. Traditionally, good turfgrass managers apply supplemental nutrients, primarily nitrogen, before or after an aerification to stimulate recovery growth. Additional irrigation also is a good idea.

Mechanical aerification opens up holes in the turfgrass which provides an opportunity for the turfgrass manager to modify his soil profile by topdressing with sand, prolonging the benefits of cultivation.

Aerification is not without potential problems, including that of actually creating compaction. Any implement pushed into the soil will cause some compaction. For example, repeated aerification to a depth of 3 inches could well create a compacted zone 4 inches deep in the profile over a period of time. These localized compacted zones are created immediately beneath the coring zones, regardless of whether hollow tines or solid tines are used. Factors influencing this are tine spacing, soil texture and frequency of cultivation. Cultivating with closely spaced tines in moist clay or silty soils is the most likely scenario for creating these compacted zones.

These zones can be broken up with deeper aerification devices like Verti-Drain, Deep Drill and air injection cultivation.

A typical cultivation program on a high use turfgrass area facility like a golf course would include core aerification in the spring or fall with water injection, pin spiking of solid-tine cultivation in the summer with Verti-Drain and drill aerification once every two or three years, depending on turfgrass use.

Soil moisture content is a critical factor in cultivation. When shattering or vibrating actions are part of the aerification process, it is best to have soil conditions somewhat drier than field capacity. However, the soil should not be so dry that the implement does not penetrate the soil.

For operations that penetrate the soil, but have minimal loosening action, soil moisture near field capacity is best. Of course, cultivation should be avoided when soil moisture is above field capacity.

Thatch Control

Most turfgrasses are perennial plants living in a continuous stage of renewal. New plants are produced and old plants die. Ideally, under proper management, the lawn achieves a balance between the rate at which organic matter is produced and decomposed. This organic matter has value. It contains various plant nutrients which, after decomposition by microorganisms, may be returned to the soil for possible future use by new turfgrass plants.

What is Thatch?

When organic material is produced faster than it can be decomposed, the turf develops an excessive amount of thatch. Thatch primarily consists of partially decomposed stem and root tissue and some living stem and root tissues that develop in the organic layer between the base of the turfgrass plant and the true soil (Figure 3). Stem, crown and root tissues are high in cell wall material called lignin that's very slow to decompose. Leaves cut off in mowing are rapidly decomposed by bacteria and fungi and do not contribute to thatch.

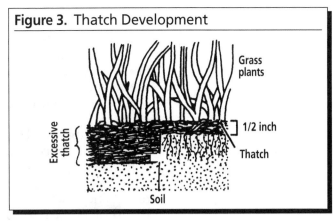

Figure 3. Thatch Development

A certain amount of thatch is desirable, because it forms a cushion that increases wear tolerance in the turf. Thatch helps turf withstand the wear and tear associated with moderate levels of traffic. Thatch also insulates the soil from high temperatures and reduces water evaporation losses from the soil surface. Thatch adds resiliency to the golf course green and helps the ball "bite."

When thatch accumulations top 1/2 inch, problems usually develop. A heavy thatch layer reduces water movement into the soil. It may also reduce soil aeration, which is necessary for good root growth.

Increased disease and insect problems can be associated with a heavy thatch layer. Also, a thatch layer in excess of 1/2 inch can create a barrier for the movement of fertilizer and insecticides (such as those used for grub control) deep into the soil. If the thatch layer is thick enough, the grass's roots may no longer be in contact with the soil.

Why Does Thatch Accumulate?

Some turf areas develop a thatch fairly easily and some do not. One reason is that turfgrasses vary in their tendency to thatch. Some turfgrasses like common bermudagrass simply do not build thatch.

There are several basic causes for excessive thatch buildup. Improper use of water can encourage thatch development. Turf excessively watered, especially areas watered daily, tends to develop heavy thatch. Heavy use of pesticides on turf may promote thatch accumulation by destroying many of the soil organisms that decompose thatch.

Perhaps the major cause of thatch buildup is the use of high rates of soluble nitrogen fertilizers. Nitrogen is a plant nutrient that can stimulate high vegetative growth rates in turfgrass. As stated previously, in an ideal turf management system, the growth rate of the plant should equal the rate which turfgrass residues are decomposed. Because of the strong influence of soluble nitrogen on growth, excessive application rates add plant residues to the system faster than they can be decomposed. As a result, thatch accumulates.

Thatch Measurement

A turf that has too much thatch is spongy. Mowers tend to scalp areas with excessive thatch. To estimate the depth of thatch, use a knife, spade, or soil probe to remove a small section of turf. Make sure the cut extends deep enough to go through the thatch layer to the true surface of the soil. Measure the amount of thatch. If it is thicker than ½ inch, the turf should be dethatched.

Thatch Removal

The best time to remove thatch is in the spring before the turf turns green. Machines specifically designed for the removal of thatch are called vertical mowers (because the blades rotate vertically), power rakes or dethatching mowers.

In using this type of equipment, make sure the blades, or knives penetrate through the thatch just to the surface of the soil. If thatch is excessively deep, it may be necessary to remove a little at a time rather than all at once. Many golf course greens are verticut weekly or biweekly as a thatch prevention program. The addition of topdressing in conjunction with vertical mowing and core aerification will help reduce the amount of thatch in a turf. This top- dressing should be the same type of soil as the lawn. The soil will help by introducing organisms responsible for thatch decomposition into the layer.

Topdressing and Thatch Control

Golf and sports turfs require intensive management to maintain the color, density, playability and recuperative potential that is desired. The large levels of fertilizers and other chemicals typically applied to highly maintained turf result in accelerated growth rates, and often the accumulation of plant material exceeds its rate of decomposition in the soil. When this imbalance occurs, the development of a thatch layer begins.

A limited amount of thatch (usually 0.3 inches or less) is beneficial for golf and sports turf. This depth of thatch offers resiliency to traffic, serves as an insulator in moderating soil temperatures, and can lessen the likelihood of soil compaction. However, excessive thatch accumulation results in turf that is much more difficult to maintain.

The removal of thatch can be done mechanically using a vertical mower or dethatcher. This practice results in significant surface disruption and thinning of the turfgrass if it is used for thatch removal. The removal of the debris can also be very labor intensive if sweeping equipment is not available. Further, the timing of the vertical mowing should coincide with environmental conditions that are favorable for the turf to recuperate from the damage.

Due to the problems associated with mechanical thatch removal, many turf managers utilize a program of light and frequent topdressing applications for thatch control. Topdressing is a highly effective means of biological thatch control. The application of soil material over the turfgrass canopy controls thatch in two ways: (1) the topdressing material itself contains microbial populations that will aid in decomposing thatch and; (2) the addition of the topdressing creates an environment that is more conducive to thatch decomposition. Some turfgrass managers are going as far as incorporating natural organic fertilizers into their topdressing to further stimulate microbial activity. Research data on the results of this concept in topdressing is limited, but there is an indication that this practice does enhance microbial populations of turfgrass soils.

The key to success with topdressing for thatch is that you must apply the topdressing lightly and frequently. Normal application levels in this type of topdressing program are between 0.05-0.1 cubic yards per 1000 ft^2 in bi-weekly to monthly applications. Many golf superintendents with the budget and equipment to do so apply a light "dusting" of topdressing materials on a weekly basis. Such applications function for thatch control, as well as provide a smooth, fast-playing surface.

Larger levels and more frequent applications of topdressing are usually required for the more aggressively growing warm-season turfgrasses than for cool-season turfgrasses. Also, keep in mind that the topdressing material should closely match the characteristics of the soil if you do not desire to modify the profile. Alternating topdressing materials can result in undesirable soil layering that can slow water infiltration and percolation. ❦

CHAPTER 10

Pruning

The problem with pruning a woody plant is that no two plants are exactly alike. Consequently, a great deal of care must be taken with each plant. Follow proven guidelines (Table 1) to help make the right pruning decision. All pruning should be done while the plant is dormant.

Many woody plants never need pruning at all. When a plant does not have a normal growth pattern or has suffered structural damage, it should be pruned (Figure 1).

Removal of Large Limbs

When removing limbs that are over 3 inches or so in diameter, it is best to use a three-cut method (Figure 2). Note that the first cut is made slightly away from the trunk and is made cutting from the underside of the limb. The second cut is slightly outward from the first and will remove the limb. The last cut is flush with the main tree trunk. If only one cut is used, either the bark could peel down the trunk or the limb itself might split (Figure 3).

A pruning paint or a wound dressing may slow the healing process when applied to the cambium tissue. These materials can prevent the entry of diseases or insects into the tree through cracks that might develop in the exposed woody tissue. Make sure only the wood, not the cambium, is treated. Inspect the treated wound periodically and retreat if necessary.

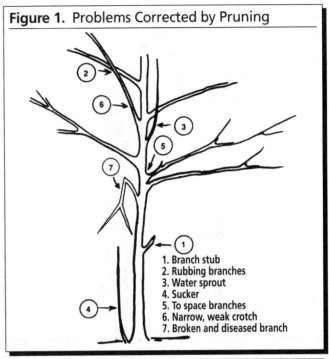

Figure 1. Problems Corrected by Pruning

1. Branch stub
2. Rubbing branches
3. Water sprout
4. Sucker
5. To space branches
6. Narrow, weak crotch
7. Broken and diseased branch

Table 1. Reasons for Pruning

- To improve the chance of survival at transplanting time.
- To direct or correct growth in shade trees or avoid later problems.
- To maintain the natural shape of the tree.
- To maintain or limit the size of a plant so it doesn't grow out of bounds.
- To remove undesirable growth that detracts from the plant.
- To remove broken, unsightly, diseased or insect-damaged growth.
- To remove suckers or water sprouts.
- To improve future flowering and/or fruiting by removing old flowers and fruit.
- To remove storm damage.
- To remove rubbing branches.
- To remove existing stubs that allow diseases and insects to enter the plant.
- To develop a particular form such as a hedge.
- To produce compact growth and prevent legginess.
- To maintain maximum coloration on plants selected for twig or stem color.
- To improve or maintain flowering by selectively removing some branches, allowing light to penetrate to the interior of the plant.
- To rejuvenate old or declining plants by removing older wood so young growth can develop.
- To increase safety to humans or property under trees by removing large branches that are weak, broken or interfering with the house or other landscape features.

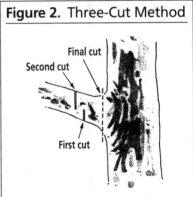

Figure 2. Three-Cut Method

Final cut
Second cut
First cut

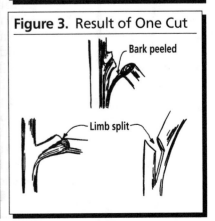

Figure 3. Result of One Cut

Bark peeled
Limb split

Figure 4. The Healing Process

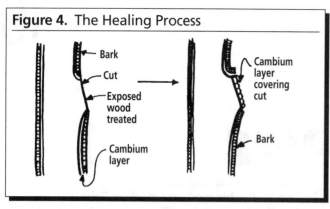

Bark
Cut
Exposed wood treated
Cambium layer

Cambium layer covering cut
Bark

Figures 5 and 6. Potential Problems

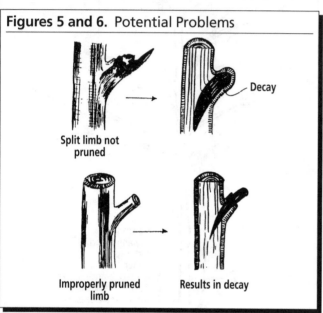

Decay

Split limb not pruned

Improperly pruned limb

Results in decay

Figure 8.

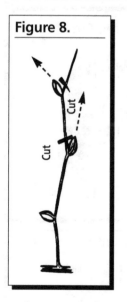

Cut
Cut
Cut

Figure 7. Bud on Inside

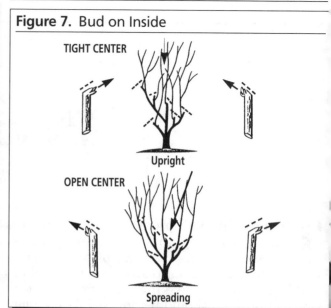

TIGHT CENTER

Upright

OPEN CENTER

Spreading

After a branch is cut off, a healing process begins. New wood (xylem) cells and new bark (phloem) cells grow from the outside of the wound toward the middle (Figure 4). The layers meet at the middle and unite to form a solid layer over the cut area. There is no connection between the old wood and the new wound-covering wood. If the cut surface is smooth and free of infection after a few years, a wound should be difficult to find.

When pruning, do not leave stubs since they usually die back, resulting in decay that can be serious, especially if large branches on the main trunk are involved. Once dieback starts, the disease may spread easily to perfectly healthy tissue. The problem is the same if the branches are broken off rather than cut (Figures 5, 6). Always finish the pruning operation with a cut flush with the tree trunk.

Pruning Small Branches

The direction the plant grows can be determined to some degree by selective pruning. If a vertically growing branch is pruned so the last or top bud is on the outward side of the branch, the plant will tend to have an open form of growth. If the remaining bud is on the inside of the branch the plant will tend to become more dense (Figure 7).

If the branches are growing horizontally, buds pointing downward rarely grow downward but usually continue a horizontal growth pattern. An upward-pointing bud will produce growth that is upward and outward in direction (Figure 8). If the plant has opposite buds on the upside and down-side of the branch, growth will favor the upper bud and it will grow up and out. If the opposite buds are across from each other in a horizontal plane, each will keep growing horizontally at the same rate (Figure 9). It is important that the cut not be made too close or too far from the bud (Figure 10).

Conifers or evergreens require different pruning techniques (Figures 11a and 11b).

Prune pines in late spring by removing one-half of the candle, or new shoot (Figure 11a).

Keep side branches from growing of bounds by removing the terminal bud. This not only slows outward growth but also helps make the plants more bushy (Figure 11b).

Flowering Shrubs

Time of pruning is important to achieve a balance between the plant's negative growth and the plant's ability to produce a maximum display of flowers. Woody plants have two flowering patterns. They will either flower on the current season's growth in the summer or fall, or they will flower on one-year old wood in the spring.

Spring flowering plants should be pruned at the end of the flowering season just before new growth starts. If these plants were pruned during the winter, the pruning might remove all the flower buds.

Summer and fall flowering plants may be pruned during the dormant season, when all other plants may be pruned.

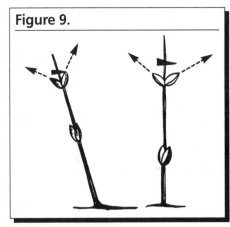

Figure 9.

Pruning Hedges

Hedges may be used to control traffic, hide or screen objects, reduce noise, form a wind break or fit into some aesthetic scheme. Hedges may be very formal or completely natural. Formal hedges require special pruning techniques to produce the desirable shape and density (Figure 12). It may be necessary to prune or shear a formal hedge at least twice a year. Three or four times a year will help keep the hedge even thicker.

Special Pruning Problems

Many trees have a strong central leader, but when they are young they may produce a competing leader. For normal growth, only one leader can remain. This competing leader should be removed as soon as possible.

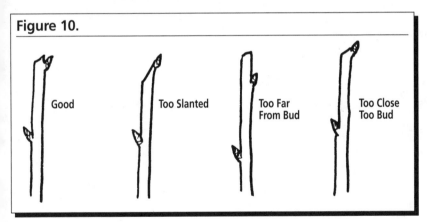

Figure 10.

Good   Too Slanted   Too Far From Bud   Too Close Too Bud

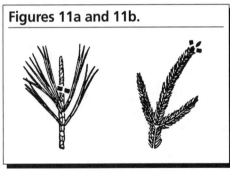

Figures 11a and 11b.

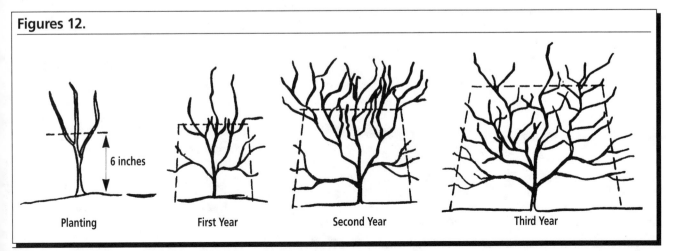

Figures 12.

6 inches

Planting   First Year   Second Year   Third Year

Figure 13.

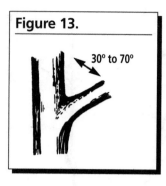

30° to 70°

As a tree grows, the strongest limbs are those that have a crotch angle from 30 to 70 degrees (Figure 13). If the crotch angle is too small, the tree may be headed for serious problems. The crotch may split just from its own limb weight or a windstorm could break the tree. If the tree isn't too large, removal of one side of the crotch may be in order. The young tree may still grow enough to reestablish its shape, but an old one may not. Older trees with a narrow crotch can be helped by bracing.

Shrub growth may be controlled or shaped using one of several methods, including thinning out the plant or heading back. The method used should depend on the desired result.

Selective pruning can reduce the height of a mature tree, open up the tree while still maintaining the tree's natural shape.

Pruning is an art. Basic pruning techniques will produce high quality plant material with a high aesthetic value. ❦

Notes

CHAPTER 11

Organic Lawn Care

There's no doubt that American consumers today are more aware of their health, as well as the impact materials used around the home have on the environment. Because the term "organic" normally conjures thoughts of "natural" and "safe" in most consumers' minds, the demand for organic lawn care programs has increased. Likewise, the number of organic products and lawn care providers has also increased.

While most lawn care professionals currently classify the organic market as a "niche market," many recognize it as one that is growing. As biological pest control products are developed, organic lawn care services will become even more attractive and competitive.

What Is Organic?

A quick look in the dictionary reveals several definitions of organic. The most basic definition or organic is any carbon containing compound. Some of these compounds occur naturally (natural organic), while some are man-made (synthetic organic).

If you were to ask your customer to define organic, they would likely describe a natural organic. True organic lawn care practitioners use natural products. In fact, certification standards for natural lawn care professionals have been developed by an ad-hoc group of the Natural Organic Farmers Association (NOFA).

There are some basic philosophical differences between natural organic and traditional lawn care programs. Practitioners of natural organic lawn care believe that the biotic character of the soil must be maintained. The organic matter in particular must be preserved because of its many benefits: nutrient and moistureholding abilities, soil aggregation, and the ability to support a diverse array of organisms. They further believe that using synthetic materials such as chemical fertilizers and pesticides will adversely affect the organic matter and the organisms it sustains. In fact, there is some documentation to support this. If the soil is healthy, the plant life it supports will be healthy as well.

Traditional lawn care programs have evolved to utilize the technologies and products developed that will produce attractive, lush lawns. Regard for how these practices affect the soil or the long-term well-being of the lawn area is often an afterthought.

Regardless of the philosophical differences between the two approaches, their goals are the same—a satisfied customer. In fact, the means to that end are also quite similar. Both traditional and natural organic lawn care programs rely on the basics of sound turfgrass management. Proper mowing, fertilization, irrigation and grass species and cultivar selection are the first defenses to pest encroachment or damage. The main differences between the two programs lie in the materials used.

Fertilizers

A fertile soil will yield a healthy lawn. Thus, lawn fertilization is the basis of most lawn care services. All lawn services should use soil testing to assess the nutrient status of the soil. Once this is known, fertilizer programs can be adjusted to make up any nutrient deficiencies or imbalances, or to alter soil pH.

You should have soils tested prior to establishing a new lawn, and every 3 to 5 years thereafter. Here are a couple of suggestions to improve the quality of information you receive from soil testing: select a competent lab and stick with them (don't switch labs); sample at the same time of year and at the same depth; be sure the sample is representative of the area; and keep records, so that nutrient levels for specific areas can be monitored over time.

Nitrogen

There are several natural organic nutrient sources to select for your lawn care program. Natural organic fertilizers contain between 3% and 10% nitrogen, the nutrients derived from bone meal, dried blood, manures, vegetable meals, feather meal, fish scraps, sludge, or any other organic source.

Most of the nitrogen in natural organic fertilizers is tied up in complex organic molecules. When applied to the soil, micro-organisms quickly begin to use the organic carbon in the fertilizers as a food source. As the organic fertilizer degrades, nitrogen and other nutrients become available to the plant. Most of the nitrogen in natural organic fertilizers is in a slow-release form. In fact, some of the nitrogen will not become available for several weeks to months after application. Therefore, the burn potential, and the potential for leaching and gaseous loss of nutrients is small.

Since nitrogen in natural organics releases very slowly, the visual turfgrass response to these problems may not be on par with their synthetic counterparts in the first year or two. With continued use, however, the release of this reserve nitrogen should enable organic fertilizers to perform very well. In one of our trials, we have noticed our organic program to be comparable to our "IPM" program in the second year.

Micro-organism activity is slow during cool periods of the year, so nutrient availability is limited. One major hurdle organic lawn care providers have had to overcome is providing good quality turf during the cooler times. For this reason, organic certifying groups will sometimes allow the use of Chilean nitrate (sodium nitrate), a naturally occurring inorganic source to improve performance at these times.

The main drawback of natural organic fertilizers is cost. A 50-pound bag of a processed manure product with 5% nitrogen contains 2.5 pounds of nitrogen. If that bag costs $14, the cost per pound of nitrogen is $5.60. Compare that to a 50-pound bag of product that contains 32% nitrogen from synthetic sources that costs $12.95 per bag. the cost per pound of nitrogen is $0.81. You can see immediately that you will have a cost disadvantage compared to the provider of traditional lawn care programs.

The short-term performance and cost disadvantages of natural organic fertilizers have forced some to fortify these products with synthetic organic and inorganic nutrient sources. There is one company with an entire line of "organic" products that supplements their manure-based product with methylene urea—a synthetic organic. While the manure makes up most of the product in bulk, nearly 90% of the nitrogen comes from the methylene urea.

Selling natural/synthetic organic or inorganic combination products is becoming more common. It brings the cost of the product down, and improves the short-term performance. Using synthetic materials, however, would be in violation of the organic lawn care certification standards—a decision you would have to make.

Other Nutrients

Most natural organic fertilizers and composts are excellent sources of other plant nutrients. Manures, for example, contain phosphorus, calcium, magnesium, and several micro-nutrients.

Phosphorus is an essential plant nutrient that is most important during new lawn establishment. Small seeded grass species such as bentgrass and Kentucky bluegrass are especially responsive to phosphorus applications in the seed bed. Once established, turfgrasses are more efficient at obtaining available phosphorus. Therefore, phosphorus needs should be determined by a soil test on established lawns.

Phosphorus sources approved by organic certification groups include bone meal and rock phosphates. Bone meal is derived from the skeletons of vertebrates. It is sold raw, or as a processed by-product of one of several industries. Elemental phosphorus content can range from 10-20%. The phosphorus in bone meal products is more readily available than other phosphorus sources accepted by certifying groups. Bone meal fertilizers may have an offending odor, however, or may be in a physical form that makes it difficult to spread.

Rock phosphate is an inorganic, naturally-occurring mineral (apatite) that contains between 12-17% elemental phosphorus. Untreated rock phosphate is very stable and of limited value to plants, unless it is ground to a very fine particle size. On alkaline (high pH) soils, rock phosphates are of little value. On acid soils, rock phosphates are of very little value. On acid soils, rock phosphates may be of some benefit, but rates as high as five times normal (compared to treated phosphates) are often needed to produce comparable results.

Acid-treated phosphate sources such as ordinary super phosphate (0-20-0) or triple super phosphate (0-46-0) are more readily available and have better physical properties than rock phosphate. They are not allowed by organic certifying groups because of the belief that acid-treated phosphates are more prone to runoff than rock phosphates. This belief is unfounded.

Potassium is another essential nutrient that is required in fairly large quantities by turfgrasses. It is also commonly deficient in New York soils. Unlike nitrogen, potassium fertilizer will usually not provide an immediate improvement in the appearance of the turf. When the turf is subjected to heat, cold, or drought stress, however, adequate levels of potassium will help the turf through these adverse conditions.

Composts are a natural source of potassium allowed by organic certifying associations. Composts may contain up to 1% potassium, which means that large quantities of compost are needed to increase soil levels. This is possible in new seedings where large quantities of compost could be incorporated into the soil.

Wood ashes are a naturally-occurring inorganic source that may contain up to 4% elemental potassium. Ashes are actually a better liming source than a fertilizer and should be used sparingly, especially on high pH soils.

Potassium sulfate (0-52-0) is a naturally-occurring, inorganic potassium source that is allowed (on a limited basis) by organic certifying groups. The potassium in potassium sulfate is soluble, meaning that it is readily available to the plant. It has a lower burning potential than other inorganic sources, and can easily be found with fertilizer dealers.

Humates

We have recently seen a host of humate products introduced on the market. Sometimes these products are a form of well decomposed organic matter from several possible sources; such as seaweed or peat bogs. While research data on many of these products has been lacking, there are many testimonials to their merits.

Because of the wide array of products available, be cautious. If you're interested in any of these products, try them out on a section of a lawn making sure you leave an untreated area for comparison. Better yet, do little in-house research. Try a number of products on two or three lawns, take notes, and compare the results over an entire growing season.

Organic Pest Management

Controlling pests is the most challenging part of any lawn care program. Traditional and organic programs alike should rely on proper turf-grass culture to minimize pest pressures.

The two best defenses for preventing weeds are mowing height and fertilization. In dry years, irrigation can be equally important. Bluegrass and ryegrass lawns should receive about 3 pounds of actual nitrogen per 1000 square feet per year. Fine fescue and tall fescue lawns should receive slightly less. Mowing heights should be at least 2 inches. If you don't provide mowing services to your customers, be sure to teach them how to mow and water properly. Not only will it help keep the weeds out, it will make your program look better.

Once weeds are in a lawn, there is little you can do, short of hand pulling, to eliminate them. Again, you must educate your customers on the realities of organic lawn care. They must be willing to either accept weeds in the lawn, go through the labor-intensive process of pulling them, or apply a herbicide. The latter option, of course, violates organic certification standards.

There may be some hope on the horizon for organic weed control options. Corn gluten meal is an organic product that has shown some preemergence herbicidal activity on crabgrass. The selectivity of this material is very narrow, however, and is not yet commercially available.

There has been far more success in genetic or biological control of diseased and insects. Any chance you have to introduce improved cultivars into a lawn area, do so. Most lawn grasses available today have resistance to diseases that were a scourge 20 years ago. Check with your local cooperative extension service for genetic resistance to specific diseases and insects.

Biological control of diseases is taking giant steps forward, thanks in large part to research conducted at Cornell. Dr. Eric Nelson and his associates have found suppression of diseases such as dollar spot and brown patch with natural organic fertilizers, such as Ringers Greens Restore and Sustane. Sustane also has been shown to reduce the severity of red thread.

Some composts have also exhibited disease suppression. The problem is, not all composts are disease suppressive. Research is now focusing on identifying the organisms in composts that are suppressive, and how to predict if a compost is suppressive.

Chemical-free means of controlling insects has also jumped forward in recent years. Perhaps one of the most significant contributions to natural insect control was the introduction of endophytic turfgrass varieties. These are varieties that have resistance to surface-feeding insects such as chinch bugs, billbugs and sod webworms. At his point, we have insect-resistant ryegrasses, tall fescues and fine fescues available. Once again, check with your local cooperative extension service to identify cultivars that have this natural resistance to insects.

There are several biological control options for insects. Entomogenous nematodes include several species of nematodes, which are microscopic worms that parasitize insect larvae. Research conducted by Dr. Mike Villani at Cornell has found that *Heterorhabdtid bacteriophora*, one species of these nematodes, was more effective on white grubs than other nematode species. It should be mentioned that control grub control with nematodes has been mixed. Another nematode species, *Steinernema carpocapsae*, has been shown to be effective on sod webworm and cutworm larvae, but not on white grubs.

The costs of nematodes can vary from being comparable to insecticides in cost to 10 times the cost. Some practitioners of organic lawn care have found it cost effective to scout lawns for the presence of grubs, and to spot treat only those areas found to be infested. Before starting an organic lawn care business or program, assess your market. Is there a demand for organic lawn care? At what cost can you offer an organic program, and still make a profit? Then, is your market willing to pay those costs? ❧

There is still much to be learned about organic lawn care, and more products to be developed. Many individuals, though, have successful businesses based on organic lawn care programs. Perhaps you can too.

Credit: Norman W. Hummel, Jr.,
Dept. of Floriculture and
Ornamental Horticulture,
Cornell University Turfgrass Times.

Notes

12 CHAPTER

Pesticides & the Environment

A pest is anything that:
- competes with desirable plants for food or water;
- injures desirable plants; or
- spreads disease to desirable plants.

Types of Pests Include:
- insects;
- insect-like organisms, such as mites;
- microbial organisms, such as fungi, bacteria, nematodes and viruses; and
- weeds, which are any plants growing where they are not wanted.

    Most organisms are not pests. A species may be a pest in some situations and not in others. An organism should not be considered a pest until it is proven to be one. Categories of pests include:
    - continuous pests that are nearly always present and require regular control;
    - sporadic, migratory or cyclical pests that require control occasionally or intermittently;
    - potential pests that do not require control under normal conditions, but may require control in certain circumstances.

Pest Identification

Accurate identification is the first step in an effective pest management program. Never attempt a pest control program until you are sure of what the pest is. The more you know about the pest and the factors that influence its development and spread, the easier, more cost-effective and more successful your pest control will be. Correct identification of a pest allows you to determine basic information about it, including its life cycle and the time that it is most susceptible to being controlled.

As a certified applicator, you must be familiar with the pests you are likely to encounter in the type of work in your certification category. To be able to identify and control pests, you need to know:
- the physical features of the pests likely to be encountered.
- characteristics of the damage they cause.
- their development and biology.
- whether they are continuous, sporadic, or potential pests.
- what your control goal is.

If you need help in identifying a pest, contact your commodity or industry organization, cooperative extension agent, or state land-grant university.

Pest Control

Any time you are considering whether pest control is necessary, remember:

Control a pest only when it is causing or is expected to cause more harm than is reasonable to accept.

Use a control strategy that will reduce the pest numbers to an acceptable level.

Cause as little harm as possible to everything except the pest.

Even though a pest is present, it may not do very much harm. It could cost more to control the pest than would be lost because of the pest's damage.

Pest Control Goals

Whenever you try to control a pest, you will want to achieve one of these three goals, or some combination of them:
- *prevention*—keeping a pest from becoming a problem.
- *suppression*—reducing pest numbers or damage to an acceptable level, and;
- *eradication*—destroying an entire pest population.

Prevention may be a goal when the pest's presence or abundance can he predicted in advance. Continuous pests, by definition, are usually very predictable. Sporadic and potential pests may be predictable if you know the circumstances or conditions that will favor their presence as pests. For example, some plant diseases occur only under certain environmental conditions. If such conditions are present, you can take steps to prevent the plant disease organisms from harming the desirable plants.

Suppression is a common goal in many pest situations. The intent is to reduce the number of pests to a level where the harm they are causing is acceptable. Once a pest's presence is detected and the decision is made that control is necessary, suppression and prevention often are joint goals. The right combination of control measures can often suppress the pests already present and prevent them from building up again to a level where they are causing unacceptable harm.

Eradication is a rare goal in outdoor pest situations, because it is difficult to achieve. Usually the goal is prevention and/or suppression.

Threshold Levels

Thresholds are the levels of pest populations at which you should take pest control action if you want to prevent the pests in an area from causing unacceptable injury or harm. Thresholds may be based on aesthetic, or economic considerations. These levels, which are known as "action thresholds," have been determined for many pests.

A threshold often is set at the level where the economic losses caused by pest damage, if the pest population continued to grow, would be greater than the cost of controlling the pests. These types of action thresholds sometimes are called "economic thresholds."

Pest Monitoring

In most pest control situations, the area to be protected should be monitored (checked or scouted) often. Regular monitoring can answer several important questions:
- What kinds of pests are present?
- Are the numbers great enough to warrant control?
- When is the right time to begin control?
- Have the control efforts successfully reduced the number of pests?

Monitoring of insect and insect-like pests usually is done by trapping or scouting. Monitoring of weed pests usually is done by visual inspection. Monitoring of microbial pests is done by looking for the injury or damage they cause.

Monitoring also can include checking environmental conditions in the area being managed. Temperature and moisture levels, especially humidity, are often important clues in predicting when a pest outbreak will occur or hit threshold levels.

Avoiding Harmful Effects

Pest control involves more than simply identifying a pest and using a control tactic. The treatment site, whether it is an outdoor area or inside a structure, usually contains other living organisms (such as people, animals, and plants) and nonliving surroundings (such as air, water, structures, objects, and surfaces). All of these could be affected by the pest control measures you choose. Unless you consider the possible effects on the entire system within which the pest exists, your pest control effort could cause harm or lead to continued or new pest problems. Rely on your own good judgment and, when pesticides are part of the strategy, on the pesticide labeling.

Most treatment sites are disrupted to some degree by pest control strategies. The actions of every type of organism or component sharing the site usually affect the actions and well-being of many others. When the balance is disrupted, certain organisms may be destroyed or reduced in number, and others—sometimes the pests—may dominate.

Integrated Pest Management

Integrated pest management is the combining of appropriate pest control tactics into a single plan (strategy) to reduce pests and their damage to an acceptable level. Using many different tactics to control a pest problem tends to cause the least disruption to the living organisms and nonliving surroundings at the treatment site. Relying only on pesticides for pest control can cause pests to develop resistance, cause outbreaks of other pests, and can harm surfaces or nontarget organisms. With some types of pests, use of pesticides as the only tactic will achieve very poor control.

To solve pest problems, you must:
- identify the pest or pests and determine whether control is warranted for each;
- determine your pest control goal(s);
- know what control tactics are available;
- evaluate the benefits and risks of each tactic or combination of tactics;
- choose a strategy that will be most effective and will cause the least harm to people and the environment;
- use each tactic in the strategy correctly;
- observe local, state, and federal regulations that apply to the situation.

The strategy you choose will depend on the pest you have identified and the kind and amount of control you need.

Natural Controls

Some natural forces act on all organisms, causing the populations to rise and fall. These natural forces act independently of humans and may either help or hinder pest control. You may not be able to alter the action of natural forces on a pest population, but you should be aware of their influence and take advantage of them whenever possible. Natural forces that affect pest populations, include climate, natural enemies, natural barriers, availability of shelter, and food and water supplies.

Climate

Weather conditions, especially temperature, day length, and humidity, affect pests' activity and their rate of reproduction. Pests may be killed or suppressed by rain, freezing temperatures, drought, or other adverse weather. Climate also affects pests indirectly by influencing the growth and development of their hosts. Unusual weather conditions can change normal patterns so increased or decreased damage results.

Natural Enemies
Many predatory and parasitic insect and insect-like species feed on pest organisms. Pathogens such as bacteria, fungi and viruses often suppress pest populations.

Geographic Barriers
Features such as mountains and large bodies of water restrict the spread of many pests. Other features of the landscape can have similar effects.

Food and Water Supply
Pest populations can thrive only as long as their food and water supply lasts. Once the food source is exhausted, the pests die or become inactive. The life cycle of many pests depends on the availability of water.

Shelter
The availability of shelter can affect some pest populations. Overwintering sites are important to the survival of many pests.

Applied Controls
Unfortunately, natural controls often do not control pests quickly or completely enough to prevent unacceptable injury or damage. Then other control measures must be used. Those available include:
- host resistance
- biological control
- cultural control
- mechanical control
- sanitation, and
- chemical control

Host Resistance
Some plants resist pests better than others. Some varieties of plants are resistant to certain pests. Use of resistant types, when available, helps keep pest populations below harmful levels by making conditions less favorable for the pests.

Host resistance works in three main ways:
- Chemicals in the host repel the pest or prevent the pest from completing its life cycle.
- The host is more vigorous or tolerant than other varieties and thus less likely to be seriously damaged by pest attacks.
- The host has physical characteristics that make it more difficult to attack.

Biological Control
Biological control involves the use of natural enemies—parasites, predators, and pathogens. You can supplement this natural control by releasing more of a pest's enemies into the target area or by introducing new enemies that were not in the area before. Biological control usually is not eradication. The degree of control fluctuates. There is a time lag between pest population increase and the corresponding increase in natural controls. But, under proper conditions, sufficient control can be achieved to eliminate the threat to the plant to be protected.

Biological control also includes methods by which the pest is biologically altered, as in the production and release of large numbers of sterile males and the use of pheromones or juvenile hormones.

Pheromones can be useful in monitoring pest populations. Placed in a trap, for example, they can attract the insects in a sample area so that pest numbers can be estimated. Pheromones also can be a control tool. Sometimes a manufactured copy of the pheromone that a female insect uses to attract males can be used to confuse males and prevent mating, resulting in lower numbers of pests. Applying juvenile hormones to an area can reduce pest numbers by keeping some immature pests from becoming normal, reproducing adults.

Cultural Control

Cultural practices sometimes are used to reduce the numbers of pests that are attacking cultivated plants. These practices alter the environment, the condition of the host plant, or the behavior of the pest to prevent or suppress an infestation. They disrupt the normal relationship between the pest and the host plant and make the pest less likely to survive, grow, or reproduce.

Mechanical (physical) Control

Devices, machines and other methods used to control pests or alter their environment are called mechanical or physical controls.

Light, heat, and cold can alter the environment enough to suppress or eradicate some pest populations. Altering the amount of water, including humidity, can control some pests, especially insects and disease agents.

Sanitation

Sanitation practices help prevent and suppress some pests by removing the pests themselves or their sources of food and shelter.

Chemical Control

Pesticides are chemicals used to destroy pests, control their activity, or prevent them from causing damage. Some pesticides either attract or repel pests. Chemicals that regulate plant growth or remove foliage also are classified as pesticides. Pesticides are generally the fastest way to control pests. In many instances, they are the only tactic available.

Pest Control Failures

Sometimes you may find that even though you applied a pesticide, the pest has not been controlled. You should review the situation to try to determine what went wrong. There are several possible reasons for the failure of chemical pest control.

Pest Resistance

Pesticides fail to control some pests because the pests are resistant to the pesticides. Consider this when planning pest control programs that rely on the use of pesticides. Rarely does any pesticide kill all the target pests. Each time a pesticide is used, it selectively kills the most susceptible pests. Some pests avoid the pesticide. Others withstand its effects. Pests that are not destroyed may pass along to their offspring the trait that allowed them to survive.

When one pesticide is used repeatedly in the same place, against the same pest, the surviving pest population may be more resistant to the pesticide than the original population was. The opportunity for resistance is greater when a pesticide is used over a wide geographic area or when a pesticide is applied repeatedly to a rather small area where pest populations are isolated. A pesticide that leaves a residue that gradually loses its effectiveness over time will help select out resistance. Rotating pesticides may help reduce the development of pest resistance.

Other Reasons for Failure

Not every pesticide failure is caused by pest resistance. Make sure that you have used the correct pesticide and the correct dosage and that you have applied the pesticide correctly. Sometimes a pesticide application fails to control a pest because the pest was not identified correctly and the wrong pesticide was chosen. Other applications fail because the pesticide was not applied at an appropriate time—the pest may not have been in the area during the applications or it may have been in a life cycle stage or locations where it was not susceptible to the pesticide. Also remember that the pests that are present may be part of a new infestation that developed after the chemical was applied.

Protecting Ground Water

Ground water is water located beneath the earth's surface. Many people think that ground water occurs in vast underground lakes, rivers, or streams. Usually, however, it is located in rock and soil. It moves very slowly through irregular spaces within otherwise solid rock or seeps between particles of sand, clay, and gravel. An exception is in limestone areas, where ground water may flow through large underground channels or caverns. Surface water may move several feet in a second or a minute. Ground water may move only a few feet in a month or a year. If the ground water is capable of providing significant quantities of water to a well or spring, it is called an aquifer. Pesticide contamination of aquifers is very troubling, because these are sources of drinking, washing, and irrigation water.

Pesticide Contamination of Ground Water

When water that is moving downward from the surface contains pesticides—or comes into contact with them as it moves—the pesticides may be carried along with the water until they eventually reach the ground water. Five major factors determine whether a pesticide will reach ground water:
- the practices followed by pesticide users;
- the presence or absence of water on the surface of the site where the pesticides are released;
- the chemical characteristics of the pesticides;
- the type of soil in the site where the pesticides are released;
- the locations of the ground water—its distance from the surface and the type of geological formations above it.

By being aware of these considerations, you can handle pesticides in ways that will make the potential for ground water contamination less likely.

Practices for Pesticide Users

The best way to keep from contaminating ground water is to follow labeling directions exactly. Be sure to note whether the labeling requires you to take any special steps to protect ground water. In addition remember the following:
- Avoid the temptation to use more pesticide than the labeling directs. Overdosing will increase both the cost of pest control and the odds that the pesticide will reach ground water. Overdosing is also illegal. Keeping the use of pesticides to a minimum greatly reduces the risk of ground water contamination.
- Consider whether your application method presents any special risks. For example, soil injection of some pesticides may not be wise when ground water is close to the surface.
- Take precautions to keep pesticides from backsiphoning into your water source.

Locate pesticide storage facilities at least 100 feet from wells, springs, sinkholes, and other sites that directly link to ground water to prevent their contamination from runoff or firefighting water.
- Whenever possible, locate mix-load sites and equipment-cleaning sites

at least 100 feet from surface water or from direct links to ground water. This will help prevent back-siphoning runoff and spills from contaminating the water sources. If you must locate one of these work sites near a water source, use methods such as dikes, sump pits, and containment pads to keep pesticides from reaching the water.

- Do not contaminate ground water through improper disposal of unused pesticides, pesticide containers, or equipment and container rinse water. Dispose of all pesticide wastes in accordance with local, state, tribal, and federal laws.

Water on the Treated Surface

If there is more water on the soil than the soil can hold, the water (along with any pesticides it contains) is likely to move downward to the ground water. Prolonged heavy rain or excessive irrigation will produce excess water on the soil surface.

Rain

If weather forecasts or your own knowledge of local weather signs cause you to expect heavy rain, delay outdoor handling operations—including mixing and loading application, and disposal—to prevent wash-off, surface runoff, or leaching.

Irrigation

Pesticide movement into ground water is affected by both the amount of water used in irrigation and how soon before or after a pesticide application the irrigation is done. If irrigation water contains pesticides, be careful to prevent it from flowing into water sources.

Pesticide Factors

Some pesticide chemicals are more likely than others to move to ground water. Such movement depends mainly on:

- solubility—Some pesticides dissolve easily in water and are more likely to move into water systems.
- adsorption—Some pesticides become tightly attached (strongly adsorbed) to soil particles and are not likely to move out of the soil and into water systems.
- persistence—Some pesticides break down slowly and remain in the environment for a long time.

These factors are all related to one another. Pesticides that are most likely to move into ground water are highly soluble, moderately to highly persistent, and are not strongly adsorbed to soil. A non-persistent pesticide would be less likely to move to ground water, even if it is highly soluble or not strongly adsorbed to soil. A pesticide that is strongly adsorbed to soil would be less likely to move to ground water even if it is persistent.

Pesticide labeling usually does not tell you about these properties of the pesticide product. The Soil Conservation Service, Cooperative Extension Service, your trade association, or your pesticide dealer may have specific information about the characteristics of the pesticides you are using.

Soil Factors

Soil is also an important factor in the breakdown and movement of pesticides. Your local cooperative extension service or soil conservation service can help you determine the types of soil in your area and how they affect breakdown and movement. The three major soil characteristics that affect pesticides are soil texture, permeability, and organic matter.

Soil texture is an indication of the relative proportions of sand, silt, and clay in the soil. Coarse, sandy soils generally allow water to carry the pesticides rapidly downward. Finer textured soils generally allow water to move at much slower rates. They contain more clay, and sometimes organic matter, to which pesticides may cling.

Soil permeability is a general measure of how fast water can move downward in a particular soil. More permeable soils must be managed carefully to keep pesticides from reaching ground water.

Soil organic matter influences how much water the soil can hold before it begins to move downward. Soil containing organic matter has greater ability to stop the movement of pesticides. Soils in which plants are growing are more likely to prevent pesticide movement than bare soils.

Geology

The distance from the soil surface to the water table is the measure of how deep the ground water is in a given location. If the ground water is within a few feet of the soil surface, pesticides are more likely to reach it than if it is farther down. In humid areas, the water table may be only a few feet below the surface of the soil. In arid areas, the water table may lie several hundred feet below the soil surface. The depth to the water table does not stay the same over the course of the year. It varies according to:

- the amount of rain, snow, and irrigation water being added to the soil surface;
- the amount of evaporation and plant uptake;
- whether the ground is frozen, and;
- how much ground water is being withdrawn by pumping.

The Soil Conservation Service can provide you with valuable information on the geology of an area and on the potential for ground water contamination on your property.

Spring and fall generally are the times when the water table is closest to the soil surface. The water table often moves downward during the summer when evaporation and plant uptake are high and when larger-than-normal amounts of ground water are being used for irrigation and other hot-weather needs. The water table also moves downward in winter if surface water cannot move down through the frozen soil to recharge the ground water.

The permeability of geological layers between the soil and ground water is also important. If surface water can move down quickly, pesticides are more likely to reach ground water. Gravel deposits are highly permeable. They allow water and any pesticides in it to move rapidly downward to ground water. Regions with limestone deposits are particularly susceptible to ground water contamination, because water may move rapidly to the ground water through caverns or "rivers" with little filtration or chemical breakdown. On the other hand, layers of clay may be totally impermeable and may prevent most water and any pesticides in it from reaching the ground water.

Sinkholes are especially troublesome. Surface water often flows into sinkholes and disappears quickly into the ground water. If a pesticide is released into an area that drains to a sinkhole, even a moderate rain or irrigation may carry some of the pesticide directly to the ground water.

Protection of Endangered Species

An endangered species is a plant or animal that is in danger of becoming extinct. There are two classifications of these plants and animals in danger—"endangered species" and "threatened species." The term "endangered species" is used here to refer to the two classifications collectively. Scientists believe that some pesticides may threaten the survival of some of America's endangered species if they are used in the places where these plants and animals still exist.

A federal law, the Endangered Species Act, requires the U.S. Environmental Protection Agency (EPA) to insure that endangered species are protected from pesticides. EPA's goal is to remove or reduce the threat that pesticide use poses to endangered species. Reaching this goal will require some limitations on pesticide use. These limitations usually will apply only in the currently occupied habitat or range of each endangered species at risk. Occasionally the limitations will apply where endangered species are being reintroduced into a habitat they previously occupied.

Habitats, sometimes called "critical habitats," are the areas of land, water, and air space that an endangered species needs for survival. Such areas include breeding sites; sources of food, cover, and shelter; and surrounding territory that give room for normal population growth and behavior.

Limitations on Pesticide Use

Read all pesticide labeling carefully to find out whether the use of a product requires you to take any special steps to protect endangered species. The label may direct you to another source for details about what you must do. When limitations do apply, they usually will be in effect only in some specific geographic locations. Use of a particular pesticide is usually limited in a particular location when:
- the site is designated as the current habitat of an endangered species, and
- the endangered species that uses the site might be harmed by the use of the pesticide within (or close to) its habitat.

Habitats of Endangered Species

The U.S. Fish and Wildlife Service is responsible for identifying the current habitat or range of each endangered species. For aquatic species, the restricted habitat often will include an additional zone around the body of water to keep any drift, runoff, or leachate in the watershed from reaching the water.

The U.S. Fish and Wildlife Service is attempting to identify the habitats as accurately as possible so that pesticide use will need to be limited only in locations where it is absolutely necessary. For this reason, limitations on pesticide use may apply on one property, while a similar adjoining property may not have these limitations.

Sources of Contamination

When environmental contamination occurs, it is the result of either point-source or non-point-source pollution. Point-source pollution comes from a specific, identifiable place (point). A pesticide spill that moves into a storm sewer is an example of point-source pollution. Non-point-source pollution comes from a wide area. The movement of pesticides into streams after broadcast applications is an example of non-point-source pollution.

Non-point-source pollution from pesticide applications is the source that has most commonly been blamed for pesticide contamination in the outdoor environment. But more and more studies are revealing that, in fact, much environmental contamination does not result from non-point-source pollution. Contamination also results from point sources, such as:
- wash water and spills produced at equipment cleanup sites;
- improper disposal of containers, water from rinsing containers, and excess pesticides;
- pesticide storage sites where leaks and spills are not correctly cleaned up, and;
- spills that occur while mixing concentrates or loading pesticides into application equipment.

These kinds of tasks are involved with nearly every pesticide use, whether the pesticide is applied outdoors or in or around an enclosed structure.

As a pesticide handler, especially if you use and supervise restricted-use pesticides, you must become aware of the potential for environmental contamination during every phase of your pesticide operation. Many pesticide uses are restricted because of environment.

Always consider:

• whether there are sensitive areas in the environment at the pesticide use site that might be harmed by contact with the pesticide;

• whether there are sensitive off-site areas near the use site that might be harmed by contact with the pesticide;

• whether there are conditions in the environment at the pesticide use site that might cause the pesticide to move off-site, and;

• whether you need to change any factors in your application or in the pesticide use site to reduce the risk of environmental contamination.

Sensitive Areas

Sensitive areas are sites or living things that are easily injured by a pesticide.

Sensitive areas outdoors include:

• areas where ground water is near the surface or easily accessed (wells, sinkholes, porous soil, etc.);

• areas in or near surface water;

• areas near schools, playgrounds, hospitals, and other institutions;

• areas near the habitats of endangered species;

• areas near apiaries (honeybee sites), wildlife refuges, or parks, and;

• areas near ornamental gardens, food or feed crops, or other sensitive plantings.

Sensitive areas indoors include:

• areas where people—especially children, pregnant women, the elderly, or the sick—live, work, or are cared for;

• areas where food or feed is processed, prepared, stored, or served;

• areas where domestic or confined animals live, eat, or are otherwise cared for, and;

• areas where ornamental or other sensitive plantings are grown or maintained.

Sometimes pesticides must be deliberately applied to a sensitive area to control a pest. These applications should be performed by persons who are well trained about how to avoid causing injury in such areas.

At other times, the sensitive area is part of a larger target site. Whenever possible, take special precautions to avoid direct application to the sensitive area. For example, leaving an untreated buffer zone around sensitive areas is often a practical way to avoid contaminating them.

In still other instances, the sensitive area may be near a site that is used for application, mixing/loading, storage, disposal, or equipment washing. The pesticide users must take precautions to avoid accidental contamination of the sensitive area. For example, a permanent site for mixing/loading or equipment washing could be equipped with a collection pad or tray to catch and contain leaks, spills, or waste water.

Typical pesticide labeling statements that alert you to these concerns include:

Remove all animals from a building prior to treatment and keep animals out until spray has dried.

Applications prohibited in areas where food is held, processed, prepared or served.

Do not use around home gardens, schools, recreational parks, or play-grounds.

In living areas, make applications in such a manner as to avoid deposits on exposed surfaces or introducing the material into the air.

Do not use in or around residences.

Pesticide Movement

Pesticides that move away from the release site may cause environmental contamination. Pesticides move away from the release site both indoors and outdoors and may cause harm in both environments. Pesticides move in several ways, including:

- in air, through wind or through air currents generated by ventilation systems;
- in water, through runoff or leaching;
- on or in objects, plants, or animals (including humans) that move or are moved offsite.

Air

Pesticide movement away from the release site in the air is usually called drift. Pesticide particles, dusts, spray droplets, and vapors all may be carried off-site in the air. People who mix, load, and apply pesticides outdoors usually are aware of the ease with which pesticides drift offsite. People who handle pesticides indoors may not realize how easily some pesticides move off-site in the air currents created by ventilation systems and by forced-air heating and cooling systems.

Particles and Droplets

Lightweight particles, such as dusts and wettable powders, are easily carried by moving air. Granules and pellets are much heavier and tend to settle out of air quickly. Small spray droplets also are easily carried in air currents. High-pressure and fine nozzles produce very small spray droplets that are very likely to drift. Lower pressure and coarse nozzles produce droplets with less drift potential.

The likelihood that pesticide particles and spray droplets will drift off-site depends partly on the way they are released. Pesticides released close to the ground or floor are not as likely to be caught up in air currents as those released from a greater height. Pesticides applied in an upward direction or from an aircraft are the most likely to be carried on air currents.

Vapors

Pesticide vapors move about easily in air. Fumigant pesticides are intended to form a vapor when they are released. Persons using fumigants must take precautions to make sure the fumigant remains in a sealed container until it is released into the application site, which also must be sealed to prevent the vapor from escaping. Some non-fumigant pesticides also can vaporize and escape into the air. The labeling of volatile pesticides often includes warning statements that the pesticide handler should heed. Any time you release a volatile pesticide in an enclosed area, consider the hazards not only to yourself and to fellow workers, but also to people, animals, and plants that are in or near the release site or that may enter the area soon after the release.

Typical pesticide labeling statements that alert you to avoid drift include:

Do not apply when weather conditions favor drift from areas treated.

Do not allow drift onto plants intended for food or feed.

Drift from treated areas may be hazardous to aquatic organisms in neighboring areas.

Water

Pesticide particles and liquids may be carried off-site in water. Pesticides can enter water through:

- drift, leaching, and runoff from nearby applications;
- spills, leaks, and back-siphoning from nearby mixing, loading, storage, and equipment cleanup sites, and;
- improper disposal of pesticides, rinsates, and containers.

Most pesticide movement in water is across the treated surface (runoff) or downward from the surface (leaching). Runoff and leaching may occur when:

- too much liquid pesticide is applied, leaked, or spilled onto a surface, or;
- too much rainwater, irrigation water, or other water gets onto a surface containing pesticide residue.

Runoff water in the outdoor environment may travel into drainage ditches, streams, ponds, or other surface water where the pesticides can be carried great distances off-site. Pesticides that leach downward through the soil in the outdoor environment sometimes reach the ground water.

Runoff water in the indoor environment may get into domestic water systems and from there into surface water and ground water. Runoff can flow into floor drains or other drains and into the water system. Sometimes a careless pesticide handler washes pesticide down a sink drain and into the water system.

Some pesticides can leach downward in indoor environments. In a greenhouse, for example, pesticides may leach through the soil or other planting medium to floors or benches below. Some pesticides used indoors may be absorbed into carpets, wood, and other porous surfaces and remain trapped for a long time.

Typical pesticide labeling statements that alert you to these concerns include:

Do not contaminate water through runoff, spills, or improper disposal of excess pesticide, spray mixtures, or rinsates.

Do not allow runoff or spray to contaminate wells, irrigation ditches, or any body of water used for irrigation or domestic purposes.

Do not apply directly to water and wetlands (swamps, bogs, marshes, and potholes).

Maintain a buffer zone (lay-off distance) of 100 feet from bodies of water.

This product is water soluble and can move with surface runoff water. Do not contaminate cropland, water, or irrigation ditches.

On or In Objects, Plants, or Animals

Pesticides can move away from the release site when they are on or in objects or organisms that move (or are moved) off-site. Pesticides may stick to shoes or clothing, to animal fur, or to blowing dust and be transferred to other surfaces. When pesticide handlers bring home or wear home contaminated personal protective equipment, work clothing, or other items, residues can rub off on carpeting, furniture, and laundry items and onto pets and people.

Pesticides may stick to treated surfaces, such as food or feed products that are to be sold. To protect consumers, there are legal limits (tolerances) for how much pesticide residue may safely remain on crops or animal products that are sold for food or feed. Products that exceed these tolerances are illegal and cannot be sold. Crops and animal products will not be over tolerance if the pesticides are applied as directed on the product labeling. Illegal pesticide residues usually result when:

- too much pesticide is applied to the crop or animal;
- the days-to-harvest, directions on the pesticide labeling are not obeyed, or;
- pesticides move out of the release site and contaminate plants or animals nearby.

Typical pesticide labeling statements that alert you to these concerns include:

Do not apply within 5 days of harvest.

Do not apply under conditions involving possible drift to food, forage, or other plantings that might be damaged or the crops thereof rendered unfit for sale, use, or consumption.

Harmful Effects from Direct Contact

Pesticides may harm non-target organisms that are present during a pesticide application. Poorly-timed applications can kill bees and other pollinators that are active in or near the target site. Pesticides may harm other wildlife, too. Even tiny amounts of some pesticides may harm them or destroy their source of food.

Pesticides applied over large areas, such as in mosquito, biting fly, and forest pest control, must be chosen with great care to avoid poisoning non-target plants and animals in or near the target site. Read the warnings and directions on the pesticide label carefully to avoid harming non-target organisms during a pesticide application.

Drift from the target site may injure wildlife, livestock, pets, sensitive plants, and people. For example, drift of herbicides can damage sensitive nearby plants, including crops, forests, or ornamental plantings. Drift also can kill beneficial parasites and predators that are near the target site.

Pesticide runoff may harm fish and other aquatic animals and plants in ponds, streams, and lakes. Aquatic life also can be harmed by careless tank filling or draining and by rinsing or discarding used containers along or in waterways.

Typical pesticide labeling statements that alert you to these concerns include:

Phytotoxic. Do not spray on plants.

Do not apply this product or allow it to drift to blooming crops or weeds if bees are visiting the treatment area.

Extremely toxic to aquatic organisms. Do not contaminate water by cleaning of equipment or disposal of wastes.

This product is toxic to fish, shrimp, crabs, birds, and other wildlife. Keep out of lakes, streams, ponds, tidal marches, and estuaries. Shrimp and crabs may be killed at application rates. Do not apply where these are important resources.

Harmful Effects From Residues

A residue is the part of a pesticide that remains in the environment for a period of time following application or a spill. Pesticides usually break down into harmless components after they are released into an environment. The breakdown time ranges from less than a day to several years. The rate of pesticide breakdown depends mostly on the chemical structure of the pesticide active ingredient. The rate of pesticide breakdown also may be affected by environmental conditions at the release site such as:

- surface type, chemical composition, and pH;
- surface moisture;
- presence of microorganisms;
- temperature, and;
- exposure to direct sunlight.

Persistent pesticides leave residues that stay in the environment without breaking down for long periods of time. These pesticides are sometimes desirable, because they provide long-term pest control and may reduce the need for repeated applications. However, some persistent pesticides that are applied to or spilled on soil, plants, lumber, and other surfaces or into water can later cause harm to sensitive plants or animals, including humans, that contact them. Clues on pesticide labeling that a particular pesticide product is likely to be persistent include:

Can remain in the soil for 34 months or more and cause injury to certain crops other than those listed as acceptable on the label.

This product can remain phytotoxic for a year or more.

When using persistent pesticides, consider whether their continued presence in the environment is likely to harm plants and animals.

When pesticides build up in the bodies of the animals or in the soil, they are said to accumulate. When the same mixing/loading site or equipment cleaning site is used frequently without taking steps to limit and clean up spills, pesticides are likely to accumulate in the soil. When this occurs, plants, animals, and objects that come into contact with the soil may be harmed. When pesticides accumulate in the soil, there is also a higher likelihood that the pesticides will move offsite and contaminate the surrounding environment or move into surface or ground water.

Sometimes animals can be harmed when they feed on plants or animals that have pesticide residues on or in them. A special concern is for predator birds or mammals that feed on animals that have been killed by pesticides. The predators may be harmed by the pesticide residues remaining on or in the bodies of the dead animals.

Typical pesticide labeling statements that alert you to these concerns include:

Toxic to fish, birds, and wildlife. This product can pose a secondary hazard to birds of prey and mammals.

Do not use fish as food/feed within 3 days of application.

Animals feeding on treated areas may be killed and pose a hazard to hawks and other birds-of-prey. Bury or otherwise dispose of dead animals to prevent poisoning of other wildlife.

Harmful Effects on Surfaces

Sometimes surfaces are harmed by pesticides or pesticide residues. Some surfaces may become discolored by contact with certain pesticides. Other surfaces may be pitted or marked by contact with some pesticides. Some pesticides can corrode or obstruct electronic systems or metal. Sometimes a pesticide will leave a visible deposit on the treated surface.

Typical pesticide labeling statements that alert you to these concerns include:

Do not apply to carpeting, linoleum, or other porous floor coverings, as discoloration may result.

Do not spray on plastic, painted, or varnished surface.

May cause pitting of automobile and other vehicle paint.

Do not spray directly into any electronic equipment or into outlets and switches, or any other location where the pesticide may foul or short-circuit contacts and circuits.

A visible deposit may occur on some dark surfaces.

Pesticide Adjuvants

Adjuvants are products that are designed to enhance the performance of pesticides. By making the pesticides as effective as possible, in the long term, less pesticide is used. This also reduces the possible damage to non-target organisms and lessens any negative environmental effects.The pest control program can benefit from an understanding of the availability and function of each adjuvant.

1. Surfactants or Wetting Agents.

These may also be called spreaders. They simply make water—wetter. That is, the surface tension of water or the spray solution, is reduced so it will move into much smaller spaces. Pesticide solutions containing a surfactant do a better job of coating the plant, in the case of a fungicide or insecticide, than the same solution without the surfactant. Surfactants help move an insecticide down into the soil to improve the control of all below-ground pests. Surfactants may also be used to help increase the efficiency of a herbicide by making it easier for the toxic chemical to get into the undesirable plant.

2. Stickers.

Many times it's desirable to coat the plant with a protectant chemical like a fungicide or insecticide to prevent pest problems for an extended period. A sticker in the spray solution will help keep the rain or irrigation water from washing the protectant chemical off the plant too soon. A surfactant may be added to the sticker making it a spreader-sticker. This will help assure good coverage of the sticker.

3. pH Modifers.

The pH of the spray solution can affect the stability of the pesticide in the solution. Many pesticides are most effective at certain pHs. If the pH of the solution is too high or too low, the effectiveness of the pesticide may be seriously reduced. Determine the recommended pH range for each pesticide used. There are materials available to either raise or lower the pH of the spray solution.

4. Defoaming Agents.

When some spray solutions are agitated, a foam may be produced. Excessive foam can cause problems, so a defoamer may prove helpful.

5. Colorants.

These dyes are most helpful in identifying areas that have been sprayed, since most spray solutions are colorless.

Area Measurement

The area to be treated with a pesticide must be accurately determined in order to apply any material at the proper rate. The most commonly-used unit of area for small turf areas has been 1,000 square feet (sq. ft. and for large areas, the acre (A).

Under the metric system, the square meter (sq. m.) (1 sq. m. = 10.76 sq. ft.) may be used for smaller areas while the hectar (ha.) (1 hectar = 2.47 acres) is suggested for large areas. There are several methods that may be used to measure areas in the field or from a map.

A. The first method involves the division of the area to be measured into geometric figures such as rectangles, trapezoids, circles and triangles.

1. Rectangle: The area of a rectangle is found by multiplying the length by the width.

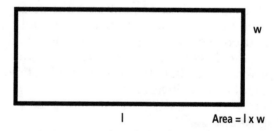

Area = l x w

Example 1: l = 100 ft. (30.48 m.)
             w = 50 ft.(15.24m.)

Area = 100 ft. (30.48 m.) x 50 ft. (15.24 m.)
    = 5,000 sq. ft. (464.5 sq. m.)

2. Trapezoid: A trapezoid is a four-sided figure with two sides parallel. The area is found by multiplying the average length of the parallel sides by the height.

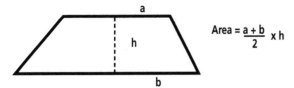

$$\text{Area} = \frac{a+b}{2} \times h$$

Example 2: a = 200 ft. (60.98 m.)
            b = 300 ft. (91.44 m.)
            h = 50 ft. (15.24m.)
Area= 200 ft. (60.98 m.) + 300 ft. (91.44 m.)
                        2
    x 50 ft. (15.24 m.)
    = 500 ft. (152.42 m.) x 50 ft. (15.24 m.)
                        2
    = 250 ft. (76.21 m.) x 50 ft. (15.24 m.)
    =12,500 sq. ft. (1,161.4 sq. m.)

3. Circle: The area of a circle is the radius (r.) (one-half the diameter) squared and then multiplied by 3.14.

$\text{Area} = 3.14r^2$

Example 3: r = 100 ft. (30.48 m.)
Area = 3.14 x 1000 ft. (30.48² m.)
     = 31,400 sq. ft. (2,917.1 sq. m.)

4. Triangle: The area of a triangle is one half the base multiplied by the height.

$\text{Area} = \frac{bh}{2}$

Example 4: b = 200 ft. (60.96 m.)
           h = 400 ft. (121.92 m.)

Area= 200 ft. (60.96 m.) x 400 ft. (121.92 m.)
                        2
    = 80,000 sq. ft. (7,432 sq. m.)
                   2
    = 40,000 sq. ft. (3,716 sq. m.)

Thus, irregularly-shaped landscape areas can be reduced to one or more of the geometric figures shown above. The area of each is calculated and added together to obtain the total area.

Example 5: GOLF COURSE HOLE

Area A is a circle.

Area = $3.14r^2$
  r = 40 ft. (12.2 m.)
Area = 3.14 x 40^2 ft. (12.2² m.)
    = 5,024 sq. ft. (467.4 sq. m.)

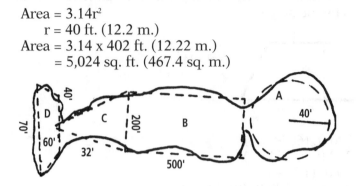

Area B is a rectangle.

Area = lw
  l = 500 ft. (152.4 m.)
  w = 200 ft. (61.0m.)
Area = 500 ft. (152.4 m.) x 200 ft. (61.0 m.)
    = 100,000 sq. ft. (9,296.4 sq. m.)
    = 100,000 sq. ft. or 9,296.4 sq. m.
      43,560 sq. ft./A   10,000 sq. m./ha.
    = 2.3 A. or 0.93 ha.

Area C is a triangle.

Area = $\dfrac{bh}{2}$
  h = 32 ft. (9.8 m.)
  b = 200 ft. (61.0 m.)
Area = $\dfrac{32 \text{ ft. (9.8 m.) x } 200 \text{ ft. (61.0 m)}}{2}$
    = 16 ft. (4.9 m.) x 200 ft. (61.0 m.)
    = 3,200 sq. ft. (298.9 sq. m.)

Area D is a trapezoid.

Area = $\dfrac{a+b}{b}$ h

  a = 40 ft. (12.2m.)
  b = 70 ft. (21.3m.)
  h = 60 ft. (18.3m.)
Area= $\dfrac{40 \text{ ft. (12.2 m.) + } 70 \text{ ft. (21.3 m.) x}}{2}$
    60 ft. (18.3 m.)
Area= $\dfrac{110 \text{ ft. (33.5 m.) x } 60 \text{ ft. (18.3 m.}}{2}$
    = 55 ft. (16.8 m.) x 60 ft. (18.3m.)
    = 3,300 sq. ft. or 307.4 sq. m.

The Total Area is then A + B + C + D:

	sq. ft.	sq. m.
Area A	5,024	467.4
Area B	100,000	9,296.4
Area C	3,200	298.9
Area D	3,300	307.4
Total	111,524	10,370.1

B. Another method that may be used to determine the size of an area is the use of offsets from straight lines.

Irregular areas can be reduced to a series of trapezoids by right angles (90°) offsets from points at regular intervals along a measured line.

In using the offset method, first establish points A and B as in the example. Next, measure the distance between A and B.

The irregularity of the area must be considered when determining the number of offsets to use. Uniform areas will require fewer offsets than those that are not uniform. The more offsets used, the more accurately the area will be measured.

Example 6:

In determining the area of a fairway 300 yards (900 ft.) long, one may want an offset every 30 yards if the shape of the fairway is fairly regular. If it is irregular, one may use offsets every 15 yards (45 feet). The offsets must be at regular intervals and of an even number (i.e., offset line C must be the same distance from offset line D as D is from E, E from F, and so on).

In the example fairway, Point A is 300 yards from Point B. The shape of the fairway is fairly uniform, so the best approach is to use an offset every 30 yards (lines C through K).

The lengths of the offset lines (measured from one edge of the fairway to the other) were found to be as follows:

A= 0   B = 0   C = 20 yds.   D = 25 yds.
E = 25 yds. F = 30 yds.   G = 40 yds.   H = 50 yds.
I = 60 yds. J= 70 yds.   K = 65 yds.

Add the lengths of all the offset lines and multiply by the distance (on line A-B) between them. In this example the total length of all offset lines is 385 yards. The distance between offsets is 30 yards.

30 yds. x 385 yds. = 11,550 sq. yds.

In acres the fairway would be:

$$\frac{11,550 \text{ sq. yds}}{4,840 \text{ sq. yds./A}} = 2.4 \text{ A.}$$

In square feet:

11,550 sq. yds. x 9 sq. ft./sq. yd. = 103,950 sq. ft.

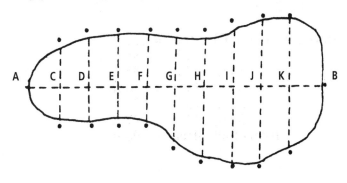

In square meters:
    11,550 sq. yds. x 0.84 sq. m./sq. yd. = 9,702.0 sq. m.
In hectares:
$$\frac{9,702.0 \text{ sq. m}}{10,000 \text{ sq. m./ha.}} = 0.97 \text{ ha}$$

Pond areas may be measured using a variation of the offset method.

The first step is to construct a rectangle around the pond with lines A-C and B-D touching the ends of the pond. The distance between A and B should be the same as between C and D. The distance between A and C should be the same as between B and D.

The offset lines are measured from the two outside lines to the edge of the pond. There will be two measurements for each offset line (E, and E, F, and F2, etc.). Each set (E, + E2, etc.) subtracted from the A-C distance will provide the distance across the pond at that point.

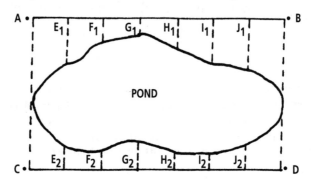

Example 7: Length of A to B or C to D = 70 ft.
            Length of A to C or B to D = 50 ft.

The total area inside the rectangle is:
            70 ft. x 50 ft. =3,500 sq. ft.
The following measurements were taken:
E1 = 14 ft.; F, = 8 ft.; G, = 7 ft.; HI = 10 ft.; 1, = 14 ft.; J, = 17 ft.

E_2 = 6 ft. F_2= 4 ft G_2 = 8 ft
    20 ft.   12 ft.   15 ft.
H_7= 4 ft. 1_2= 4 ft. J_2=6 ft.
    14 ft.   18 ft.   23 ft.

Total offset E = 20 ft.
              F = 12 ft.
              G = 15 ft.
              H = 14 ft. I= 18 ft.
              J = 23 ft.

50 ft. (distance from A to C) - 20 ft. =   30 ft.
                    50 ft. - 12 ft. =   38 ft.
                    50 ft. - 15 ft. =   35 ft.
                    50 ft. - 14 ft. =   36 ft.
                    50 ft. - 18 ft. =   32 ft.
                    50 ft. - 23 ft. =   27 ft.
        Total of all offsets = 198 ft.

Total of all offset (198 ft.) x 10 ft. (distance between offsets) = 1,980 sq. ft.
The pond is 1,980 sq. ft. or in square meters:
$$\frac{1,980 \text{ sq. ft.}}{10\ 76 \text{ sq ft /sq. m.}} = 184 \text{ sq. m.}$$

C. A method for measuring greens has been suggested by Palmer Maples, Jr., CGCS. In his method, an irregularly-shaped green is converted into a circle by determining the average radius of the green.

From a central point on the green, distances to the edge of the green are measured in 10° increments. From the average of the 36 measurements (360° in a circle) the area is calculated from the formula for a circle (Area = $3.14r^2$). This method is quick, simple and easy to calculate, and works best with greens that are circular in shape. In some cases 18 measurements every 20° could be used.

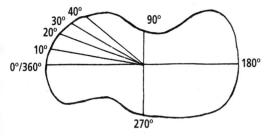

Example 8: Total measurements (36) =1,731.6 ft.
$$\frac{1,731.6 \text{ ft.}}{36} = 48.1 \text{ ft. (average radius)}$$
Area = 3.14 x 48.1^2
      =7,264.8 sq. ft.
      or in square meters,
$$\frac{7,264.8 \text{ sq. ft.}}{10.76 \text{ sq. ft./sq. m.}} = 675.2 \text{ sq. m.}$$
The area of the collar may be determined by extending the 36 measurements to the outer edge of the collar. Calculate the entire collar-green area and then subtract from it the area of the green.

Example 9: For the green above, the
    36 collar-green measurements
    were 1,998.5.
$$\frac{1,998.5 \text{ ft.}}{36} = 55.5 \text{ ft.}$$
Area = 3.14x55.5^2
    = 9,671.9
    -7,264.8
      2,407.2 sq. ft. of collar

If greens are less circular in shape, such as long and narrow or hourglass shaped, then additional steps must be taken in the calculation. To calculate these areas you must square (multiply each radii by itself) each of the 36 radii you have measured and then average them. Then multiply this figure by 3.14 and you will have a better estimate of the area of irregular-shaped greens.

Pesticide Application Calculations

Most pesticide application rate recommendations are given as the amount of the active ingredient (a.i.) per 1,000 square feet (sq. ft.) or per acre (A.).

EXAMPLE 1:

If an insecticide contains 4 lbs. a.i. per gallon (gal.) and the recommended rate of application is 1 pound (lb.) a.i. per A., how much would be needed (in fluid ounces, fl. oz.) to treat 20,000 sq. ft.?

If one gal. of the insecticide contains 4 lbs. a.i., then one gal. can be used to treat 4 A. at the rate of 1 lb. a.i. per A.

1 gal. = 4 lbs. a.i.
¼ gal. = 1 lb. a.i.

The next step is to convert 6 gals. to fl. oz. There are 128 fl. oz. per gal., so ¼ gal. = 32 fl. oz. Thirty-two (32) fl. oz. of the insecticide would contain 1 lb. a.i. and would treat one A.

Next, determine what percent of an A. is 20,000 sq. ft.

$$\frac{20,000}{43,560} = 46\%$$

Since 32 fl. oz. of the insecticide will treat one A. and the area to be treated (20,000 sq. ft.) is 46% of an A., then 46% of 32 fl. ozs. will treat the area at the recommended rate.

0.46 (46%) x 32 oz. = 14.7 oz.

14.7 fl. oz. of the insecticide will treat 20,000 sq. ft. at the rate of 1 lb. a.i. per A.

EXAMPLE 2:

The label on a liquid pesticide indicates a recommended rate of application of 2 fl. oz. of product per 1,000 sq. ft. How much of the pesticide will it take to treat nine (9) greens that are 6,000 sq. ft. in size?

Since the rate is 2 fl. oz. per 1,000 and the greens are 6,000 each, then

2 fl. oz. x 6 = 12 fl. oz. per green
12 fl. oz. x 9 = 108 fl. oz. of pesticide required.

EXAMPLE 3:

A pesticide is labeled as a 75% wettable powder. The rate of application is 10 lbs. a.i. per A. How much of the pesticide is required for three (3) A.?

First, find how much of the pesticide is needed to get 10 lbs. of the a.i. Since it is 75% active, divide 75 into 100.

$$\frac{100\%}{75\%} = 1.3$$

1.3 x 10 lbs. a.i./A. = 13 lbs. of the pesticide contains 10 lbs. a.i. There are three (3) A. to treat, so 3 x 13 lbs. = 39 lbs. needed.

EXAMPLE 4:

Using the following information, which pesticide is the better buy, assuming both are equally effective?

Pesticide A	Pesticide B
$ 1.45/1b.	$8.90/lb.
Rate: 8 oz./1,000 sq. ft.	Rate: 1 oz./1,000 sq. ft.

Since there are 16 oz. in a pound,

Pesticide A costs $\dfrac{\$1.45}{16} = \$.09$

per oz. and Pesticide B costs

$\dfrac{\$8.90}{16} = \$0.56$ per oz.

Pesticide A is cheaper per ounce but the rate is eight (8) times (8 oz. per 1,000 sq. ft.) that of Pesticide B. It will therefore cost 8 x $0.09 or $0.72 per 1000 sq. ft. to use Pesticide A compared to $0.56 per 1,000 sq. ft. to use Pesticide B. Pesticide B is the better buy.

Calibration of Boom Sprayer

1. Run clear water through the sprayer to see that all nozzles are clean and the discharge of water is the same from each nozzle.
2. Determine the amount of water the sprayer will use to cover 1,000 square feet (sq. ft.).
   a. Fill the spray tank and run the sprayer at 30 pounds per square inch.
   b. Divide 1,000 by width of the boom. That will indicate the distance the sprayer must run at a constant rpm. It is very important that a constant speed be maintained over this distance.
   c. Refill the tank, noting how much water was used. This amount is how much the sprayer is applying at that pressure setting and at that ground speed per 1,000 square feet.

   Example: If your boom is 10 feet wide, divide 1,000 by 10 (1,000/10). The result is 100 feet. Drive the sprayer 100 feet at a steady speed with the sprayer operating at 30 pounds of pressure. You have just sprayed 1,000 square feet. If it takes 2 gallons to refill the tank, then this sprayer has applied 2 gallons per 1,000 sq. ft. at the selected speed and pressure.
3. Determine the amount of chemical to put in the tank.
   a. Divide the number of gallons the tank holds by the application rate determined in step 2c. This will tell how many 1,000 square foot units the tank will hold.

   Example: If the tank holds 100 gallons and in step 2c it was determined that the sprayer was applying 2 gallons per 1,000 square feet, then 100 divided by 2 (100/2) = 50. One tank full can cover 50 1,000 square foot units or 50,000 square feet.
   b. Check the chemical's label and determine how much is suggested for 1,000 square feet. Multiply this number by the number of 1,000 square foot units the tank holds (step 3a). This is how much total chemical to put in the tank.

   Example: If the label rate for the chemical is 1½ oz. per 1,000 sq. ft. and our tank holds 50 1,000 sq. ft. units, then a total of 75 oz. should be placed in the tank. ✺

13 CHAPTER

Weed Management

Probably the most serious and frustrating pest problem associated with most landscapes is weeds. No landscape is immune from weeds. Weeds are the opportunists of the plant world, ready to take advantage of any failure of the maintenance program.

In considering weed control, there are two factors to realize. First, weed seed is in virtually every soil; and second, weed seed can live in a soil for years waiting for a chance to germinate.

In developing a control program, there is absolutely no question the front line in the weed war is adherence to a good landscape maintenance program that produces a thick, dense turf. Weeds have a difficult time invading high- quality turf. A lot of money can be spent on herbicides, but if the turf is not maintained properly, chances are the weeds will just return.

Once a weed is in place, it must be removed mechanically by digging or by herbicides. If the choice is digging, all the underground parts of the weed capable of growing a new plant, such as the rhizome, must be completely removed. Rhizomes may extend, undetected, from above the soil several inches to a foot beyond the base of the weed. If not completely removed, the weed simply re-establishes itself in a short period of time.

Generally, perennial weeds have underground parts like rhizomes, thickened tap roots or tubers while annual weeds do not.

When considering chemical control, remember that a herbicide is being used to remove an undesirable plant (the weed) from a population of desirable plants (the turf). Sometimes this is difficult. An example of this process is the fact that it takes more MSMA to kill common bermuda than it does to kill crabgrass. If the proper rates of MSMA are used, the crabgrass dies and the worst that happens to the bermuda is that it turns a little yellow for a short time.

Weeds can be hard to control even though the right herbicide is applied properly. Basically, the herbicide which can kill the weed must enter the plant, either through the leaf cuticle or through the root system. If it is a hot, dry day, the leaf loses hydration and it is more difficult to get the herbicide into the plant. If soil moisture levels are low, the root system might not take up the herbicide. The rule of thumb is that the weed must be actively growing to be controlled. A warm, but not excessively hot, day coming a few days after a good rain is ideal for applying herbicides. A lot of weed control failures can be traced to unfavorable weather conditions. Also, the younger a weed is, the easier it is to control. Old weeds can pose a difficult control challenge. Annual weeds should be controlled when they are in the seedling stage. Perrenial weeds should be controlled in the spring or fall when root reserves are depleted.

Developing a Weed Control Program

A weed control program should be carefully planned and coordinated, with an understanding of how and why weeds are present, what chemical control options are available and the proper timing and application technique to use for control.

Weed identification is the first step. This handbook provides information regarding certain weeds and grasses that should help with identification.

Weed identification begins with classifying the weed type. Broadleaves, or dicotyledonous plants, have two seed cotyledons (young leaves) at emergence and have net-like veins in their true leaves. Examples of winter broadleaf weeds include clover, lawn burweed, henbit, speedwell and chickweed, among others.

Grasses, or monocotyledonous plants, have only one seed cotyledon present when they emerge from the soil. Grasses also have rounded hollow stems with nodes (joints), and parallel veins in their true leaves. Annual bluegrass is an example of a winter grass weed.

Weeds complete life cycles in either one growing season (annuals), two growing seasons (biennials), or three or more growing seasons (perennials). Annuals that complete life cycles from spring to fall generally are referred to as summer annuals. Those that complete life cycles from fall to spring are referred to as winter annuals.

Understanding the biology and the growth and reproductive characteristics of a weed is the second most important step in developing a control strategy. Environmental and cultural practices that discourage weed infestations, and how a turf manager can use them, are important in producing an acceptable and uniform weed-free turf. Turf weakened by improper cultural practices, pest invasion or excessive traffic is much more likely to become weed infested and will take longer to recover.

Common Weeds

The following are descriptions of some weeds and grasses encountered by landscape managers in various regions of the United States.

Annual Bluegrass (*Poa annua*)

Low-growing, compact, tufted winter annual that grows well in cool weather but may not be summer hardy. Some flattened stems may lie close to the ground but stems can grow 1 to 12 inches tall. It does not have rhizomes. Roots are shallow and easily pulled from the soil. Leaves are a soft, light green and boat-shaped at the tip. Panicles are very small in clipped lawns. It may die suddenly during summer months.

Annual Bluegrass

Barnyardgrass

Coarse warm-season annual with fibrous, rather shallow roots. It has a flattened stem, especially near the base, that reaches 1 to 4 feet in height. The lower portion of the plant tends to be reddish purple. The seed head branches into 6 or 8 compact segments.

Bedstraw

Cool-season annual often found in the dense shade of trees and shrubs. Square stems, 1 to 3 feet long, are weak, sprawling and have tiny, saw-toothed appendages. Leaves and leaflike parts form whorls at distinct intervals along the stems. Small flowers have four white petals. Roots are branching, short and shallow.

Barnyardgrass

Bindweed

Deep-rooted perennial vine in the morningglory family that is difficult to control. Spade- shaped leaves have rounded tips and vary in size. Funnel-shaped flowers vary from white to light pink and are about the size of a nickel. It spreads by seed and an extensive root system that may go down 20 to 30 feet. Stems are smooth, slender and 2 to 7 feet long, often twining or spreading over the ground surface.

Catchweed Bedstraw

Field Bindweed

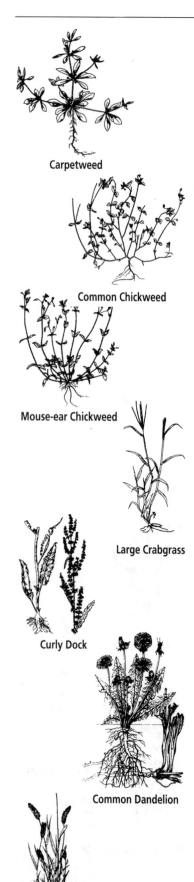

Carpetweed

Common Chickweed

Mouse-ear Chickweed

Large Crabgrass

Curly Dock

Common Dandelion

Green Foxtail

Carpetweed

Rapidly growing, summer annual with green, smooth stems that branch along the ground in all directions from the root, forming a flat circular mat on the soil surface. Light green, smooth, tongue-like leaves are grouped five to six together, forming whorls at each joint on the stem. Flowers are small and white, with several at each joint.

Chickweed (*Common*)

Low growing annual or winter annual with creeping stems that root at the nodes. It has a fibrous, shallow root system. It is green most of the year in milder climates. Small opposite leaves are oval-shaped and smooth. Small starlike flowers, with five deeply-notched petals, are white. It is often found in the shade of trees and shrubs and especially on the north side of buildings.

Chickweed (*Mouse-ear*)

Perennial with creeping stems that root at the nodes. Stems are hairy, slender, and partly spreading to erect. Leaves are opposite, two to three times longer than wide, small and very hairy. Flowers are small with five white petals notched at the tips, surrounded by an equal number of hairy sepals. The root system is shallow and fibrous.

Crabgrass

One of the most common warm-season annual grassy weeds. Stems grow mostly prostrate, branch freely and send down roots where each joint comes into contact with the soil or moist grass. The seed head is divided into several fingerlike segments. Large crabgrass, sometimes known as hairy crabgrass, has stems up to 3 feet long and at least somewhat hairy leaf blades ¼ to ⅓ inch wide. Smooth crabgrass is similar but not as coarse or as tall. It is less hairy and more purplish or bluish.

Curly Dock

A perennial with a large, yellow and somewhat branched taproot. Its stems are smooth and erect, growing from 1 to 4 feet tall. Leaves are mostly smooth, 6 to 12 inches long, and with wavy-curled edges. Upper leaves alternate. Flowers are in dense clusters on branches at the tip of the stem. Flowers are without petals, small and greenish before becoming reddish brown at maturity. A relative, broadleaf dock, is similar with leaves broad, flat and heart-shaped at the base.

Dandelion

Cool-season perennials with yellow flowers. The thick fleshly taproot, often branched, can give rise to new shoots. The stem never elongates but produces a rosette of leaves that are simple, variously lobed, 3 to 10 inches long and contain a milky juice. Flower heads are 1 to 2 inches in diameter, borne on a long hollow stalk.

Foxtail

Warm-season annuals with flattened stems that are often reddish in color on the lower portion. The stems of green foxtail are round and erect. Leaves are hairless. It usually grows between 1 to 3 feet tall and has green seeds. Yellow foxtail stems are erect and 1 to 2 feet tall. Leaves are flat and often have a spiral twist, with many long hairs on the upper surface near the base. The seed of yellow foxtail is four times as large as green foxtail. It also is commonly known as pigeongrass.

Goosegrass

Warm-season annual that germinates later than crabgrass. Stems, which tend to be flattened and whitish in color at the base, can be upright but usually are nearly prostrate, 6 inches to 2 feet long. Flower heads are thicker and more robust than common crabgrass. Goosegrass also is a darker green and grows in tufts. Leaves are smooth with blades 3 to 12 inches long. A fibrous root system makes it difficult to pull.

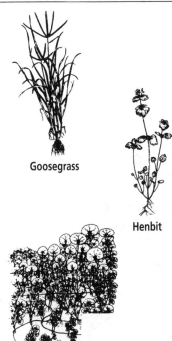

Goosegrass

Henbit

Winter annual with squarish stems 4 to 16 inches tall. Plants are usually upright. Flowers are lavender to blue and found in whorls in the axils of upper leaves. Flowers are surrounded at the base by calyx with five sharp teeth. Roots are fibrous. Leaves are opposite, hairy, and have rounded teeth.

Henbit

Ground Ivy

Cool-season perennial that thrives in the shade but also grows in the sun. Leaves are almost round or kidney-shaped, with round-toothed edges, and are bright green. It produces an abundance of lavender to blue funnel-formed flowers, borne in small clusters in the axils of the leaves. Square stems may root at each joint where they touch the ground.

Ground Ivy

Knotweed (*Prostrate*)

Annual with bluish-green stems that extend 4 to 24 inches in all directions from the small, white taproot, forming a dense mat. Leaves often have a bluish cast, alternate and are oblong, narrowed at the base and pointed at the tip. Flowers are very small, yellow or white and borne in clusters in the leaf axils.

Prostrate Knotweed

Lambsquarters (*Common*)

Annual with a short, branched taproot. Stems are 3 to 4 feet tall, smooth, and often have red or light green stripes. Leaves alternate, are 1 to 3 inches long, and are smooth. Flowers are small, green, and without petals.

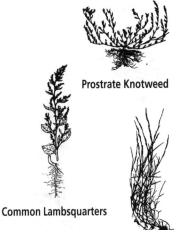

Common Lambsquarters

Nimblewill

Warm-season, shade-tolerant perennial with wiry, fine stems that root at the nodes. Stems are very slender and spreading. It has a root system that is shallow and fibrous. Leaf blades are flat. It forms circular patches or may be distributed throughout the lawn.

Nimblewill

Sedges (*Yellow, purple, and green kyllings*)

Warm-season perennial with erect, triangular stems that produce 3-ranked leaves near the ground. Leaves are light yellowgreen, narrow and grasslike. The lower portion of the plant is fibrous and brown. Roots are fibrous and often terminate with small nutlets. It reproduces by seed and by tubers produced at the tips of scaly rhizomes.

Yellow Nutsedge

Pigweed (*Prostrate*)

Warm-season prostrate annual that grows from a pink taproot. Leaves are very shiny. Stems are smooth, light-green to reddish green and may spread 1½ to 3 feet. Stems are long, nearly smooth, reddish and spread flat over the ground. Leaves are small, alternate and egg-shaped.

Prostrate Pigweed

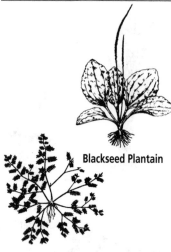

Blackseed Plantain

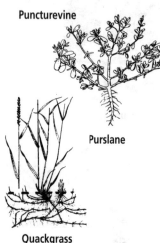

Puncturevine

Purslane

Quackgrass

Shepherdspurse

Red Sorrel

Prostrate Spurge

Plantain (*Blackseed and Broadleaf*)

Cool-season perennials forming rosettes with prominently veined leaves. The leaves of blackseed are oval shaped and 2 to 3 inches across, with purplish stalks. Broadleaf plantain has smaller leaves without the purplish coloration. Both have rattail-like seed heads several inches long. Roots are mostly fibrous.

Puncturevine

Annual with a simple taproot and hairy, prostrate stem branching from the base to form dense mats of slender tailing branches 6 to 8 feet long. Leaves are oblong, opposite, hairy and divided into pinnate leaflets that are bright green. Flowers are small, yellow and five-petaled, each having two sharp, Iong spines.

Purslane (*Common*)

Warm-season annual with leaves and stems fleshy and reddish in color. Flowers are small, yellow, and in axils of leaves and branches. The root system tends to be fibrous and stems root wherever they touch the ground, particularly if the main root has been destroyed.

Quackgrass

Cool-season perennial wheatgrass that spreads by long white rhizomes. Rhizomes vary from 2 to 8 inches in depth, depending on soil type and soil treatment. Roots arise only at nodes. Stems are 1½ to 3 feet tall, with 3 to 6 joints. Leafblades are typically rough in texture and a claw-shaped protrusion of the leaf, called an auricle, clasps the stem. A distinguishing characteristic is a ring of root hairs every ¾ to 1 inch along the rhizomes.

Sandbur

Warm-season annual grass typically found in sandy turf areas on low-maintenance programs. Stems are flattened and branched. Roots are fibrous and rooting may occur at the nodes of the stems when they come into contact with the soil. Stems are erect, or sometimes spreading and matlike, 6 inches to 2 feet long. Spikes are composed of spikelets enclosed in sharp, tiny burs.

Sedges

Warm-season perennials with erect triangular stems. Purple nutsedge is only found in the southern tier of the U.S. whereas yellow can be found anywhere in the U.S. Yellow and purple nutsedge produce mutlets and the end (yellow) or along the (purple) in chains. Green kyllinga is also found in the southern tier of states and produces rhizomes but not mutlets. Green kyllinga is a perennial mat-forming sedge that spreads rapidly.

Shepherdspurse

A winter annual with deeply lobed leaves that form rosettes in the fall. Stems are erect, 1 to 1½ feet tall, and covered with gray hairs. Flowers are small white and 4-petaled. Flowers develop into triangular seed pod filled with numerous tiny, red dish brown seeds.

Sorrel (*Red*)

Low growing, cool-season perennial that reproduces by creeping roots and seeds. Leave are spear shaped, 1 to 3 inches long. Lacy flowering stalks bloom in mid-spring with a definite reddish color. Roots and rootstocks are extensive but rather shallow Stems are 6 to 18 inches high an branched at the top.

Spurge *(Prostrate)*

Warm-season annual with prostrate stems that form a mat, unlike spotted spurge which has erect stems that spread. Leaves and seed pods are hairy. Leaves are spotted like those of spotted spurge. Also called milk spurge, due to its milky sap.

Wild Garlic

Perennial with slender, smooth leaves that are hollow and attached to the lower portions of waxy stems. Stems are 1 to 3 feet tall and smooth. Bulbs and bulblets are produced underground, and small, green to purple flowers are often replaced with bulblets. It has a characteristic onion/garlic odor.

Wild Garlic

Wild Onion

Wild Onion

Similar to wild garlic but does not produce underground bulblets. Stems are 1 to 2 feet tall. Leaves are flat, not hollow and arise from the base of the plant.

Herbicides

An important consideration when choosing herbicides is knowledge of proper handling procedure for safety purposes. Knowing herbicide effectiveness at different weed-growth stages and at what level of tolerance a given turf species has against damage from it also is important. The amount of time required for a given herbicide to provide weed control and the economic factors of using it also are part of the herbicide selection process.

Many variables influence successful herbicide application. These include proper use of equipment; the environmental factors at the time of application; proper and constant calibration of equipment; and adequate agitation of the herbicide solution. Most herbicide failures involve using the wrong chemical at the wrong date, or the chemical is applied at the wrong time, in the wrong manner or at the wrong site. Failure is usually not the fault of the herbicide itself.

Commonly-available herbicides are divided into two large groups: those that kill the weed as it germinates (called a pre-emergence herbicide) and those that control the weed after it germinates (a post-emergence herbicide).

Pre-emergence Weed Control

In this process, a herbicide is applied evenly over the landscaped areas and forms a barrier at the soil surface. As seeds germinate in this barrier, the seedlings absorb the herbicide and are killed. If undisturbed, the barrier can remain in place from a few months to about a year. The type of soil and the amount of water used on the lawn has much to do with the persistence of the chemical.

Incorporation and activation of the herbicide after its application is required by most pre-emergence herbicides. This can be accomplished by irrigation. Normally, ¼ to ½ inch of water is required within seven to 10 days of application to optimize herbicidal activity. By not irrigating within this time frame, many herbicides will not be in position to control the germinating weed, or they may lose their effectiveness by being broken down by sunlight or volatilization. The biggest problem with the use of pre-emergence herbicides is timing. The chemical must be in place before the weed seed begins growth. For example, crabgrass begins to germinate in the spring when the soil temperature at a 2-inch depth gets just above 50 degrees F. Goosegrass, on the other hand, which is a warm-season annual, needs soil temperatures in the 60-65 degree F range to germinate. Since the germinating shoot and root tips are the two major sites of cell division, pre-emergence herbicides need to contact these in the soil. Herbicide application should therefore be timed prior to weed seed germination since most preemergence herbicides are ineffective on emerged (visible) weeds. The beginning of weed growth in most cases is tied to weather patterns. A host of annuals like henbit and annual bluegrass germinate in the fall as soon as the weather cools. There could be as much as a month's difference in the arrival of the climatic conditions that trigger germination.

The same situation is present in the spring. Many annuals like knotweed and crabgrass germinate in early spring, depending again on temperatures. The success of a good pre-emergence program, aside from considerations like using the proper rate and obtaining an even distribution, is dependent on weather changes. Early or late falls and springs make preemergence programs difficult, with regard to determining specific application dates. Follow the averages and accept that the program may fail once in awhile.

Repeat applications of pre-emergence herbicides are often necessary. When exposed to the environment, most herbicides begin to degrade. Usually the level of degradation that occurs from six to 16 weeks after application reduces the herbicide level to the point that its effectiveness on germinating weeds is lost. Repeat applications therefore become necessary for prolonged pre-emergence weed control.

Post-emergence Weed Control

Post-emergence chemicals are used to control weeds after they come through the soil (visible weeds).

The application should be made when weeds are young (two- to four-leaf stage) and actively growing. At this stage, herbicide uptake and translocation is favored and turfgrasses are better able to fill in the voids left by the dying weeds.

Broadleaf weeds such as chickweed, henbit, clover and dandelion normally are controlled with 2,4-D, 2,4-DP, MCPP, MCPA or dicamba. Many manufacturers also market two- or three-way combinations of these herbicides. All are selective, systemic and foliar applied. Usually two- or three-way combinations of these provide better control than the single herbicide; however, repeat applications are commonly necessary for satisfactory control of older weeds. Sequential applications should be timed 10 to 14 days apart.

When selecting a post-emergence chemical, make sure the herbicide will control the weed without harming the turfgrass or any ornamentals in or near the lawn. Not all chemicals can be used in every state. You may not be able to use a specific herbicide on every variety of the same turfgrass. You must READ THE LABEL.

Combination Products

There are a number of combination fertilizer/herbicide products offered on the market. Most are a combination of fertilizer and a preemergence herbicide. These are generally good products, if applied properly. The only real problem that can occur at times is determining timing of the application. For example, if a preemergence herbicide must be applied in early spring to be effective, it could be too early to fertilize the turfgrass. Sometimes the right time to apply a herbicide is not necessarily the right time to apply a fertilizer. But if the dates are the same or close, the use of these products makes sense and is effective, but check to make sure the timing is compatible for fertilizer application and herbicide application.

Liquid vs. Dry

Some herbicides are offered in both liquid and dry forms. Since pre-emergence herbicides must be watered into the soil, it makes little difference which form is used. Just read and follow the label.

Liquid post-emergence herbicides are generally considered to be superior to dry or granular forms of the same chemical. Since most of these herbicides must enter the plant through the leaves, coating the leaf with a liquid increases the chances of killing the weed.

Herbicide Resistance

Some species of weeds which were previously susceptible to herbicides are now resistant. The problem of herbicide-resistant weeds was first reported in the mid 1960s in a nursery in Washington state. Since the discovery of the triazine-resistant weeds, the number of weed species and their distribution has increased.

Triazine-resistant weeds include common lambsquarters, redroot pigweed, smooth pigweed, common ragweed, kochia, annual bluegrass and others. Fortunately, not many resistant weeds species have been identified in turfgrass.

Records

Keeping accurate records on application dates, weather conditions (temperature, rainfall, etc.), application rates, and observation of control response will assist in next year's timing schedules.

Pest Control Recommendations

The rules and regulations concerning the use of chemicals for pest control are in a state of change. Many chemicals are under review by various levels of government and there may be some changes in which chemicals may be used, and for what purpose.

The requirements associated with becoming a pesticide applicator also vary greatly between governmental jurisdictions. This state of change and the possible differences between localities make it nearly impossible to make any absolute, across-the-board recommendations. Additionally, some states require that turfgrass areas treated with pesticides be posted with signs informing the public of their application.

The best way to be sure of absolute legality in making an application of any pesticide is to check with the state's Department of Agriculture or other agencies having control over the use of pesticides. Your local county extension agent can also help. There is an agent in nearly every county in the United States.

Illustrations were obtained from many sources, including *Weeds of the North Central States*, North Central Regional Research Publication No. 281.

Material for this chapter
furnished by Dr. Fred Yelverton,
Extension Weed Specialist,
North Carolina State University.

For current control measures, please refer to the annual March issue of *Landscape Management*. 🌿

14 CHAPTER

Disease Management

Figure 1. Symptoms Caused by Plant Pathogens (modified from Agrios, 1988)

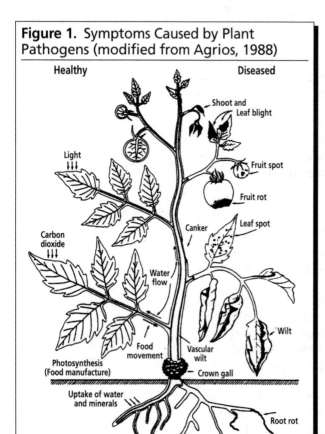

Healthy

Diseased

Shoot and Leaf blight

Light ↓↓↓

Fruit spot

Fruit rot

Canker

Leaf spot

Carbon dioxide ↓↓↓

Water flow

Wilt

Photosynthesis (Food manufacture)

Food movement

Vascular wilt

Crown gall

Uptake of water and minerals

Root rot

Identifying a disease can range from being very easy to extremely difficult. In many cases, symptoms are characteristic and visual identification is simple (Figure 1). Other diseases, however, require extensive study to identify.

The first step in disease identification is to decide whether the cause of the problem is cultural or environmental, an insect or a plant pathogen. Answering the following questions may help eliminate or point to possible causes.

• How old is the plant and how long has it been in place?

• Is only one species of plant affected or are multiple types of plants affected?

• Where is the plant located—in a low spot, next to buildings, shaded area?

• What are the environmental conditions—temperature, moisture, light, soil type?

• What pesticides or herbicides have been applied in the area recently?

• Have there been any recent changes in the landscape—underground cables, sidewalks, pools, driveways, building additions?

Plant pathogens (fungi, bacteria, viruses, nematodes) usually are specific to a given host plant. If many types of plants, such as turf, woody ornamentals, and bedding plants are all affected, the probable cause is cultural or environmental. Construction or other changes in the environment can affect plant root growth by cutting through roots, compacting the soil, and changing the soil level.

Types of Diseases
Fungi

All plants are subject to infection by one or more fungal diseases. And there are many different fungi. While most are beneficial, about 80,000 of them cause plant diseases. Most pathogenic (disease-causing) fungi attack only specific plants or groups of plants. Since they can't produce their own food, they must obtain food from living plants or dead organic matter.

Fungi have a wide range of shapes, sizes and growth habits. Most grow in a threadlike mass of hyphae, a term from the Greek word for web. A single strand is called a hypha. Mycelium, a mass of hyphae, may be visible without a microscope. In certain fungi, the hyphal strands form highly-organized structures called mushrooms.

Many fungi multiply by means of spores similar to plant seeds. When environmental conditions are favorable, the spores germinate and the fungus begins to grow (Figure 2). Some fungal spores last years in the environment waiting for the proper host, the right temperature and the right humidity to germinate.

Fungal spores usually germinate and damage plants only when environmental conditions are favorable. Spore germination generally requires high humidity or free moisture. A common exception is the fungus that causes powdery mildew. These spores germinate under low moisture conditions.

When spores germinate, they grow over the surface of the plant. Fungi enter plants by one of three methods.

(1) Some fungi produce a structure called an infection peg or appressorium. This infection peg puts tremendous pressure on the plant cell wall and if it isn't strong enough, the fungus enters the cell.

(2) Some fungi enter the plant through natural openings in the leaf called stomates or through wounds. Once inside the plant, the fungus is free to grow and feed on the plant cell nutrients.

(3) Other fungi, such as Pythium, produce organic acids that cause the plant cell wall to dissolve. The contents then leak into the surrounding tissue where the fungal hyphae can absorb it.

Figure 2. Stages of Infection and Disease Development

1. Fungal spore lands on susceptible host plant
2. Spore germinates and starts infection
3. Fungus grows using plant nutrients
4. Mycelial mass, symptoms may be visible
5. Produces more spores for other infections
6. Survival spores may last years

Bacteria

Bacteria are microscopic one-cell organisms that reproduce very rapidly. Fortunately, most bacteria are beneficial and are important decomposers, releasing valuable nutrients. However, more than 80 species cause plant diseases.

Bacteria cannot penetrate directly into plants. They must enter through stomates or wounds or be deposited by feeding insects. When bacteria are present in a plant, even in low numbers, any cutting is likely to spread the bacteria to healthy plants. They need water, wind-blown water, insects, or tools to move from one plant to another.

Bacteria are very susceptible to desiccation (drying out), limiting their ability to survive outside a host plant and to disperse rapidly to distant places. Bacterial diseases are more common in warm humid climates such as the southeastern states and greenhouses where there is adequate moisture for them to move around and infect new plants.

Viruses

Virus particles are so tiny that they are visible only under an electron microscope. They multiply only inside living plant cells. Plant viruses consist of two components, a protein coat and a nucleic acid, the component that causes disease.

Viruses enter plants by abrasion, insect feeding, or vegetative propagation. Cigarette smokers are common carriers of tobacco mosaic virus and transmit it to tomato and related plants. Viruses also are carried in seeds, tubers, and bulbs.

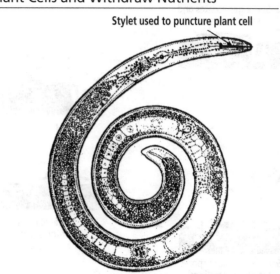

Stylet used to puncture plant cell

Once inside the plant, a virus forces the plant's genetic material to make more viral particles. Viruses are the only plant pathogens that cause systemic infections. In general, viruses seldom kill the host plant, but they do severely affect quality and health.

Nematodes

Nematodes that attack plants are microscopic roundworms (Figure 3). They have a spearlike stylet that they use to puncture plant cells to withdraw plant juices. Nematodes are obligate parasites; they obtain their food only from living plants.

Some plant nematodes feed in the buds, stems and leaves, but most feed in or on the roots or below ground structures. Some species feed from outside the roots while others feed by tunneling through the plant tissue.

Nematodes are aquatic animals that live in the water film around soil particles. They can spread rapidly with surface or irrigation water. Soil clinging to equipment, hoses and shoes can spread the nematodes to new areas. Transplanting infected plants also can introduce them to new areas.

Enlisting the help of a plant pathologist or plant disease diagnostic laboratory may be necessary when the cause of the disease problem is not obvious. In addition, a plant pathologist can decide whether the presence of a disease organism is having a negative affect on the plant.

Disease Management

It takes three things to have a disease problem: the right environmental conditions for a disease to develop and infect, a plant susceptible to that disease, and the presence of a disease-causing agent (pathogen). Removal or significant alteration of any one of these factors prevents disease development.

Cultural Practices

- Select plants adapted to the planting site. Consider light, moisture and soil type when choosing plants. Plants under stress are more susceptible to disease.
- Choose resistant varieties. Resistant varieties are available for many common diseases, e.g., crepe myrtles resistant to powdery mildew or Raleigh St. Augustinegrass resistant to St. Augustine decline.
- Plant disease-free materials. Inspect plants before planting to insure they are healthy.
- Avoid soil compaction. Several diseases are worse in areas where soil is compacted. Aerate by coring to improve soil texture and stimulate vigorous root growth.
- Add organic matter to the plant site. Organic matter increases the number and types of microorganisms in the soil, many of which compete with pathogens.
- Rotate plants. Rotate bedding plants of different types to avoid a pathogen buildup in the soil. Closely-related plants often are susceptible to the same soilborne diseases.
- Change the planting date. Proper timing of planting dates to allow soils to warm or dry out sufficiently can control some diseases. Timing of planting dates can allow you to avoid virus-carrying insect flights. For example, wait to plant periwinkles until after the soil dries out in early summer to avoid aerial blight caused by Phytophthora.
- Space plants properly. Crowded plants reduce air circulation, enhanc-

ing conditions for leaf spot diseases.

- Fertilize appropriately. Plants receiving adequate nutrients resist some plant pathogens. Over-fertilization causes excess new growth that is more susceptible to disease.
- Avoid root pruning. Cutting roots while planting or cultivating reduces plant vigor and provides openings for pathogens to enter.
- Use mulches. Mulches keep pathogens from splashing onto lower leaves from soil. However, some micro organisms can overwinter in mulches, so it's a good idea to replace mulches yearly.
- Avoid overwatering or underwatering. Proper water management is critical to disease control. While water is necessary for good plant growth, too much water floods the air pores in the soil, causing the roots to drown. Water infrequently but deeply, to a depth of six inches. This stimulates good root growth and reduces root rots.
- Use drip or furrow irrigation. Diseases caused by fungi and bacteria need water to spread, germinate and infect plants. Dry leaves reduce diseases by preventing infection. Overhead (sprinkler) irrigation encourages leaf spot disease by allowing leaves to remain wet over extended periods. If you use a sprinkler, water in the early morning to allow leaves to dry quickly.
- Remove diseased plants or plant parts. This reduces the ability of the pathogen to reproduce or overwinter.
- Avoid thatch buildup in turf areas. When thatch is more than ½ inch thick, it reduces nutrient and water absorption and harbors insects and disease pathogens. Prevent thatch formation by reducing fertilizer and proper mowing. Mechanically remove thick thatch in spring or late summer when turf can recover faster.

Prevention is the key to any plant disease control whether you use chemical or non-chemical methods. Disease prevention practices are most effective when combined and used simultaneously. While some practices are more effective against certain diseases than others, many apply to a variety of diseases.

Chemical Control

In spite of preventive measures, plant disease sometimes still occurs. Fungicides, bactericides and nematicides are pesticides used to prevent or control fungi, bacteria and nematodes, respectively. There are no pesticides available to control viruses.

Most pesticides are designed to control the specific diseases listed on the label. Therefore, proper identification of the disease problem is essential for effective use of a pesticide. A fungicide that controls Pythium, for example, will not control Rhizoctonia or powdery mildew.

Fungicides are the most commonly-used pesticide for disease control. There are two basic types of fungicides available. Contact fungicides form a protective shield on the surface of the plant that prevents or halts infection. Applied before a fungus attacks the plant, contact fungicides have the disadvantage of being exposed to weathering, and on turf, to mowing. In addition, new leaves are unprotected. Absorbed by the plant, systemic fungicides protect new growth since they also move in the plant. They persist longer (up to three to four weeks) as well. While systemic fungicides provide protection against some diseases not controlled by contact fungicides, other pathogens have developed resistance to some of them.

Knowing when the most common diseases occur aids in scheduling pesticide applications (Tables 1-3). Often it takes several days after infection occurs before symptoms appear. Sometimes infection and disease development occur in the fall and symptoms aren't visible until spring. Applying a pesticide after symptoms are seen may be too late to provide adequate control.

One can't depend solely on pesticides for disease control. No amount of pesticide will control disease if proper cultural practices are not in place. Proper variety selection, fertilization, site maintenance, and cultural practices reduce disease pressure and increase the effectiveness of pesticide applications.

Examples of Common Diseases
Turfgrass-Foliar

Brown Patch *(Rhizoctonia solani)*

Table 1. When Diseases strike warm-season turfgrasses.
•Note: chart gives general times for turf diseases to occur. They may occur at other times, however, depending on location and environmental conditions.

Jan.	Feb.	Mar.	Apr.	May	June	July	Aug.	Sep.	Oct.	Nov.	Dec.
		▓	▓	▓ Brown Patch	█			▓	▓ Brown Patch	▓	
	▓	▓	▓ Pythium blight	▓	▓			▓	▓ Pythium blight	▓	▓
		█	█	█	█	█	█		▓	▓ Spring dead spot	▓
				▓	▓ Gray leaf spot	▓	▓	▓			
				▓	▓ Rusts	▓	▓	▓			
		█	█	█	█	█			▓ Take-all patch*	▓	▓
		▓	▓ Dollar-spot	▓	▓						
				▓	▓ Helminthosporium diseases	▓	▓	▓	▓	▓	

* The timing of take-all patch varies by climate. The fungus is active during the rainy seasons and symptoms become visible when the dry (and/or hot) season gets started.

Table 2. When Diseases strike cool-season turfgrasses.
•Note: chart gives general times for turf diseases to occur. They may occur at other times, however, depending on location and environmental conditions.

Jan.	Feb.	Mar.	Apr.	May	June	July	Aug.	Sep.	Oct.	Nov.	Dec.
				▓	▓ Dollar spot	▓	▓	▓	▓		
				▓	▓ Brown patch	▓	▓	▓			
					▓	▓ Pythium	▓				
		▓	▓	▓	▓ Helminthosporium diseases	▓	▓	▓	▓		
				▓	▓ Anthracnose	▓	▓	▓			
			▓	▓ Necrotic ring spot	▓	█	█	▓			
					▓	█ Summer patch	█	▓			
	▓	▓	▓ Red thread	▓	▓	█	█				
▓	▓ Snow molds	▓	█							▓	▓

* The timing of take-all patch varies by climate. The fungus is active during the rainy seasons and symptoms become visible when the dry (and/or hot) season gets started.

▓	Fungus most active	█	Persistent symptoms often still visible

Table 3. When Diseases strike landscape ornamentals.

•Note: chart gives general times for turf diseases to occur. They may occur at other times, however, depending on location and environmental conditions.

Jan.	Feb.	Mar.	Apr.	May	June	July	Aug.	Sep.	Oct.	Nov.	Dec.
		░	░Anthracnose░	░	░	░					
	░	░Bacterial░	░diseases░	░							
									░	░	
		░	░Fire blight░	░	██	██					
	░								░	░Peach leaf curl░	
░	░	░	░	░Fungal leaf spots░	░	░	░	░	░	░	░
░	░	░	░Powdery mildew░	░	░	░	░	░	░		
		░	░Cedar apple rust░	░							

* The timing of take-all patch varies by climate. The fungus is active during the rainy seasons and symptoms become visible when the dry (and/or hot) season gets started.

░ Fungus most active   ██ Persistent symptoms often still visible

Susceptible turfgrasses: all turfgrasses

Symptoms: Symptoms of brown patch vary according to species of turfgrass. On closely-mowed turf, patches are roughly circular and, under high humidity, a "smoke ring" consisting of water-soaked dark leaves, and fungal mycelium may be present around the outer margin of the diseased area. On turf mowed higher, smoke rings usually are not present and patches may have an irregular rather than circular shape. In cool-season turfgrasses, the fungus primarily causes a blight or dieback from the leaf tip, giving the diseased turf its brown color. In warm- season turfgrasses, the fungus attacks the base of the leaf sheath.

Occurrence and Management: Brown patch is a common, summer-time disease of cool-season turfgrasses. In warm-season turfgrasses, the disease is more severe in the fall and causes extensive damage during cool, wet periods prior to entering winter dormancy.

Cultural practices that reduce brown patch include avoiding nitrogen applications when the disease is active, increasing mowing height, and irrigating early in the day. Also, improve drainage and aerate to improve the root system. Dragging, poling, or mowing early in the morning speeds leaf drying and may reduce disease activity and improve the residual effectiveness of fungicides. Brown patch is a disease in which infection takes place long before symptoms are evident. Careful timing of preventive fungicide applications is critical.

Dollar Spot (Sclerotinia homoeocarpa)

Susceptible turfgrasses: bentgrasses, bluegrasses, bermudagrass, centipedegrass, fescues, perennial ryegrass, St. Augustinegrass, and zoysiagrass

Symptoms: Symptoms vary with species and management practices. On fine-textured turfgrasses maintained at a low mowing height, it appears as small, circular, straw-colored spots about the size of a silver dollar. On coarser-textured grasses at higher mowing heights, patches are larger and irregularly shaped. Grass blades die from the tip back and have straw colored spots shaped like an hourglass. The spots are highlighted on the healthy side by a distinctive narrow brown, purple or black band.

Occurrence and Management: Dollar spot is prevalent in late spring-early summer and again in the fall. It is more damaging in poorly nourished turf, especially if soils are dry and high humidity or heavy dew are present. Cultural practices that reduce disease pressure include avoiding drought stress, irrigating deeply during early morning hours so foliage dries quickly, maintaining a balanced fertility program and controlling thatch and compaction. Fungicides labeled for dollar spot provide effective disease control.

Gray Leaf Spot *(Pyricularia grisea)*

Susceptible turfgrasses: St. Augustinegrass, perennial ryegrass

Symptoms: Entire planting may have a scorched appearance as if suffering from prolonged drought. Leaf spots first appear as tiny brown to ash-colored spots, with purple to brown margins, that enlarge and become diamond shaped. Spots usually have a depressed gray center and may have a velvet appearance.

Occurrence and Management: Gray leaf spot is a summer disease associated with high humidity and high temperatures. Irrigate early in the morning to allow foliage to dry quickly. Avoid excessive nitrogen or applying nitrogen during hot, humid weather. Rapidly-growing turf is more susceptible. Control of leaf wetness and fertility reduces the need for fungicides.

Powdery Mildew *(Erysiphe graminis)*

Susceptible turfgrasses: primarily cool-season turfgrasses

Symptoms: The appearance of grayish-white mycelium on upper leaf surfaces is a sign of the disease. Lower and older leaves generally are more heavily infected than upper, younger leaves.

Occurrence and Management: Powdery mildew is generally confined to shaded areas. Peak fungal activity occurs when days are warm and nights are cool. Reducing shade and improving air circulation are ideal management strategies but often impractical. To minimize damage from powdery mildew and promote turfgrass growth, increase mowing height, avoid drought stress, and use a balanced fertility program. Apply fungicides where the disease is yellowing plants and thinning the stand.

Red Thread *(Laetisaria fuciformis)*

Susceptible turfgrasses: bentgrasses, bermudagrass, bluegrasses, fescues, ryegrasses

Symptoms: Symptoms are concentrated in circular or irregularly shaped patches from 2 inches to 3 feet in diameter. From a distance, infected turf appears to be suffering from lack of water. When there is morning dew or rain, a reddish layer of jelly-like mycelium can be seen on leaves and sheaths. Infected leaves often appear water soaked. During the final stage of the disease, bright red, hard and brittle strands of mycelium are visible extending from cut leaf tips.

Occurrence and Management: Red thread is a disease of slow-growing turf, whether from a lack of nitrogen or cold temperatures. Disease development is favored by cool, wet and extended overcast weather in the spring and fall. Red thread causes the most damage to poorly-nourished turfgrasses. Timely applications of nitrogen help reduce damage from red thread. On high-maintenance turfgrasses, fungicide treatments may be necessary to prevent severe turf loss.

Rust *(Puccinia spp)*

Susceptible turfgrasses: Kentucky bluegrass, perennial ryegrass, zoysiagrass

Symptoms: Rust-affected turf has a yellowish to reddish-brown appearance from a distance. Closer inspection of diseased leaves reveals the presence of red, black, orange, or yellow pustules.

Occurrence and Management: Rusts are most damaging to poorly-nourished turf and turf grown under low mowing height. Prolonged periods of overcast weather or shaded environments favor disease development. Generally, rust-affected turf can be effectively maintained by employing sound cultural practices. A balanced fertility program, deep and infrequent irrigation, and increased mowing height and frequency are preferred to using fungicides. Fungicides may be necessary on slow-growing turf, turf grown for seed production and on turf that is not mowed.

Turfgrass-Foliar and/or Root Rots
Anthracnose (Colletotrichum graminicola)
Susceptible turfgrasses: cool-season turfgrasses and centipedegrass

Symptoms: Turf is affected in irregularly- shaped patches and has a yellow-bronze appearance. Initially, elongated reddish-brown spots appear on the leaves. As the disease progresses, these spots enlarge and cover the entire leaf blade. As the disease progresses, numerous black fruiting bodies, with protruding black spines, of the fungus can be seen on the foliage and stems.

Occurrence and Management: This disease is found when there is prolonged moist weather. Generally, it is only a problem if the turf is weakened by some stress factor such as heat, drought, or low fertility. Proper fertility, alleviating soil compaction and traffic, and providing adequate water are important measures for reducing disease levels. Avoid nitrogen deficiencies and N:K imbalances. Water turf deeply and infrequently and avoid watering during late afternoon or evening. Fungicides may be necessary to help bring the disease under control once it gets established.

Helminthosporium Complex Leaf Spot and Melting Out
(Bipolaris and Dreschlera spp.)
Susceptible turfgrasses: bentgrasses, buffalograss, bermudagrasses, bluegrasses, fescues, perennial ryegrass

Symptoms: Symptoms range from leaf spots and blotches to crown and stolon rots. During the leaf spot phase, distinctive purplish-brown spots with tan centers are found on older leaves. During favorable disease conditions, the spots may increase in size to encompass the entire width of the blade, causing a dieback from the tip. If environmental conditions remain favorable, successive layers of leaf sheaths are penetrated and the crown is invaded. Once the crown is invaded, the disease enters the melting out phase. During the melting out phase, spots with purplish margins can be seen on the stolons.

Occurrence and Management: The Helminthosporium complex would more appropriately be called either Drechslera or Bipolaris, depending on the disease, but the common name persists. Use of resistant varieties has reduced the damage caused by Helminthosporium-type diseases. Both warm- and cool-season diseases are part of this complex. Melting out, netblotch, and brown blight are cool-weather diseases. Leaf spot and red leaf spot are warm-weather diseases.

Cultural practices that reduce injury from any of these include raising the mowing height, proper watering practices, and reducing the thatch layer. Avoid spring application of high rates of fast-release nitrogen fertilizers. These fungi produce huge numbers of spores when the thatch is subjected to frequent wetting and drying cycles, so irrigation should be applied deeply and infrequently. If necessary, a fungicide may be applied to reduce the amount of disease present.

Pythium Cottony Blight, Grease Spot, Crown and Root Rot
(Pythium spp.)

Susceptible turfgrasses: creeping bentgrass, annual bluegrass and perennial ryegrass

Symptoms: Circular reddish-brown spots appear in affected turf. When the turf is wet, from either dew or irrigation, infected leaf blades appear water-soaked and dark, and may feel slimy. As they dry, the blades shrivel and turn reddish-brown. A purplish-gray or white and cottony fungal growth may be visible on the outer margins of a spot, depending on the turf and species of Pythium. Root-infecting Pythium species may cause damage in irregularly-shaped areas. Infected plants turn yellow or reddish-brown and symptoms may mimic Helminthosporium melting out or anthracnose. No foliar mycelium is present on the root-infecting Pythium species.

Occurrence and Management: Pythium blight can be devastating. Several Pythium species affect turfgrasses. Warm-season Pythium species attack the foliage and are active during periods of high relative humidity, night temperatures above 70°F, and abundant surface moisture. Disease is generally more severe in shaded areas, low spots, or near surface water where air circulation is poor. Cool-season Pythium species cause foliar or root rots and generally occur during or following long cool periods when soils are excessively wet or saturated.

Water management greatly influences disease severity. Irrigate early in the day to avoid moist foliage at night. Improve drainage and increase air circulation to help reduce disease development. While fungicides are not generally used in lawn care for Pythium blight control, they are considered necessary in golf course management. However, continued use of a given fungicide often results in resistance to the fungicide. To avoid the buildup of fungicide resistant types of fungi, fungicides should always be rotated and they should be applied in tankmix combinations whenever feasible.

Snow Molds *(Typhula spp. and Microdochium nivale)*

Susceptible turfgrasses: all turfgrasses

Symptoms: Patches may be from a few inches to a few feet in size. The fungal mycelium mats the leaves and the plants eventually collapse and die.

Occurrence and Management: There are two basic types of snow molds: pink snow mold caused by Microdochium nivale and gray snow mold caused by Typhula spp. Snow molds are active at temperatures slightly above freezing. While called snow molds, snow is not necessary for disease to develop. Abundant surface moisture allows the fungus to infect turf when it's dormant or when growth is slow because of low temperatures. In susceptible areas, fungicides may be applied just prior to the first snowfall or ice storm.

Turfgrass-Root Rots
Necrotic Ring Spot (Leptosphaeria korrae)

Susceptible turfgrasses: Kentucky and annual bluegrass, red fescue

Symptoms: Affected areas have 6- to 12-inch circular to irregularly-shaped patches of light tan, matted turf. On older patches, the turf at the center of the patches will look healthy, giving a "frog-eye" appearance. Because the fungus attacks the roots, plants first wilt and eventually turn straw-colored.

Occurrence and Management: Necrotic ring spot occurs when wet weather is followed by warm, dry periods. The fungus is active during the spring and fall although symptoms may not appear until summer. A complete integrated pest management program, including biological, cultural, genetic and fungicide strategies, is effective for control of necrotic ring spot. Because necrotic ring spot is a root disease, timely application of water is required during the summer months when heat and drought severely stress the infected plants. Use of slow release and bio-organic fertilizers help to reduce disease severity. Several cultivars of Kentucky bluegrass have some resistance. Early spring applications of fungicides may reduce the damage caused by necrotic ring spot.

Spring Dead Spot (*Leptosphaeria spp., Gaeumannomyces graminis var. graminis, Ophiosphaerella herpotricha*)

Susceptible turfgrasses: bermudagrass

Symptoms: Circular patches of bleached, dead grass appear in the spring as the turfgrass breaks dormancy. Patches may range from a few inches to several feet in diameter and are usually depressed. The damage often appears similar to winterkill or winter desiccation. Patches tend to reappear and expand over the years. Rhizomes and stolons from nearby healthy plants eventually spread into and cover the dead patches. This filling-in process is slow due to toxic substances generated in the soil below the dead patches.

Occurrence and Management: The longer the period of winter dormancy and the colder the temperature, the more severe the disease. Areas experiencing spring dead spot typically have been on high-maintenance programs, especially programs high in nitrogen. Avoid excess nitrogen applications, especially in the fall just prior to dormancy. Damage is most likely to occur where thick thatch layers exist. Cultural practices that promote vigorous root growth reduce damage caused by the fungus. Very few fungicides are labeled for this disease and they may be of limited use in certain states.

Summer Patch (*Magnaporthe poae*)

Susceptible turfgrasses: Kentucky and annual bluegrass, red fescue

Svmptoms: Symptoms of summer patch are similar to necrotic ring spot but typically appear in the warm weather of summer as yellow to bronze-colored, irregularly-shaped patches. Patches may take on a crescent shape or become elongated streaks over time. Healthy turf may persist at the center of the spots giving a "frog-eye" appearance. Leaves generally die back from the tips.

Occurrence and Management: Environmental conditions that favor disease are moist soil and root zone temperatures of >78°F. To minimize summer patch, increase mowing heights, apply water deeply and only at the onset of wilt, and use slow-release nitrogen fertilizers. On closely-cut turf, preventive applications of fungicides may be necessary. Fungicides are ineffective if turf is allowed to enter drought-induced dormancy.

Take-all Patch (*Gaeumannomyces graminis*)

Susceptible turfgrasses: bermudagrasses, St. Augustinegrass

Symptoms: Patches are irregularly-shaped and plants in affected areas have root systems that are short and rotted. Plants are easily pulled or lifted from the ground. The nodes and stolons may become infected and show a brownish discoloration and rotting.

Occurrence and Management: The take-all patch fungus is generally active during the rainy season. However, symptoms often don't appear until the affected turfgrass experiences the stressful effects of high temperatures and dry weather. Low or poorly-drained areas suffered from more damage. Excessive thatch and overwatering also contribute to disease development. Cultural practices that improve the root system, such as improving surface and subsurface drainage, avoiding overwatering, prevention of thatch build-up and a balanced fertility program, reduce the damage caused by take-all patch. Preventive fungicides applied when the fungus is active may slow down disease development.

Turfgrass-General
Fairy Rings

Fairy rings may be caused by more than 60 species of fungi and grow in thatch and soil. They may appear as circles or arcs of dark green, fast-growing grass. This is a result of the fungi releasing nutrients as they degrade dead organic matter. Fairy rings also appear as circles or arcs of dead grass. This is a result of the massive build-up of fungal mycelium forming a hydrophobic barrier that prevents entry of rain or irrigation water, thus killing the plants by drought.

Control of fairy rings is extremely difficult due to the impermeability of infected soil. Chemical control is generally ineffective because the fungus grows so deeply in the soil. Suppression of symptoms is the most practical approach to managing fairy rings. A combination of aeration, deep watering, and proper fertilization mask the symptoms. Use of wetting agents helps improve water infiltration. Frequent mowing and use of labeled fungicides will control the mushroom producing fungi but deep watering is necessary to leach out toxins for the turf to recover.

Nematodes

Diagnosing nematode damage is often difficult since many other factors cause similar symptoms. These include fungi, insects, too much or too little water, too much or too little of some micronutrients, soil compaction and chemical spill. Both above- and below-ground symptoms must be observed to make an accurate diagnosis.

Above-ground symptoms typical of nematode damage include wilting under moderate moisture stress, slow recovery of wilted turf after rain or irrigation, and thinning or gradual decline of turf. Because nematodes are not distributed evenly in soils, damage is rarely uniform, appearing in areas that are irregular in shape and size. Roots damaged by nematodes are usually short and dark colored, with few lateral or 'feeder' roots. They may be rotted because of secondary fungal activity. Sometimes the root tip is swollen. The damaged root system will not hold soil together when a core or plug is lifted.

The best method for controlling nematodes is to prevent their introduction into the area. It's critical to use clean seed or sod and topdressing soil. Clean equipment thoroughly of all dirt, especially when moving from an area known to be infested with nematodes.

Effectiveness of nematicides depends on the type and texture of soil. Nematicides reduce nematode numbers but they don't completely eradicate them from the soil.

Slime Molds

Slime molds, while fungi, are not diseases because they don't feed on living turfgrasses. Fruiting structures are grayish-white and often resemble cigarette ashes. Slime molds occur in wet weather, usually in the spring or early summer. Slime molds can be removed by mowing, raking, or irrigating the turf. Fungicide use is not necessary for slime mold control.

Ornamentals-Foliar and Flower
Powdery Mildew

Susceptible hosts: many ornamentals

Symptoms: Spots or patches of whitish or grayish mildewy growth appear on young plant tissues or upper surface of entire leaves. There may be a slight reddening and curling of leaves before the fungal mycelium is noticeable. Tiny black pinhead-sized spherical fruiting bodies may be present in older areas of infection. Plants may be stunted and flower buds deformed.

Occurrence and Management: Powdery mildews are probably the most common, widespread and easily recognizable plant diseases. They seldom kill the host plant but they do reduce photosynthesis, impair growth and reduce yields. Powdery mildews absorb nutrients from plant cells near the surface of the plant. Powdery mildews are specialized pathogens that are specific to a given host. So the powdery mildew found on roses won't infect zinnias, crape myrtles, or turfgrass. Unlike most fungal pathogens, powdery mildew spores don't require free water to germinate, so mildews are more abundant in semi-arid regions than in areas of high rainfall.

Powdery mildews often occur when plants are crowded, are in low or shady locations, or in areas that lack air circulation. Proper spacing of plants and selective pruning to improve air circulation reduce the damage caused by powdery mildews. Irrigating early in the day allows the relative humidity at the leaf surface to drop quickly, preventing spores from germinating. Several ornamental species have been developed with powdery mildew resistance. Fungicides are available, when needed, to control established infections.

Rust

Susceptible hosts: many ornamentals

Symptoms: Symptoms appear as rusty, orange, yellow or even white spots that break through the leaf surface. They cause defined spots that don't enlarge, unlike most fungal leaf spots. An orange or yellow dust can be brushed off with a light finger touch to the leaf spot. Reddish discoloration (caused by spray injury, weather, or other leaf spot fungi) of a leaf is often mistaken for rust. When rusts cause disease, the tissue around the pustule is usually yellow and the pustules have a powdery, rusty "dust" in them. Frequently, plants are stunted.

Occurrence and Management: Rusts attack mostly leaves and stems, although sometimes flowers and fruits are affected. Most rusts are very specialized and can attack only specific host plants. However, there are more than 4,000 kinds of rusts and many ornamental plants are susceptible to at least one of them.

Control of rust diseases in some plants is achieved by resistant varieties. Since rust spores are spread by the wind, it's difficult to prevent rust from entering a planting. Fungicides are effective in controlling many of the rust diseases.

Botrytis

Susceptible hosts: many bedding plants

Symptoms: Symptoms vary depending on host plant but may include bud and flower blights, blossom blights, gray-mold rot and stem and crown rots. When infection occurs on leaves, they appear water-soaked and often a brownish-gray mold covers the affected area. Dark spores can be rubbed off affected areas with a light touch.

Occurrence and Management: Botrytis diseases generally occur in areas of high humidity or excessive moisture. They are especially damaging in greenhouse situations. Sanitation is an important management strategy. Remove all fading flowers and blighted foliage or the whole plant if infection is near the base. Keep greenhouse plants widely spaced with good ventilation and avoid overhead watering and too cool temperatures. In outdoor plantings avoid crowding plants, shady or low spots with little air circulation and areas subject to heavy dews. Fungicides may be necessary for control of Botrytis blights.

Ornamentals-General Foliar

Leaf spots caused by fungi are the most common of plant diseases. They are so common we seldom notice them, which is good, because it would be impossible to control all the miscellaneous leaf spots that appear.

Most leaf spot-causing fungi require a thin layer of moisture on the leaf surface for them to germinate and infect. Cultural practices which allow leaves to dry quickly after irrigation and improve air circulation greatly reduce the damage caused by fungal leaf spots. Many are unsightly but cause little damage to the plant and, in some instances, can be ignored. In situations where control is necessary, several broad-spectrum fungicides are available.

Ornamentals-Root and Stem Rots
Pythium and Phytophthora

Susceptible hosts: all ornamentals

Symptoms: Both Pythium spp. and Phytophthora spp. can cause seed rots, damping-off, root rots, and soft rots. When seeds are infected, they fail to germinate, become soft and mushy, then turn brown, shrink, and finally disintegrate. Seedlings can be infected at the roots and sometimes at or below the soil line. The succulent tissues of seedlings are easily penetrated by the fungus, which invades and kills cells very rapidly. Invaded areas become water soaked and discolored. Infection by these fungi on older roots is usually limited to the outer cortex of the root. This cortex can be easily slipped from the rest of the root by holding the infected root between the thumb and forefinger and gently tugging.

Occurrence and Management: Pythium and Phytophthora are known as water molds. Damage by these fungi is more severe in areas of poor drainage or standing water, when temperatures are unfavorable for the host plant, and when excessive nitrogen has been applied.

Cultural practices which improve surface and subsurface drainage and careful irrigation management are critical to control these diseases. Plantings should be done when temperatures are favorable for fast plant germination and/or growth. Seed treatments and foliar applied fungicides are available and, when used in conjunction with improved cultural practices, may reduce the amount of damage caused by these diseases.

Rhizoctonia, Fusarium, and Thielaviopsis

Susceptible hosts: all ornamentals

Symptoms: These fungi may cause root rots, stem rots, and in some special cases, foliar spots and blights. As soil-borne organisms, these fungi attack the root or near the soil line. As with Pythium and Phytophthora, they can cause seed rots, damping-off, and root and stem rots. In wet weather, cobwebby mycelium develops on lower portions of stems, girdling the stem and causing the plant to die.

Occurrence and Management: While Pythium and Phytophthora do best in the low oxygen content of poorly-drained soils, Rhizoctonia causes similar root rots in well-drained soils. Thielaviopsis is most destructive in heavy, cold soils with lots of organic matter. Long wet periods also increase rots caused by Thielaviopsis. All of these diseases are problems in greenhouses where cuttings are being started. Using sterile potting mix, optimizing the environmental conditions for rapid plant growth and sanitation are important control strategies. Fungicides may be necessary to bring these diseases under control once they become established.

This chapter was provided by Dr. Janell Stevens-Johnk, Extension Plant Pathologist, Texas Agricultural Extension Service.

For current control measures, please refer to the annual May issue of *Landscape Management.* ❦

CHAPTER 15

Insect Management

A wide variety of insects are present in every landscape all the time, both above and below the soil surface. Not all insects damage plants and some do such little damage that they are of no concern. Insects that do damage plants do so in one of three ways. One group of insects damage plants by chewing plant parts. Another group have specialized mouth parts that allow them to suck plant juices. Some insects may not do any significant damage themselves, but they may inadvertently transmit plant disease. Insects may also indirectly damage or kill plants by reducing the plants' vigor to the point of making the plant more susceptible to other pests.

Insects have two very different life cycle patterns; complete or incomplete metamorphosis.

Complete Metamorphosis

These insects produce four very distinct stages in their life cycle. They are egg, larvae, pupae, and finally adult. The larvae stage may also be referred to as caterpillars, maggots, or grubs. Only the adult stage has wings and is capable of reproduction. Usually the larvae stage cause the most damage to plants. (Figure 1)

Examples are:

Billbug	Cankerworm
Cutworm	Leaf minor
Bagworm	Sod webworm
Fall webworm	Army worm
Crane fly	Hyperodes weevil
Beetles	

Incomplete Metamorphosis

These insects have different stages in their life cycle, but they aren't as distinct as those that go through complete metamorphosis. Following the egg stage, the insect which hatches is an exact miniature of the adult, then goes through several nymph stages. The nymphs feed on the same materials as do the adults. Wings are not fully developed until they reach the adult stage. Both the nymphs and the adults can damage plants. (Figure 2)

Examples are:

Chinch bug	Lace bug
Mole cricket	Aphids
Ants	Elm leaf beetle
Spittle bug	Bark beetle
Ground pearls	Wood borers
Leaf hopper	

Insects That Damage Turf (Figures 3 and 4)
Above-Ground Feeders

1. Army worm—The young larvae is pale green and when fully grown is about 1—1½ inches long. It then is striped and is yellow to brownish

Figure 1. Complete metamorphosis

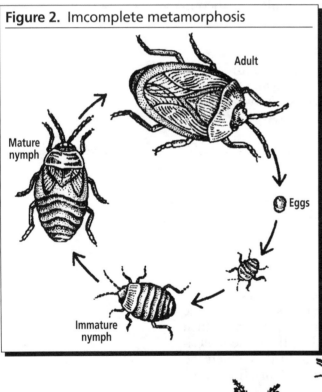

Adult (butterfly)

Eggs

Larvae (caterpillar)

Pupae (chrysalis)

Figure 2. Imcomplete metamorphosis

Adult

Mature nymph

Eggs

Immature nymph

Mites

Sod Webworms

Billbugs and Weevils

Chinch Bugs

Leafhoppers

green in color. It curls into a "C" shape when disturbed. They have a distinct inverted yellow "Y" on the head area. (Note: while all caterpillars have inverted Y's, they are only yellow on army worms).

The habit of the larvae to move en masse from one feeding area to another give this insect its name. High populations may develop very quickly and then may disappear just as quickly.

Usually populations of parasites and diseases keep army worm populations in check.

2. Billbugs—These are dark- colored beetles that have a snout with chewing mouth parts. The larvae feed on roots, and the adults burrow into the grass stems at the soil surface.

Damage from these insects may resemble a fertilizer burn or a dried-out area. In the case of billbugs, the grass can be easily pulled up.

3. Chinch bug—The ¼-inch long adults are black with white or opaque wings. Nymphs are reddish in color. Both feed on the grass plant by sucking plant juices. Damage is greatest during hot, dry weather.

The southern chinch bug is primarily a problem on St. Augustine while the hairy chinch bug prefers cool-season grasses.

4. Cut worms—Cut worms are fat, dull colored caterpillars from 1½ to 2 inches long when full grown. They feed at the base of the plant, cutting it off. They are found in all climates and may attack any turfgrass.

5. Hyperodes weevil—This may also be known as the annual bluegrass weevil because most of its damage is confined to shorter cut bluegrasses as found on golf course fairways. This weevil's snout has a conspicuously knobbed antenna on each side near the tip.

6. Leaf hopper—These ¼-inch long insects hop or fly short distances as you walk across the turf surface. They can retard grass growth by sucking sap through their needle-like mouth parts.

7. Sod webworm—The larvae, which are ⅔ to ¾-inch long when full grown, live in small silk-lined tunnels. They cut off grass blades and feed on them in their tunnels. Their damage appears as small brown patches of closely-cut grass.

8. Spittle bug—The nymphs of this insect produce a white, frothy mass or spittle. This mass serves to protect the insect as it feeds.

9. Mites—The bermudagrass mite causes an abnormal growth pattern that is described as rosetting or tufting. The plant's internodes are great-

Figure 3. When Northern Turfgrass Insects are most active

	Jan	Feb	Mar	Apr	May	June	July	Aug	Sept	Oct	Nov	Dec
Hairy chinch bugs						D/C	D/C	D/C	D/C			
Sod webworms						C	C	D	C			
Bluegrass billbugs			D	D			D		C	D		
Cutworms				C	C	C	C	C	C	C		
Ants				C	C	C	C	C	C	C	C	
Black turfgrass ataenius			D	D	D	C	D	C				
Grubs					D			D	D/C	D		
Clover mites	C	C	C	C	C	C	C	C	C	C	C	C
Greenbug aphids					D	D	D	C	C	C		
Winter grain mites			D	C								
Annual bluegrass weevil				D/C	C			D/C	C			

■ Periods of insect damage.   ■ Periods when control is needed.

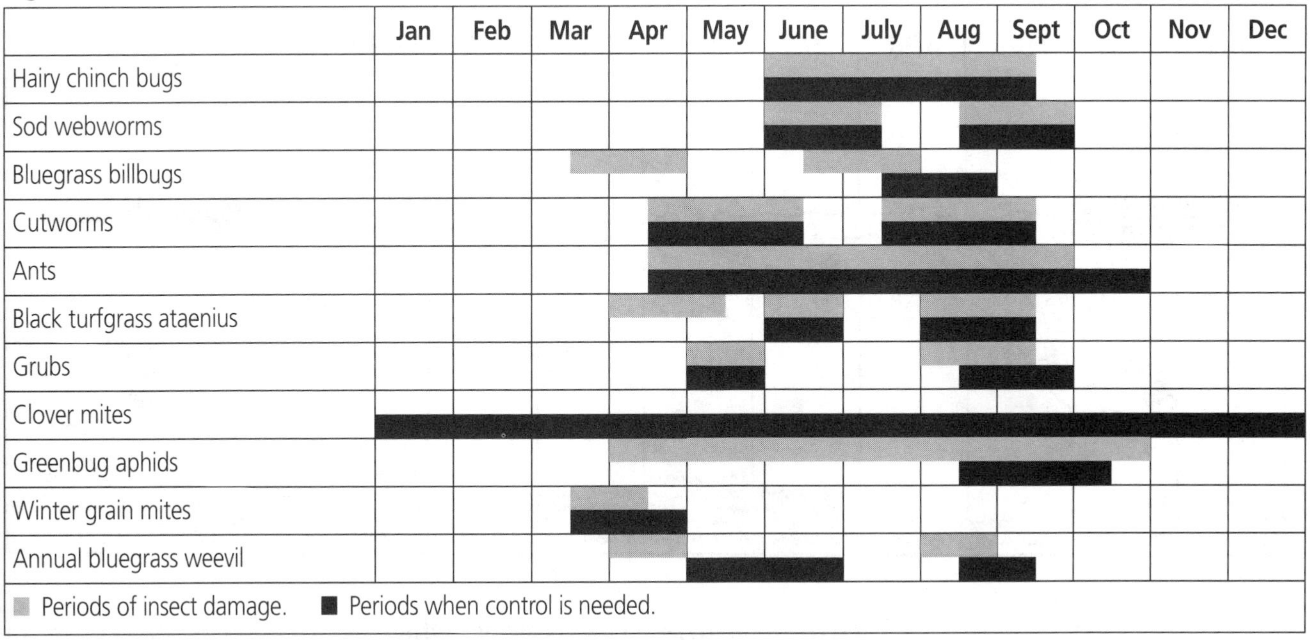

Figure 4. When Southern Turfgrass Insects are most active

	Jan	Feb	Mar	Apr	May	June	July	Aug	Sept	Oct	Nov	Dec
Southern chinch bugs		C	D/C	D/C	D/C	D/C	D/C	D/C	D/C	D/C	C	D
Sod webworms				D	C	C	C	C	C	C	D	D
Armyworms			D/C	D/C	D/C	D/C	D/C	D/C	D/C	D/C		
Cutworms			C	C	C	C	C	C	C	C		
Fire ants	C	C	C	C	C	C	C	C	C	C	C	C
Mole crickets			C	C	C	C	C	C	C	C		
Grubs			D/C	C	C			C	C	C		

■ Periods of insect damage.   ■ Periods when control is needed.

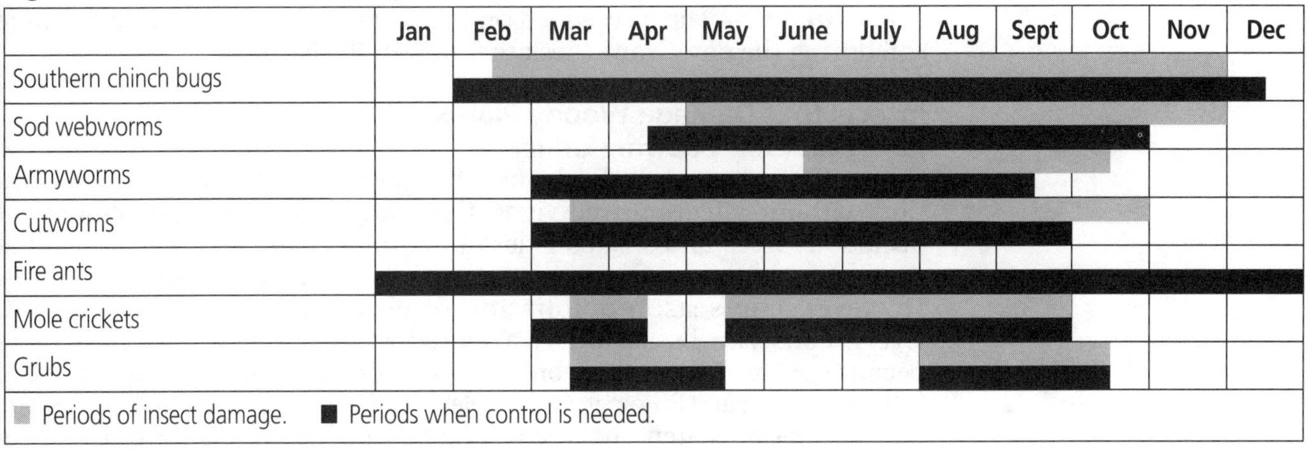

ly shortened. These mites seem to prefer hot, dry locations.

The winter grain mite feeds on cool-season turfgrasses during winter months.

Below-Ground Feeders

1. Grubs—Grubs are the immature forms of several different beetle species. Included are the ataenius, the Japanese, the Green June, the May, and the Oriental beetles. Also included in this group are the masked and European chafers.

They all feed on root systems and if populations are high enough, the grass plant may be killed. It's not unusual to find a few grubs in the soil at any time of the year. (Figure 5)

If the turf is actively growing, it is possible that some grubs can be present without any significant damage.

Since grubs feed on roots, heavy feeding may result in a nearly complete loss of the whole root system and the plant's ability to take up water. The turf dries out but will not respond to watering.

2. Mole crickets—These are fairly large insects that burrow through the soil and feed on root systems. They seem to prefer sandier soils because of the ease in burrowing.

Figure 5.

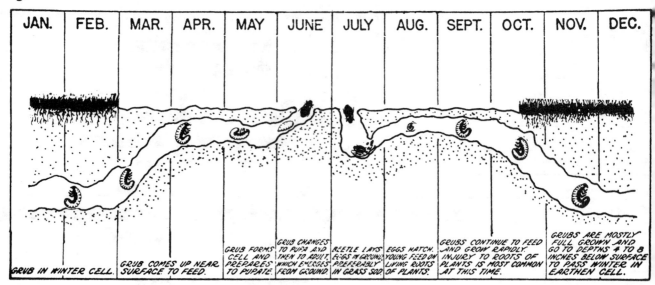

| JAN. | FEB. | MAR. | APR. | MAY | JUNE | JULY | AUG. | SEPT. | OCT. | NOV. | DEC. |

GRUB IN WINTER CELL. — *GRUB COMES UP NEAR SURFACE TO FEED.* — *GRUB FORMS CELL AND PREPARES TO PUPATE.* — *GRUB CHANGES TO PUPA AND THEN TO ADULT, WHICH EMERGES FROM GROUND.* — *BEETLE LAYS EGGS IN GROUND, PREFERABLY IN GRASS SOD.* — *EGGS HATCH. YOUNG FEED ON LIVING ROOTS OF PLANTS.* — *GRUBS CONTINUE TO FEED AND GROW RAPIDLY. INJURY TO ROOTS OF PLANTS IS MOST COMMON AT THIS TIME.* — *GRUBS ARE MOSTLY FULL GROWN AND GO TO DEPTHS 4 TO 8 INCHES BELOW SURFACE TO PASS WINTER IN EARTHEN CELL.*

3. Ground pearls—The nymphs, which feed on roots, protect themselves by forming a pearl-like shell around their bodies. They feed mostly on St. Augustine and centipede grasses.

4. Crane fly—The larvae feed on the surface at night, remaining in the soil during the day. Crane flies are found in the Northwest.

Insects that Damage Woody Plants
Leaf Feeders—Chewing Injury

Deciduous trees and shrubs usually can tolerate considerable defoliation without affecting tree vigor. Generally, late-season defoliation of deciduous trees and shrubs is less important than early-season defoliation, because food necessary for growth has been produced and stores. However, late season defoliation of evergreens can be important. Evergreens can be seriously affected by heavy defoliation. This is because evergreens replace only a portion of their total complement of foliage each year. (Pines, for example, replace about one-third, and if the new needles are eaten, the tree will be missing about one-third of its needles for three consecutive years.) Also, evergreens usually use their leaves or needles to produce growth regulators (hormones) and to store food reserves for the next year. If these leaves or needles are destroyed, so are sites for growth regulator production and food storage. New foliage is the most efficient producer of photosynthate (plant food). If this foliage is lost to defoliators, the current year's food production can be reduced considerably.

The two most common types of leaf-chewing insects are caterpillars and leaf beetles.

Caterpillars

Caterpillars feed on the foliage of tress. Some form webs or tents on branches and some have more than one generation per year. Several important caterpillars are bagworm, mimosa webworm, fall webworm, and cankerworm. Note: These pests can be controlled with bacterial products (Bacillus thuringiensis). Where environmental and personal safety are critical considerations, you might wish to consider B.t. products in lieu of "classical" synthetic insecticides in your control program.

BAGWORMS — Bagworms will attack and defoliate most evergreen and deciduous trees and shrubs, but prefer arborvitae, red cedar, juniper, bald cypress, several species of pine and boxelder. Bagworms live inside a spindle-shaped bag which they construct while they are in the larval or caterpillar stage. The bags are dragged with the caterpillars wherever they go and are made of silk and bits of foliage. The front part of the larvae protrude from the bag for feeding movement. Full-grown larvae are three-fourths to one inch long, dark brown with white to yellowish heads and a black spotted thorax.

Life History. Bagworms overwinter as eggs inside the bags of the females. The eggs hatch in late spring (May to early June) and the larvae begin feeding and constructing their protective case. As the caterpillars grow in size, the bag is constantly enlarged. The larvae pupate in late summer and the males emerge from their bags as black moths with furry bodies, feathered antennae, and clear wings with a wing span of almost one inch. The female is a wingless moth that remains in a wormlike form and never leaves the bag. She is fertilized by the male, lays 500 to 1,000 eggs inside the bag, and then dies. There is one generation per year.

Management. Light infestations, particularly on small shrubs and trees, can be effectively controlled by hand-picking all the bags from the infested plants and destroying the bags before they hatch.

Half-grown to nearly full-grown bagworm caterpillars can be difficult to kill with insecticide. The key to successful control with insecticide sprays is to spray when the bagworms are small (late May to mid-June, when their cases are a half-inch or less in length). To be able to time sprays exactly so they will do the most good, collect a few bags before the eggs hatch in late May and place them outdoors in a fine-screen cage. When the newly-hatched larvae are seen leaving the caged bags, it is time to spray. When collecting bags for this purpose, keep in mind that male bags will not have any eggs, so collect enough bags to ensure that at least some of them have eggs.

FALL WEBWORM — The fall webworm is the larval stage of a moth that is responsible for unsightly webbing seen on shade and nut trees from mid-summer to fall. These webs should not be confused with tent caterpillars, which appear on fruit trees in the spring. The larvae feed on the leaves of more than a hundred kinds of fruit, ornamental, and woodland trees. Favored trees include persimmon, pecan, English walnut, black walnut, and hickory. Larvae confine their feeding to leaves they have covered with webbing. Larvae characteristically web only the outer ends of branches. One or more branches may be defoliated, often with no damage to the tree other than appearance.

Life History. The moth is satiny white and may have black or brown spots on the forewings. They have a wing span measuring slightly over one inch. Moths emerge from overwintering pupae in late spring (late April to May) and lay clusters of up to 500 greenish eggs on leaf surfaces of host trees. The eggs are partly covered with white hairs or scales and usually occur on leaves near the ends of branches.

Depending on the weather, tiny larvae hatch from eggs in early June. Larvae immediately begin weaving their webbing over the leaves at the end of branches. The web is small at first, but soon becomes large as the larvae extend the web to cover more leaves. Feeding is done entirely in the protection of the web. Only the tender portion of leaves are eaten, leaving the veins intact. As the larvae grow, the web becomes filled with dead leaves, cast skins, and feces. The larvae are about one inch long when full grown and are pale yellow with dark spots down the back. The body is covered with long, silky, gray-white hairs. When full grown, they crawl down the tree to spin a cocoon and pupate in the ground litter in July. There are two generations a year—the first in early June (into July) and the second and normally the largest and most damaging generation of larvae present in August and September (sometimes early October). Larvae from the second generation remain in the pupal stage until the next spring, when the moths emerge to begin the cycle again.

Management. When pruning out webs is not practical, insecticidal sprays, including bacterial sprays, will give excellent control if sufficient pressure is used to penetrate webbing. Control will be most effective if treatment is made while the webs are still small.

CANKERWORMS — Cankerworms are known also as measuring worms, inch worms, or loopers. They attack early in the spring just as the leaves are beginning to appear, or they sometimes attack the buds before the leaves open.

Life History. The spring cankerworm adult emerges in late February and March as winged male and wingless female moths.

The females crawl up the trunk of the tree to deposit eggs. Eggs hatch in Aril or early May and the larvae devour developing leaves for three to five weeks. Dispersal is accomplished when small caterpillars are blown from one tree to another. There is one generation per year. Defoliation is often not readily apparent, although trees may appear dead because they are late in leafing out. Note: Even if this pest causes virtual defoliation of new spring foliage, trees normally recover and "re-leaf."

Caterpillars first chew holes in leaves, then progress to eating the whole leaf as the larvae get bigger. Elms, hackberry, oaks, and apple are favorite hosts. These caterpillars are often seen dangling from the foliage of infested trees on fine strands of silk (as from being dislodged by wind or disturbed foliage); however, the worms quickly climb the silk strands back up into the foliage.

Management. Applying bands of sticky material to the trunks of individual trees to catch the wingless females as they crawl upwards to lay their eggs is an old technique that can work. However, because large numbers of the small caterpillars are dispersed to other trees by the wind, the use of sticky bands works best when done on a community-wide basis.

Insecticides including bacterial (B.t.) products are effective in reducing damage to trees from this pest, if applied in April or early May to kill the newly-hatched caterpillars.

Leaf Beetles

The most damaging leaf beetle is the elm leaf beetle. The elm leaf beetle is an introduced pest from Europe which feeds only on elm. Although most elm species are subject to attack, the beetles usually prefer Siberian elm, Ulmus pumila (commonly called Chinese elm), and hybrid elms. The true Chinese elm, U. parvifolia, is seldom attacked, and the American elm, U. americana, seldom suffers any significant damage from this pest.

Elm leaf beetle feeding damage may result in partial or complete defoliation of the tree. Severely damaged/eaten leaves will turn brown and often drop prematurely. Sometimes the entire tree may be defoliated by mid-summer. Most of the damage is caused by the larvae as they feed on the lower side of the leaves. Trees which lose their leaves as a result of elm leaf beetle damage commonly put out a new flush of growth which may also be consumed by the insects on the tree or later generations of larvae.

Feeding damage by elm leaf beetles seldom kills an elm tree. However, severe feeding will weaken a tree, making it more susceptible to attack by other pests.

Life History. Elm leaf beetles overwinter as adult beetles in houses (where they are a nuisance), sheds, and protected places out-of-doors (under loose bark or house shingles). Adults are about one-fourth inch long, yellow to olive green, with dark stripes along the outer edge of each wing cover. Adults emerge from their overwintering quarters during late April to early May, fly to nearby elms, mate, and lay eggs. The adults eat small, circular holes in the expanding leaves. The orange-yellow, spindle-shaped eggs are laid on end in groups of five to 25, always parallel rows on the underside of leaves. A female will lay 600 to 800 eggs in her lifetime. Small black larvae feed on the undersurface of the leaves for about three weeks. Mature larvae are about one-half inch in length, dull yellow, with two black stripes down the back.

Larvae feed in groups, eating the undersides of the leaves, leaving only the upper leaf surface intact, giving a skeletonized appearance. At the end of the feeding period (larval stage), the larvae move to the lower parts of the tree to pupate in cracks, crevices, or crotches on the trunk or larger limbs. Adults emerge in about eight days and lay second-generation eggs. There are three full generations and sometimes a partial or complete fourth generation of elm leaf beetles.

Management. Spraying infested trees should be timed to kill the young first brood larvae in May. Other treatments will likely be needed as later generations of larvae appear. Rain within 24 hours of treatment may result in having to re-treat the tree to ensure sufficient insecticide residue to kill larvae. Also, properly labeled systemic insecticides can be applied to the soil to control elm leaf beetles. (Check product labels for specific application procedures.) Note: New varieties/strains of Bacillus thuringiensis (var. tenebrionsis) are available for control of this pest.

Leaf Miners

Leaf miners are larvae of certain species of small flies, wasps, moths, or beetles. They feed inside the leaf between the upper and lower surface. Damage appears as brown or discolored blotches or winding trails in leaves. There may be more than one generation per year, depending on the species of mining insect. Leaf miners are difficult to control after they have entered leaves. A systemic insecticide will best reduce leaf miner numbers in hawthorn, birch, oak, holly, and other infested plants. Treatment should be made when miners first appear in new foliage (in late spring or early summer).

Leaf Feeders—Sucking Injury
Aphids

Few plants exist, cultivated or wild, that are not hosts to one or more aphid species. Aphids, scale insects and the true plant bugs obtain their food by sucking the sap from plant tissue. Some species feed only on foliage, others on twigs, branches, flowers, or fruit, and still others on roots. Many live on several distinct hosts, spending part of their seasonal development on one host and the remainder on another.

Appearance and Damage. Aphids are small (seldom over ⅛ inch in length), soft-bodied, pear-shaped insects of many colors, such as green, black, gray, or red. They usually can be distinguished from other insects by the presence of cornicles—a pair of "tailpipe" or tubelike structures projecting upward and backward from the upper surface of the abdomen. (One group of aphids, the most common member of which is the wooly apple aphid, does not have these structures.) Cornicles may be either long and narrow, short and broad, or somewhere in between, depending upon the species.

Most aphids attack en masse, preferring young shoots or leaves. The feeding of large numbers of aphids can cause serious damage to plants by 1) robbing plants of sap, 2) the toxic action of their salivary secretions injected during feeding, and 3) serving as vectors of viruses which cause plant diseases. Aphid damage stunts growth, deforms leaves and fruit, or causes galls on leaves, stems and roots.

Besides this damage, many aphid species excrete a sticky substance known as "honeydew." This material falls onto the leaves, twigs and fruit, and a black, sooty mold soon begins to grow in it. This mold not only mars the appearance of the plant, but also restricts certain physiological functions, such as photosynthesis. Honeydew attracts ants and flies and is a nuisance on cars, chairs, tables, or other objects that happen to be under infested plants.

Biology of Aphids. Much variation is found in the biology of aphids; however, there are certain general biological facts that may be applied to the group as a whole. Aphids usually reproduce without mating and give birth to living young. Species of aphids are usually rather restricted to specific host plants, feeding on a group of more or less related plants. Some species have alternate hosts on which they are found at different seasons.

Aphids are frequently held in check by natural forces, primarily adverse weather conditions, such as beating rains and high and low temperatures; fungus diseases; and naturally-occurring insect predators and parasites. The natural insect enemies of aphids are lady beetles, syrphid fly larvae, lacewing larvae, and small wasp parasites known as braconids.

FOLIAGE-FEEDING APHIDS — These aphids constitute a large group of small, soft-bodied insects frequently found in large numbers sucking sap from stems or leaves of plants. Such aphid groups often include individuals in all stages of development. This group contains a number of serious pests of cultivated plants. Many species affect particular plants (host specific), but a few can be found on many different types of plants. These aphids cause a curling or wilting of plant foliage, and they serve as vectors of a number of important plant diseases.

WOOLLY APHIDS — Aphids in this group vary in color from shades of brown to purple. However, they all have in common a white, woolly waxlike covering. Generally, the cornicles are reduced or absent, the sexual forms lack mouthparts, and the fertile female produces only one egg.

Nearly all members of this group of aphids alternate between host plants, with the primary host (on which the overwintering eggs are laid) usually being a tree or shrub, and the secondary host an herbaceous plant. These aphids may feed either on the roots of the host plant or on the part of the plant above ground.

Damage resulting from their feeding is characterized by prematurely opened leaf buds, distorted leaf edges curled or rolled in a gall-like manner, "clustered" leaves, or enlarged or knotty growth on twigs and branches.

MANAGING APHIDS — Beneficial insects play an extremely important role in natural aphid control. Frequent inspections will acquaint the observer with the presence of beneficial insects, their relative population level, efficiency in reducing aphid numbers, and degree of parasitization. Insecticide applications for aphid control destroy beneficial insects as well as pests, leaving trees or shrubs unprotected if aphid resurgence occurs. Where practical, try washing aphids off with a forcible stream of water, rather than using insecticidal sprays. (Apply water or insecticides during early morning or late afternoon to avoid sunscald of foliage or other tender plant parts.) When aphid populations are large and causing damage as previously noted, insecticides may be needed.

Spider Mites

Several species of mites attack trees and shrubs and cause the plants to become an off-green color as a result of these sap-sucking pests. Severely-infested plants lose their vigor, become unsightly, and may even be killed. Mites are close relatives of insects, but mites differ in that they only have two body regions, no antennae, and the adults have eight legs.

TWO-SPOTTED SPIDER MITES — This mite is perhaps the best known mite species and is often called the common red spider mite. It feeds on the lower surface of leaves on deciduous trees and shrubs. The mites suck sap from the foliage. Infested leaves become stippled with gray and may be covered with strands of silken webs.

Two-spotted spider mites overwinter as adults in protected places (soil, debris, etc.). The overwintering mites are bright orange, whereas the summer forms are usually cream to green color with two dark sots on their backs. Females deposit eggs on the lower surface of the leaves. The length of the spider mite life cycle varies greatly, but in warm weather it may require only two weeks from egg to adult. This is why a mite population may build up rapidly.

Checking for Mites. If plant foliage begins to become an off-green color and mites are suspected, one way to determine if mites are present is to make a foliage check. This is done by holding a piece of white paper under a branch suspected to have mites and striking the branch hard against the paper. The mites are only about 1/50 of an inch in diameter. That's why they may not be seen on the plant foliage. If 10 mites or more are seen at each site, management procedures need to be considered.

Management. In general, cool, humid, and rainy weather will hold mite development and numbers down to non-damaging levels so that no control measures are needed. Hot, dry weather is ideal for development. Certain mite predators feed on the destructive mites and, when abundant, they keep the population in check.

If natural controls fail to reduce mite populations below damaging levels, miticide (acaricide) sprays will likely be needed. One should consider rotation of products (pesticide classes) to reduce the chance of pesticide resistance developing in the mite population.

Lace Bugs

Lace bugs are small, broad, flat insects with clear, lacelike wings. Eggs, nymphs, and adults all may be on a plant at the same time. Both adults and nymphs suck sap and cause leaves to be off-colored, speckled, and yellowed and to drop. Many small, black, varnish-like spots of excrement on the underside of leaves are evidence of lace bug infestation. Lace bugs are common on pyracantha, hawthorn, quince, sycamore, oak and American elm.

Plant Galls

Plant galls, abnormal tumor-like plant growths, are quite abundant in both rural and urban areas. They attract attention because of their unusual shape and colors, and because many homeowners prefer damage-free ornamentals in their yards.

Large numbers of galls can appear one year and few the next, or galls may be abundant year after year on the same plant. The abundance of galls is related to the abundance of the insect or mite causing the gall. Unfortunately, there is not enough knowledge about most gall-forming organisms to predict their abundance.

How Galls Are Formed. The young of insects or mites initiate the formation of most galls through their feeding activity. Certain chemicals produced by these young cause the living plant cells to increase rapidly in size or numbers. The exact mechanism for gall formation is not fully understood, but it is most remarkable that galls produced on specific plants by a given insect or mite are similar in shape and size year after year.

Species of aphids, midges, wasps, and psyllids are the main insects which form galls. Eriophyid mites are also prominent gall formers. In addition, some galls are produced on plants by nematodes, fungi, bacteria, and viruses. With most insect-caused galls, you should be able to see the insect(s) inside galls that are cut open.

Leaf galls can appear as curling of leaf margins, shriveling of the leaf, or wartlike growths on leaf blades or petioles. These wartlike growths may be smooth, spiny, or velvety.

Bud galls deform buds in various ways. Flower structures may be altered to look like spines, leaves, or shapeless masses. Such growths can be numerous enough to destroy the aesthetic value of a tree.

How injurious are galls? Galls are rarely abundant enough to seriously affect the normal growth of most plants. However, bud galls on conifers can lead to deformed growth of the tree, and, occasionally, twig galls can kill affected twigs.

In young trees, large numbers of galls can reduce growth. Control of the causal organism may then be necessary. On mature trees, however, leaf gall control is rarely justified.

Management. For plants such as roses, galls can be pruned out when they are discovered. Gall material should be removed from the premises so that reinfestation is less likely to occur. The same is also true for leaf galls. Removing the leaves in the fall also can help reduce the numbers of gall-forming organisms. However, by the time many galls are seen, the insect or mite has left the gall and will not be back until next year.

Some simple procedures are necessary when considering using pesticide controls (including oils). The insect or mite causing the gall must be vulnerable. Once the gall is formed, insecticides will not control the pest. Insects or mites which affect new plant growth require treatment just before bud development begins. Late applications have minimal value, although they may slow the development of additional galls. Some reduction in gall formations can normally be achieved if treatments are applied in the spring (e.g., at bud swell, a second application when leaves are one-fourth grown, and a third treatment when leaves are one-half to three-quarters grown).

Shoot, Twig, Trunk, and Root Feeders — Chewing Injury

Many kinds of insects attack ornamental plants and shade trees, but the wood borers are among the most injurious. Damage by these insects is often overlooked during summer months because the immature borers (larvae) feed in tunnels constructed in twigs, shoots, branches, or trunks. Generally, plants lacking vigor are more susceptible to borer attack than are vigorous, healthy trees and shrubs. Note: Pheromone traps (male attractants) are available for monitoring the activity of some borer species. You may wish to consider integrating trapping into your IPM programs as a predictive "tool" to assist with proper timing of control efforts.

Borers can be classified in several ways; however, it is more convenient to list them by family groups, rather than by parts of the host plant attacked or by emergence periods. There are two groups of boring insects: beetles and moths.

Wood Borers—Beetles

The true beetles that attack woody tissues can be extremely injurious. Members are easily recognized because the adult insect body is hard and the wing covers meet in a straight line down the middle of the back. Two families of wood borers will be discussed: flatheaded wood borers and roundheaded wood borers.

FLATHEADED WOOD BORERS— Adults of the flatheaded wood borers generally are brightly metallic colored, boat-shaped, and one-third to one inch long. Adults are commonly called metallic wood-boring beetles because of their color. These borers are destructive to newly transplanted trees.

The larvae or grubs are one-half to two inches long, yellowish white, legless, and have a pronounced flattened enlargement just behind the head. This enlargement bears a hard plate on both the upper and lower sides.

Adult beetles emerge from host trees in the early spring and summer months, and lay eggs near cracks and wounds in the tree bark. The larvae hatch from the eggs and bore first beneath the bark, and then enter the sapwood. Their tunnels are packed with borings arranged in concentric layers, so that arc-like bands appear when the galleries are exposed. Most species complete their life cycle in one year, while others may require two to three years. The flatheaded appletree borer is a common flatheaded wood borer.

FLATHEADED APPLETREE BORER — This flatheaded wood borer attacks newly-transplanted trees. Hard and soft maple, apple, sycamore, oak, hickory, pecan, linden, poplar, and willow are preferred hosts, but several other species may be attacked. Newly-planted trees, those that have been pruned to expose the trunk to sun, and weakened trees are the most susceptible to borer infestations. A single larva may girdle a small tree. Larvae are about one inch long at maturity. They overwinter as mature larvae, and adults emerge in May, June and July. Eggs are deposited in crevices of the bark during June and July. Hatching extends over several months so that all stages of larval development may be observed on a single tree. There is one generation per year. An effective method of protection is to wrap the trunks of newly-planted or pruned trees with a good grade of wrapping paper or newspaper. Apply the paper to give continuous coverage from the ground to the first branches.

Insecticides can be applied on the trunks in May, June and July to kill newly-hatched larvae.

ROUNDHEADED WOOD BORERS—Adult beetles are cylindrical, hard-shelled, and sometimes colored in contrasting bands, spots, or stripes. Adult beetles are commonly referred to as longhorned beetles because their antennae are usually at least half as long as the body. In some species, it is nearly one-and-a-half times as long. The larval stages of the beetle have no legs, are white to yellowish in color, and are fleshy and rather round-bodied.

Adult beetles emerge from infested trees from late spring to early fall. Mated females then seek egg laying sites, often under bark scales, in crevices, or in tree wounds. Some of the longhorned beetles cut elliptical niches in the inner bark to lay eggs. After hatching, the larvae of some species may feed beneath the bark prior to entering the wood. Other species remain under the bark. Life cycles of the different species vary from one to four years. An example is the cottonwood borer.

COTTONWOOD BORER — This longhorned wood borer will attack cottonwood and other poplars. The adult is large, about one-and-a-half inches long, with a black and white patch and cross stripe design. Eggs are laid in the tree trunk at the soil surface in July to August. Larvae live for two years in the trees. They bore both beneath the bark and into the wood and exude considerable frass. Larvae may completely girdle the bases of trees, cutting off sap movement and killing the trees. Lombardy poplar may be damaged so severely that they break off near the soil surface. Barriers constructed of wrapping paper or burlap and placed around the bases of young trees will help prevent oviposition. Such barriers are needed for several years. All factors that promote good growing conditions will help in reducing losses from borers. Borers can often be cut out of their tunnels with a pocketknife if done in early September of the first season of attack.

Insecticidal control is based on preventing attacks. Spray the lower trunk and saturate the soil around the tree base with insecticides in July and/or early August.

Shoot Borers

Insects in this category feed on the surface or inside of shoots, causing shoot malformations and death. Moths and beetles cause most of the damage. The pine tip moth is the most serious borer.

PINE TIP MOTHS — The Nantucket is the primary damaging species in Oklahoma. Pine tip moths destroy new growth of pines. The damage often deforms small, young trees up to 15 feet tall, slowing their growth and detracting from their normal symmetrical form. In some cases repeated attacks can cause trees to die. Most species of two- and three-needle pines are subject to attack, except slash, Austrian, and long leaf pines, which generally suffer no significant damage. Young pines growing in full sunlight have a tendency to be most heavily infested.

Life History. The moth overwinters as a pupa in terminal buds or just under the bark near the tips of other infested shoots. Emergence of first generation adults begins early in March and is completed by late April. Larvae that develop from the overwintering generation usually enter pine shoots during April.

The adult is a small, gray moth with patches of reddish brown or copper on the forewings and buff hind wings. Wingspread is about one inch. It remains concealed among needle fascicles, where it is well camouflaged by similar coloration. It is a weak flier, flying only short distances from tree to tree during evening hours. In daylight it flies only when disturbed.

Mating takes place soon after emergence, and the female begins to lay eggs during the evening the second day after emergence. Some eggs are laid on the buds and twigs, but most are laid on needles. An adult moth lives about eight days; each female lays about 25 eggs.

The egg is small, yellow, and usually found on the upper surface of the needle about one inch above the base. Emergence from the egg begins in seven to eight days. An emerged larva is cream colored, but gradually turns light brown or orange. The head is dark brown to black.

Immediately upon emerging, the small first-instar caterpillar burrows into the needle. It continues to mine toward the base of the needle, where it tunnels to the outside and spins a web around itself and the needle fascicle. The larvae then continues to chew its way toward the terminal of the shoot, sometimes feeding only on the fascicles of needles, but at other times on materials just under the bark of the twig. Larvae per infested shoot vary from one to 10. In most years, there are four generations.

Survey Methods. In certain cases, sprays are the most practical means of controlling the pine tip moth. Since sprays are most effective when properly time, you need to know when adults are active. The simplest method is the use of pheromone traps. Note: Sex pheromones are chemical substances that adult insects secrete to lure members of the opposite sex. The pheromone traps contain an artificial sex attractant that lures male moths inside the trap. The traps are placed among or near the pine trees and checked every day or two for moths that stick to an adhesive material inside the trap. Peak emergence can occur from three to six weeks after the first moth is collected in early spring.

If populations are very large, one trap for every two acres is sufficient. More traps are suggested when smaller numbers of moths are encountered. Depending on temperature, most pheromones (lures) will remain effective for four to six weeks. Traps are not control methods for pine tip moths. It would take several hundred traps per acre to provide any chance of reducing the moth population, and this would not be economically feasible.

Pheromone traps should be in place by March 1. Moths of the overwintering generation begin emerging sometime during March in most locations during most years. However, moths can sometimes emerge in late February.

Management. The most effective method of management in most situations is provided by systemic insecticides. Research has shown labeled granules applied per label directions to the soil around each tree in November are very effective. This application usually provides good protection from the first generation larvae.

The best chance of protection by use of sprays is with a treatment program from late March through the end of June. Following this, monthly treatments in late July and late August should provide protection from later generations.

Sprays are effective only against adults and newly-hatched larvae; therefore, control can be improved by treating at the proper time.

Sprays should be timed in accordance with peak emergence of adult moths so maximum control of young larvae is achieved before they penetrate tree shoots. Generally, sprays should be applied 10 days after an emergence peak has been identified. However, grower experience suggests that this 10-day lag should be reduced in later generations as temperature decreases the time needed for egg hatch – 4 to 5 days after peak emergence in June and 2 to 3 days in August. Retreatment may be necessary if heavy rainfall occurs within a week of timed treatment.

Bark Beetles

Bark beetles are so named because most of them live and mine between the bark and wood of trees and shrubs. (These cause the scars or sculptured runs or tunnels one sees if the bark is peeled off.)

Adult beetles lay their eggs in tunnels which they make between the bark and wood After the eggs hatch, the larvae mine the area, making runs that radiate out from the egg tunnels. Larval tunnels are always packed with their feces.

Extensive tunneling of this kind can girdle stems, branches, or the trunk, and thus kill parts of or the entire tree or shrub. When adults bore out through the bark, they leave the surface as though riddled by buckshot (thus sometimes referred to as "shotholes"). Adults are small cylindrical beetles, reddish to dark brown or black, from one-sixteenth to one-fourth inch long. The larvae are grub-like, thick-bodied, legless, generally broadly C-shaped, white or cream colored, and have a distinct head. Adult egg laying habits and life cycles vary extensively with the different species.

One of the most destructive bark beetles is the smaller European elm bark beetle which transmits Dutch elm disease to American elms.

SMALLER EUROPEAN ELM BARK BEETLES — Smaller European Elm Bark Beetles (SEEBB) first entered the United States in 1909. Since that time, they have become widespread and is now the most important carriers of Dutch elm disease.

This beetle is about one-eighth inch long. A concave area is at the rear of the abdomen, and a noticeable projection points toward the rear. The female lays her eggs in niches in the side of simple, unforked egg tunnels under the bark of dead or recently-cut elm wood. The egg tunnels run with the grain of the wood. After the eggs hatch, the larvae bore small tunnels around the trunk or branch and away from the centrally located egg tunnel (thus the larvae feed across the grain).

Adult beetles emerge in late April or May, fly to healthy trees, and feed in crotches of the twigs. It is during this time—if they emerged from the bark of diseased trees or wood—that they can introduce the fungus spores from their bodies into healthy trees.

Beetles emerge from under bark of dead or dying elms in the spring and move to and feed on tender bark in twig crotches. Feeding injuries are most numerous in twig crotches near the outside crown of the tree. The beetles that emerge from late April to the first of July (overwintering and first-generation adults) are the ones most likely to vector the disease to healthy elm trees. At this time, the long vessels of the elm's spring wood are open and functioning. Feeding beetles will cut into these vessels, and they can introduce Dutch elm disease spores. The vessels that are produced later in the year are shorter and the movement of materials throughout the tree will be slower. Dutch elm disease transmission is most likely if beetles feed in one-year-old or older twig crotches in spring or early summer.

After feeding, the adults tunnel into the inner bark of weakened, dying, or recently dead elm trees. They lay their eggs in galleries which are parallel with the grain of the wood. The larvae hatch and feed in the layer under the bark of the tree. The life cycle may be completed in 35 to 40 days. The spring-flying adults produce a generation that emerges in June. These first-generation adults also feed in twig crotches and can transmit Dutch elm disease. They then produce a second generation of larvae. Many of these larvae enter a developmental diapause and overwinter, but some continue to develop and begin to emerge in August. These adults produce a partial third generation. Second- and third-generation adults also feed in twig crotches, but they usually do not transmit Dutch elm disease since the trees are not as susceptible at this time. Due to overlapping of generations, adults may be present almost continuously from April to October. Thus, this insect has three full generations per year and sometimes a partial fourth.]

Control of SEEBBs with respect to their potential spread of Dutch elm disease should be timed such that treatments coincide with the spring emergence of adults (usually May).

Shoot, Twig, Trunk and Root Feeders — Sucking Injury
Scales

Scale insects derive their name from the scale, a shell-like or waxy covering on their bodies. Generally, scale insects can be divided into two categories—soft scales and armored scales. Soft scales can be bare (or without shell) or covered, but they are commonly covered in a soft, cottony or powdery substance. Armored scales have a protective covering of wax under which they feed. Depending on the species involved, scale insects feed on plant stems, twigs, foliage, or fruit.

Damage. Scale insects feed by sucking sap from trees and shrubs and are capable of killing the entire plant or parts of the plant. Scale insect feeding can also reduce the plant's vigor, making it more susceptible to injury caused by drought, severe winters, attack by other insects (particularly borers), or infection by diseases.

Life Cycle. The scale insects most commonly found in Oklahoma overwinter either as eggs or immatures. In most species, the female deposits its eggs under her shell or scale. When the eggs hatch, "crawlers" (or nymphal scales) move away from the maternal scale to locate new feeding sites. When the crawlers settle and begin to feed, the characteristic soft or armored scale covering is developed. Good scale control is generally best accomplished if treatments are applied immediately after eggs hatch (when crawlers are active).

Monitoring Suggestions. When scale insects increase to levels that create a nuisance (unsightly, honeydew, etc.) or are causing extensive damage to a tree, insecticide control of the infestation can best be achieved at two different times of the year. Horticultural oils may be applied in the dormant season (per label instructions) to smother overwintering scales and/or eggs, or an insecticide may be applied when the crawlers are active.

Monitoring scales in the dormant season is easy, since the insects are half-grown or larger and their "coverings" quite visible. In contrast, monitoring crawlers can be tedious because of their small size and because our interest is in their numbers in relation to the entire crawler-emerge profile for the specific scale species (so we can time application with a reasonable certainty that virtually all are hatched and would be exposed to the insecticide).

Monitoring crawlers can be accomplished by visual observation with the aid of a hand lens; however, monitoring for the mobile immature can be facilitated by the use of two-sided sticky tape. Wrap strips of it tightly around scale-infested twigs or branches. Crawlers seeking a place to settle down will be stuck fast as they attempt to cross the sticky surface. Note: Try to select smooth bark as a place for bands. It is suggested that one collect the bands at least weekly and count the numbers of crawlers per band under magnification. New bands should be put back in the same place after each collection. (It helps to place a tag or indicator near such band for ease in finding it.)

The best control of the scales will normally result when treatment is made at or slightly after the peak of crawler emergence. Differences in peak crawler emergence can always be expected between years and locations because of varying environmental conditions.

If one uses some type of monitoring for crawler activity, a great deal of the "guesswork" of timing scale crawler applications will be eliminated.

EUONYMUS SCALE — The euonymus scale is an armored scale that can infest most species of euonymus. It can attack both the leaves and stems. Often, stems or leaves will become heavily encrusted with the male scales, which are small, slender, and chalky white in color. Heavy infestations make the plant appear white. The female euonymus scales are pear-shaped, brown, and about twice the size of males.

Life History. Scales overwinter as fully grown, fertilized females. Eggs are deposited in early spring beneath the dark-colored female scale covering. The eggs can hatch over a two month period from mid-April to mid-June. Nymphs, or crawlers, move to other parts of the host plant or are blown to susceptible hosts by wind. During the summer, all life stages of the scale can be found, and, in most years, there are four or five overlapping broods. Control of the first/overwintering generation crawlers can be achieved if you will check for their activity in early to mid-May before treatment.

BROWN ELM SCALE — The brown elm scale is one of the most common soft-scale insects infesting elms. Brown elm scale is a soft scale that is also known as the European fruit lecanium because of its origin and the fact that it infests fruit trees in some parts of the country. Brown elm scale has been found in Oklahoma on ash, mulberry, plum, pecan, maple, and occasionally on other trees, but it is chiefly a pest of elm. On elm, injury is usually noticed in April and May, when the female scales are conspicuous and the trees are visibly injured by the insects. Heavy infestations kill smaller branches, stunt tree growth, and weaken the tree until it is susceptible to attacks of borers and diseases. Heavy infestations result in large quantities of honeydew (a gummy, sticky secretion that is produced by aphids) which often coats leaves or falls on sidewalks, buildings, or cars parked under trees.

Life History. The mature female is brown with a smooth hemispherical-shaped covering that is one-eighth to one-fourth inch in diameter. During growth, the body is soft and plastic, but at death becomes a hard, brown shell fastened loosely to the bark that may serve as a covering for several hundred white eggs. Eggs are laid in late April and early May and hatch into tiny licelike creatures from early to mid-May. The nymphs (crawlers) come out from beneath the scale covering and migrate to the leaves and small limbs. Large numbers attach themselves on the lower leaf surfaces and to small limbs. As they grow during the summer, their bodies become opaque, and they attach along the veins of leaves as well as twigs and limbs.

Before the leaves fall in autumn, brown elm scales migrate to the bark of smaller branches, where they remain all winter. At this stage they are brown, oval-shaped, and about 1mm in length. With the beginning of sap flow in the spring, the scales start to feed. The adult male is small, brown, and gnatlike (1¼mm long). It is incapable of feeding and lives only a short time.

Material for this chapter was provided by the Oklahoma Cooperative Extension Service and by DowElanco.

The dates given in this chapter are average dates. Insect activity in your area may vary greatly. Check with your local cooperative extension service for local occurrence dates.

For current control measures, please refer to the annual April issue of *Landscape Management.* ❦

CHAPTER 16

Lake and Pond Management

Nearly every golf course, many parks, as well as other landscaped areas have lakes or ponds. A water feature is a big aesthetic plus for any landscape. The landscape manager is concerned about maintaining high water quality. This is especially difficult when dealing with impounded or slow-moving bodies of water.

Methods used to improve and maintain water quality are basically:
- chemical weed control
- dyes
- mechanical weed harvest
- plant-eating fish
- mechanical aeration

Which method is chosen is dependent on the size and depth of the pond or lake, the type of problem and the budget.

Mechanical Aeration

There are three types of aeration devices: fountains; bubblers that create water movement on the surface as the bubbles rise; and circulators which make water currents. The choice of aerator will depend on lake size, depth, use of the water and the budget.

Circulators typically have a shaft that goes straight down in the water. A turbine fan at the lower end lifts the water from the bottom of the lake or pond through a flexible hose. The water from the bottom of the pond is released horizontally and spreads across the surface giving a wide area of mixing action. One large unit can cover up to 40 acres.

Water in impounded or slow-moving lakes or ponds may tend to become stratified. Heavier cold water stays at the bottom. A circulation-type aerator can help break up the stratification and bring the cooler water to the surface. This mixing action improves the water's condition by cooling the surface and by enhancing the decomposition of materials that had been trapped under the surface. As a result of the mixing action, algae which is dependent on the warm surface water and sunlight is moved to a less ideal environment. In the winter the circulator brings warm water to the surface, helping prevent ice formation.

Fountains do not have the same type of action as circulators. Fountains generally move water in a vertical column. They pick up surface water and throw it into the air. This provides very little mixing of any present stratification, but they do add oxygen to the upper level water.

Fountains and circulators are powered by electric motors. They are held in position by anchoring or mooring and must have waterproof electrical lines to the shore.

Bubblers inject air in a powerful stream of water. These units may be positioned to operate in any part of the pond or lake. These systems can offer the benefit of bringing oxygen-poor water up from the bottom to the surface to mix with oxygen-rich water. This aids in decomposition. The pump can be on land so there aren't any electrical lines in the water.

Aeration, by any means, can provide a quick cure for poor lake water. Changes can only take place with extended use. They should be considered for use in a preventative program. These units cannot do it all; in some cases chemical weed control may be necessary.

Although plants grow naturally in ponds and small lakes and are essential for a healthy aquatic environment, they sometimes grow too thick, clog irrigation equipment and mar the pond's beauty. At that point, control is necessary.

Turf managers should consider four main types of aquatic plants: algae, floating weeds, submersed weeds and emersed weeds. Each has distinct growth characteristics resulting in varying control techniques.

The first step is to identify the problem.

Control measures include raking, grass carp, dyes, fertilization, water level drawdowns and herbicides, and pond renovation. Raking is feasible only in small ponds and where the algae grows so rapidly that carp may not be able to keep up with it.

Chemical Weed Control

The charts list recommended aquatic herbicides, target weeds, restrictions and activity expected. Consult state regulations and label restrictions before selecting any aquatic herbicide.

Herbicides may be applied as a surface acre, bottom acre-foot or total water volume treatment. Water volume treatments are expressed in a parts per million by weight (ppmw) or in product per acre basis. Although water volume can be measured in gallons, cubic feet or other increments, the most common unit used is an acre-foot. An acre-foot of water is "one surface acre of water that is one foot deep." The number of acre-feet in a pond can be determined by multiplying the number of surface acres times the average water depth. (A pond with six surface acres and an average water depth of four feet would be six surface acres x four feet average water depth = 24 acre-feet).

The following formulas can be used to determine the amount of a herbicide formulation required to treat a pond on a ppmw basis, amount of product per acre foot basis, or the amount of product per surface acre.

1. Concentration based on part per million by weight (ppmw).
   Amount of formulation = $\dfrac{A \times B \times CF \times ECC}{I}$

   A   = area of the water surface in acres.

   B   = average depth of the pond or lake in feet.

   CF = 2.72 lbs./acre foot. The Conversion Factor (CF) when total water volume is expressed on an acre-feet basis. 2.72 lbs. of a herbicide per acre-foot of water is equal to one ppmw.

   ECC = Effective Chemical Concentration of the active ingredient of a herbicide needed in the water to achieve control of the weed.

   I   = The total amount of active ingredient divided by the total amount of active and inert ingredients. Liquid products usually list the amount of active ingredient as pounds per gallon. For such products:

   I   = $\dfrac{\text{pounds of active ingredient}}{\text{one (1) gallon}}$

Non-liquid formulations usually list active ingredients as a percentage of the total formulatlon. For non-liquid formulations:

I = $\dfrac{\text{percent active ingredient}}{100\%}$

2. Amount of herbicide formulation per acre foot.
   Amount of formulation = A x D x R
   A = area of the water surface in acres
   D = average depth of the pond or lake in feet.
   R = recommended rate of product per acre foot.

3. Amount of herbicide formulation per surface acre. Amount of formulation = A x R
   A = area of the water surface in acres.
   R = recommended rate of product per surface acre.

Examples of Aquatic Herbicide Dosage Calculations

Example 1. How much Rodeo (5.4 lbs./gal) is needed to treat a 6-acre pond at a rate of 6 pints per acre?

Amount of formulation = A x R
6 surface acs. x 6 pints per surface ac. = 36 pints
= 4.5 gallons

Example 2. How much Aquathol K (4.2 lbs./ gal.) is needed to treat a pond with 6 surface acres, an average depth of 4 feet, at a rate of 1.9 gallons of product per acre foot?

Amount of formulation = A x D x R
Amount of formulation = 6 surface acres x 4 ft. depth x 1.9 gallons of product per acre foot
= 45.6 gallons of Aquathol K

Example 3. How much copper sulfate (99% copper sulfate) is needed to treat a pond with 6 surface acres, an average depth of 4 feet, at a rate of 1.0 ppm active ingredient?

Amount of formulation = $\dfrac{\text{A x D x CF x ECC}}{\text{I}}$

Amount of formulation = 6 surface acres x 4 ft. depth x 2.72 x 99%/100%
= 66 lbs. of copper sulfate

Example 4. How much Cutrine-Plus (copper complex with 0.909 lbs. of copper per gallon) is needed to treat a 6-acre pond, an average depth of 4 feet, at a rate of 0.2 ppm of active ingredient?

Amount of formulation = $\dfrac{\text{A x D x CF x ECC}}{\text{I}}$

$$\text{Amount of formulation} = \frac{6 \text{ acres} \times 4 \text{ ft.} \times 2.72 \times 0.2 \text{ ppm}}{0.909 \text{ lbs.}/1 \text{ gal.}}$$

$$= 14.4 \text{ gallons of Cutrine-Plus}$$

Lakes that suffer from problem algae and submerged aquatic weed may be helped by dyes that block sunlight. However, a major source o oxygen will be cut off in the process, possibly leading to a breakdown ii the essential part of the ecological system that keeps the water in to condition.

Depending on what is being irrigated with the lake's water, and wha is legally allowable in an irrigation water source in a specific state, th use of dyes or algaecides and aquatic herbicides may not be permitted o advisable in specific situations.

In certain states, plant-eating fish can be stocked to control aquati vegetation.

Sterile white amur (grass carp) can be carefully introduced in limitec numbers, depending upon the amount of excess vegetation and habita requirements of other fish.

Tilapia is a fish recognized for its consumption of algae. Howevei they are not sterile, can overpopulate, and cannot survive water temper atures below 50 degrees F.

Mechanical methods of aquatic weed control including dredging, har vesting and aeration.

Dredging removes bottom-rooted plants and built-up sediment. A lake' depth can be increased to prevent sunlight from reaching the bottom.

Harvesting is simply cutting and removing bottom-rooted plants Removal is essential to relieve a lake from an oxygen drain durin; decomposition. It does not prevent regrowth, and is generally followec by or used in combination with chemical treatment.

Some problems can be avoided with proper pond construction.

Ponds should be at least 3–5 feet deep and have relatively steep banks tc discourage establishment of bottom-rooted weeds. Impoundment shape and location can influence natural wave action. ❦

Dr. Tim Murphy, University of Georgia Weed Specialist, contributed to this section.

Note: The following aquatic weed control recommendations are provided as an example. All products labeled for use may not be included. Always follow label directions when using pesticides.

Aquatic Weed Control
Tim R. Murphy, Extension Agronomist-Weed Science

Use Stage/ Herbicide	Broadcast Rate/Acre		Remarks and Precautions
	Amount of Formulation	Pounds Active Ingredient	
Algae			Apply at early stages in algae development (usually April or May), repeat as needed. Read and observe all label cautions and instructions. Copper algaecides may be toxic to fish at high rates. Use the low rate in acid waters and the high rate in alkaline waters. The rates suggested should not be toxic except through oxygen depletion. Under heavy infestations, treat only 1/4 to 1/3 of the water body at any one time to avoid fish suffocation caused by oxygen depletion. Copper-containing products may be used for spot treatments of algae. Copper sulfate, copper complexes and diquat may also be used in commercial fish production ponds.
copper sulfate			
(Triangle copper-sulfate)	2.7-5.4 lbs.*	1.0-2.0 ppm*	
99% Granule	2.7-5.4 lbs.*	1.0-2.0 ppm*	
99% Snow	2.7-5.4 lbs.*	1 0-2.0 ppm*	
99% Crystal, Others	2.7-5.4 lbs.*	1.0-2.0 ppm*	
copper complex			
(Cutrine-Plus)			
0.9 lbs./gal.	0.6-1.2 gal.*	0.2-0.4 ppm*	
(Cutrine-Plus G)			
3.7% Granule	60.0 lbs.*	—	
(K-Tea)			
0.8 lbs./gal.	0.7-1.4 gal.*	0.2-0.4 ppm*	
diquat			Diquat is effective for filamentous algae control. Apply diquat as recommended in Submersed Weeds section. Use 1.0 gal. Reward per surface acre in water with an average depth of 2.0 feet. The higher rate may be used in water with an average depth greater than 2.0 feet.
(Reward)			
2 lbs./gal.	1.0-2.0 gal.*	2.0-4.0 lbs.*	
(Weed-Trine D)			
0.4 lbs./gal.	3.4-10.2 gal.*	0.5-1.5 ppm*	
dichlobenil			Apply uniformly per surface-acre in early spring either to exposed bottom or through the water. Use the low rate in water less than 2 feet deep. Use 70-100 lbs./A as a drawdown treatment. Refill pond immediately after treatment. Effective on chara. Dichlobenil may be used as a spot treatment. Not labeled for commercial fish production ponds.
(Casoron) 10G	100-150 lbs.	10.0-15.0 lbs.	
(Norosac) 10G	100-150 lbs.	10.0-15.0 lbs.	
Aquashade	1.0 gal./4 acre ft.	1.0 ppm	Aquashade is a non-toxic blue dye that controls filamentous algae by blocking light penetration for up to six weeks after application. May be used in lakes, ponds, ornamental ponds and fountains, and commercial fish production ponds that have little or no outflow. Apply one gallon of Aquashade per one acre of water that averages 4.0 feet deep in the early spring before weed growth begins, or apply when weeds may be seen on bottom of pond. Additional applications will be necessary through the year to maintain an acceptable level of dye in the water. May be used at any time of year, but is less effective when weed growth is near the surface. Do not apply to water that will be used for human consumption. Water may be used for swimming after complete dispersal of the dye in water. Aquashade is non-toxic to livestock.
Floating Weeds			Spray to wet exposed plants with 50-150 gallons of water per acre plus 1.0 pt. of nonionic surfactant per 100 gal. of spray mix. Do not apply to muddy water. Labeled also for commercial fish production ponds.
diquat			
(Reward)			
2 lbs./gal.	1.0 gal.	2.0 lbs.	
(Weedtrine-D)			
0.4 lbs./gal.	5.0 gal.	2.0 lbs.	

*Indicates rate per acre-foot of water. All other formulation rates are based on amount per surface acre.

Use Stage/ Herbicide	Broadcast Rate/Acre		Remarks and Precautions
	Amount of Formulation	Pounds Active Ingredient	

Floating Weeds

Use Stage/ Herbicide	Amount of Formulation	Pounds Active Ingredient	Remarks and Precautions
fluridone (Sonar AS)	Rates Vary	Rates Vary	Apply Sonar AS as a surface application to duckweed at labeled rates. Apply only once per year when duckweed is present. Apply Sonar to bladderwort as suggested in the Emersed Weeds section. See remarks and precautions for Sonar as listed in the Emersed Weeds and Submersed Weeds sections.
2,4-D (Esteron 99 Concentrate) 3.8 lbs./gal.			Controls water hyacinth. Do not apply to open water. Apply only to dense stands. Treat 1/3 to 1/2 of the water body to avoid oxygen depletion problems. Weed Rhap A-4D and Weed Rhap LV-4D are also labeled for commercial fish production ponds.
(Weedar 64) 3.8 lbs./gal.	2.5-4.5 pts.	1.2-2.1 lbs.	
(Weed Rhap A-4D) 3.8 lbs./gal.	2.0-4.0 qts.	1.9-3.8 lbs.	
(Weed Rhap LV-4D) 3.8 lbs./gal.	2.5-4.5 pts.	1.2-2.1 lbs.	
	2.5-4.5 pts.	1.2-2.1 lbs.	

Emersed Weeds

Use Stage/ Herbicide	Amount of Formulation	Pounds Active Ingredient	Remarks and Precautions
2,4-D (Aqua-Kleen) 19G	100-200 lbs.	19-38 lbs.	Spray to wet foliage or spread granules uniformly in infested area in spring or early summer. Read the label for specific weeds controlled and special precautions. Do not apply to more than 1/2 the pond in any one month. Do not apply to waters used for irrigation, agricultural sprays, watering dairy animals, or domestic waters. This group of products is also labeled for commercial fish production ponds.
(Weedtrine II) 1 9G	100-150 lbs.	19-28 lbs.	
(Weed Rhap A-4D 3.8 lbs./gal.	2.5-4.5 pts.	1.2-2.1 lbs.	
(Weed Rhap LV-4D) 3.8 lbs./gal	2.5-4.5 pts.	1.2-2.1 lbs.	
(Weed Rhap LV-6D) 5.6 lbs./gal.	1.6-3.0 pts.	1.1-2.1 lbs.	
(Esteron 99 Concentrate) 3.8 lbs./gal.	2.5-4.5 pts.	1.2-2.1 lbs.	
glyphosate (Rodeo) 5.4 lbs./gal.	See label.		Apply after drawdown or when water is present. Allow 7 or more days after drawdown treatment before reintroduction of water (apply within one day after drawdown). Add 2 qts. of a manufacturer-approved surfactant per 100 gal. of spray solution. Rodeo may be used in commercial fish production ponds.
dichlobenil (Casoron) 10G	100.0-150.0 lbs.	10-15 lbs.	Controls waterlily, spatterdock and alligatorweed. For alligator weed apply 40 to 80 lbs./acre of Casoron 10G in the early spring and no later than the full-size leaf stage of growth.
fluridone (Sonar AS) (Sonar SRP)	Rates vary Rates vary	Rates vary Rates vary	Controls several emersed weeds. Apply Sonar AS as a surface spray, or near the bottom with weighted trailing hoses or meter into pumping system. Uniformly broadcast the SRP formulation. Trees or shrubs growing in water treated with Sonar may be injured. Thirty to 90 days are required before desired weed control is achieved. Use Sonar SRP (slow-release pellet) in irrigation or drainage canals with slow-moving water. Not recommended for spot treatment. Labeled also for commercial fish production ponds.

Use Stage/ Herbicide	Broadcast Rate/Acre		Remarks and Precautions
	Amount of Formulation	Pounds Active Ingredient	

Submersed Weeds

dichlobenil

Use Stage/ Herbicide	Amount of Formulation	Pounds Active Ingredient	Remarks and Precautions
(C) 1 OG	100-150 lbs.	10-15 lbs.	Apply as listed for dichlobenil in "Algae" section. Controls several submersed weeds. May be used as a spot treatment. Not labeled for commercial fish production ponds.
(N) 1 OG	100-150 lbs.	10-15 lbs.	
diquat			Apply in early season where submersed growth has not reached the surface by pouring directly from the container into the water while moving slowly over the water surface in a boat. Distribute in strips 40 feet apart In late season or where submersed weed growth has reached the surface; use the high rate indicated on the label for the weeds present. Also labeled for commercial fish production ponds. Do not apply to muddy water.
(Reward) 2 lbs./gal.	1.0-2.0 gals.	2.0-4.0 lbs.	
(Weedtrine-D) 0.4 lbs./gal.	5.0-10.0 gals.	2.0-4.0 lbs.	
2,4-D granular			See comments for granular formulations in "Emersed Weeds" section Effective on parrofeather, coontail and Eurasian water-milfoil. Also labeled for commercial fish production ponds.
(Aquakleen) 19G	100-200 lbs.	19-38 lbs.	
(Weedtrine II) 19G	100-150 lbs.	19-28 lbs.	
endothall			Aquathol and Aquathol K are contact killers and must be applied as early as possible after weeds are present. Water temperature should be a minimum of 65°F. Water containing heavy weed growth should be treated in sections 5-7 days apart. Apply on a calm day. Hydrothol formulations are toxic to fish and should be used only on sections by a commercial applicator at rates below 0.3 ppm unless fish kill is not objectionable. Hydrothol formulations are not recommended for commercial fish production ponds. Aquathol formulations are also labeled for commercial fish production ponds.
(Aquathol Granular) 10.1%	13.0-81.0 lbs.*	0.5-3.0 ppm*	
(Aquathol K) 4.2 lbs./gal.	0.3-1.9 gal.*	0.5-3.0 ppm*	
(Hydrothol Granular) 5G	3.0-27.0 lbs.*	*0.05-0.5 ppm*	
Hydrothol 191 2 lbs./gal.	0.6 pts.-0.7 gal.*	*0.05-0.5 ppm*	
Aquashade	1.0 gal./4 acre ft. 1.0 ppm		Aquashade is a non-toxic dye that controls several submersed weeds, such as naiads, by blocking light penetration for up to six weeks after application. May be used in lakes, ponds, ornamental ponds and fountains and commercial fish production ponds that have little or no outflow. Apply one gallon of Aquashade per one acre of water that averages 4.0 feet deep in the early spring before weed growth begins, or apply when weeds are seen on bottom of pond. Additional applications will be necessary through the year to maintain an acceptable level of dye in the water. May be used at any time of year, but is less effective when weed growth is near the surface. Do not apply to water that will be used for human consumption. Water may be used for swimming after complete dispersal of the dye in water. Aquashade is non-toxic to livestock.
fluridone			Apply fluridone to control coontail, common elodea, egeria, hydrilla, naiad, pondweeds, and watermilfoils. See directions in Emersed Weeds section. Trees or shrubs growing in water or having roots growing in water treated with Sonar may be injured. Thirty to 90 days will be required before desired weed control is achieved. Not recommended for spot treatment. Also labeled for commercial fish production ponds.
(Sonar AS)	Rates vary	Rates vary	
(Sonar SRP)	Rates vary	Rates vary	

*Indicates rate per acre-foot of water. All other formulation rates are based on amount per surface area.

Conversion Factors

Weight Measures

1 grain (gr.)
   64.7989 milligrams = 0.03657 grams= 0.0020833 ounces = 0.0648 gram
1 milligram (mg.)
   0.001 gram = 0.015432 grain
1 gram (g.)
   1,000 milligrams = 0.035274 ounces avoirdupois = 15.432356 grains = 0.56438 dram avoirdupois = 0.0022046 pound = 0.001 kilogram
1 ounce avoirdupois (oz. av.)
   0.911458 troy ounce = 28.349527 grams = 437.5 grains = 16 drams = 0.0625 pound
1 kilogram (kg.)
   1,000 grams = 35.273957 ounce avoirdupois = 2.20462 avoirdupois pounds = 15,432.35639 grains = 0.00098421 ton (long, U.S.) = 0.00110231 ton (short, U.S)
1 ton (short, U.S.)
   2,000 avoirdupois pounds = 2,430.56 troy pounds = 0.892857 long ton = 0.907185 metric ton = 907.18486 kilograms = 32,000 ounces
1 ton metric
   2,204.6 pounds = 1.1023 short tons = 0.984 long ton = 1,000 kilograms

Square (or surface) measures

1 square millimeter (sq. mm.)
   0.01 sq. centimeter = 0.000001 sq. meter = 0.00155 sq. inch
1 square centimeter (sq. cm.)
   100 sq. millimeters = 0.155 sq. inch = 0.001076 sq. ft.
1 square inch (sq. in.)
   6.451626 sq. centimeters = 0.0069444 sq. foot
1 square foot (sq. ft.)
   144 sq. inches = 0.111111 sq. yard = 0.0929 sq. meter = 0.003673 sq. rod
1 square yard (sq. yd.)
   9 sq. ft. = 1,296 sq. inches = 0.83613 sq. meter = 0.03306 sq. rod
1 square meter (sq. m.)
   10.76387 sq. ft. = 1,550 sq. inches = 1.195985 sq. yards = 0.039537 sq. rod = 1 million sq. millimeters = 10,000 sq. centimeters
1 square rod (sq. r.)
   30.25 sq. yards = 25.29295 sq. meters = 272.25 sq. feet = 0.00625 sq. acre = 0.0025293 hectare = 625 sq. links
1 acre (A.)
   43,560 sq. feet = 4,840 sq. yards = 160 sq. rods = 4,046.873 sq. meters = 0.404687 hectare = 0.0015625 sq. mile = 10 sq. chains = 8 ft. wide strip and 1 mile long (approximate)
1 hectare (ha.)
   2.471 acres = 395.367 sq. rods = 10,000 sq. meters = 0.01 sq. kilometer

= 0.0033 sq. mile
1 square kilometer (sq. km.)
  0.3861 sq. mile = 247.1 acres = 100 hectares = 1 million sq. meters
1 square mile
  640 acres = 1 section = 258.9998 hectares = 102,400 sq. rods = 3,097,600 sq. yards = 2,589,998 sq. kilometers

Cubic measures
1 cubic centimeter (cc.)
  0.06102 cu. inch = 1,000 cu. milliliters = 0.000001 cu. meter
1 cubic inch (cu. in.)
  16.38716 cubic centimeters = 0.0005787 cu. foot = 0.004329 gallon (U.S.)
1 cubic foot (cu. ft.)
  0.80356 bushel = 1.728 cu. inches = 0.037037 cu. yard = 0.028317 cu. meter = 7.4805 U S gallons = 6.229 British or Imperial gallons = 28.316 liters = 29.922 quarts (liquid) = 25.714 quarts (dry)
1 cubic foot (cu. ft.) of water
  62.43 pounds (one pound of water = 27.68 cu inches = 0.1198 U.S.gallon = 0.01602 cu. foot)
1 cubic foot (cu. ft.) of dry soil (approximate)
  sandy (90 lbs), loamy (80 lbs), clayey (75 lbs)
1 bushel (bu.) dry soil (approximate)
  sandy (112 lbs.), loamy (100 lbs.), clayey (94 lbs.)
1 cubic yard (cu. yd.)
  27 cu. ft. = 46,656 cu. inches = 764.559 liters = 202 U.S. gallons = 168.17 British gallons = 1,616 pints (liquid) = 807.9 quarts (liquid) = 21.694 bushels = 0.764559 cubic meter
1 cubic meter (cu. m.)
  1.30794 cu yard = 35.3144 cu feet = 28.3776 bushels = 264.173 gallons = 1,000 cu. decimeters = 1.0567 quarts (liquid) = 2,113.4 pints (liquid) = 61,023 cu. inches = 1 million cubic centimeters

Volumes (dry)
1 quart (qt.) U.S.
  67.2 cu. inches = 2 pints = 1.1012 liters = 0.125 peck = 0.03125 bushels = 0.038889 cu. foot = 67.2 cu. inches
1 peck (pk.) U.S.
  0.25 bushel = 2 gallons = 8 quarts = 16 pints = 32 cups = 8.80958 liters = 537.605 cu inches
1 bushel (bu.) U.S.
  4 pecks = 32 quarts = 64 pints = 128 cups = 1 2445 cu feet = 35.2383 liters = 0.304785 barrel = 2,150.42 cu. inches = approximately 1120 cubic yard = 40 seed flats (16 x 23 x 3 inches)

Volumes (liquid)
1 milliliter (ml.)
  1 cubic centimeter (approximate) = 0.1 centiliter = 0.01 deciliter = 0.001 liter = 0.061 cu. inch = 0.0084538 gill = 0.03815 fluid ounce
1 fluid ounce (fl. oz.) U.S.
  2 tablespoons = 0.125 cup = 0.0625 pint = 0.03125 quart = 0.00781 gallon = 29.573 milliliters = 1.80469 cu. inches = 8 fluid drams = 0.25 gill = 0.029573 liter
1 tablespoon
  3 teaspoons
1 cup
  16 tablespoons = 8 fluid ounces = 0.5 pint = 2 gills = 236.6 cubic centimeters or milliliters

1 pint (pt.) U.S.
  16 fluid ounces = 32 tablespoons = 2 cups = 4 gills = 0.125 gallon = 473.167 milliliters = 1.04 pounds of water = 28.875 cu. inches = 0.473167 liter = 128 fluid drams = 0.0167 cu. foot
1 liter (1.)
  2.1134 pints = 1.0567 liquid quarts (U.S.) = 0.9081 dry quarts (U.S.) = 0.264178 gallon (U.S.) = 10 deciliters = 1,000 milliliters or cubic centimeters = 33.8147 fluid ounces = 270.5179 fluid drams = 61.025 cu. inches = 0.0353 cu foot = 0.028378 bushel = 0.001308 cu. yard
1 quart (qt.) U.S.
  2 pints = 4 cups = 8 gills = 32 fluid ounces = 57.749 cu. inches = 64 tablespoons 0.25 gallon = 0.946333 liter = 0.3342 cu. foot = 256 fluid drams
1 gallon (gal.) U.S.
  4 quarts = 8 pints = 16 cups = 128 fluid ounces = 0.1337 cubic foot = 0.83268 British or Imperial gallon= 3,785.4 milliliters or cubic centimeters = 231 cu. inches = 8.337 pounds water = 3.782 kilograms
1 barrel - U.S.
  31 5 gallons = 7,056 cu. inches = 1/2 hogshead = 0.11924 cu. meter

Linear (or distance measures)

1 millimeter (mm.)
  0.1 centimeter = 0.01 decimeter = 0.001 meter = 1,000 microns = 0.03937 inch (about 1/25 inch)
1 centimeter (cm.)
  10 millimeters = 0.01 meter = 0.3937 inch = 0.03281 foot = 0.010936 yard (U.S.)
1 decimeter (dm.)
  10 centimeters = 0.1 meter = 3.937 inches
1 inch (in.)
  25.4 millimeters = 2.54 centimeters = 0.0254 meter = 0.083333 foot = 0.027778 yard = 0.00505 rod
1 foot (ft.)
  12 inches = 0.3333 yard = 0.060606 rod = 30.48 centimeters = 0.3048 meter = 0.16667 fathom
1 yard (yd.)
  36 inches = 3 feet = 0.181818 rod = 0.9144 meter = 0.00454545 furlong
1 meter (m.)
  100 centimeters = 39.37 inches = 3.2808 feet = 1.09361 yards = 0.1988 rod = 0.001 kilometer = 0.5468 fathom
1 rod (r.)
  5.5 yards = 16.5 feet = 198 inches = 5.02921 meters = 0.003125 mile = 0.025 furlong = 25 links
1 kilometer (km.)
  1,000 meters = 3,280.8 feet = 1,093.6 yards = 0.62137 statute mile = 0.53961 nautical mile
1 mile (mi.) statute
  5,280 feet = 1,760 yards = 1,609 35 meters = 320 rods = 8 furlongs = 63,360 inches = 0.86836 nautical miles = 80 chains
1 mile (mi.) nautical
  1,1516 statute miles = 6,080.27 feet = 1.85325 kilometers

Dilutions

1 part per million (ppm)
  milligram per liter or kilogram = 0.0001 percent = 0.013 ounce by weight in 100 gallons = 0.379 grams in 100 gallons = 1 inch in nearly 16 miles = 2 crystals of sugar in a pound = 1 ounce of salt in 62,500 pounds of sugar = 1 minute of time in about 2 years = a 1 gram needle

in a 1 ton haystack = 1 ounce of sand in 31-1/4 tons of cement = 1 ounce of dye in 7,530 gallons of water = 1 pound in 500 tons = 1 penny of $10,000 = 0 007 grain per pound

1 percent (%)
    10,000 parts per million = 10 grams per liter = 1.28 ounces by weight per gallon = 8.336 pounds per 100 gallons

Miscellaneous Weights and Measures

1 micron
    0.00039 inch
1 acre-inch of water
    27,154 gallons
1 pound per cubic foot
    0.26 gram per cubic inch
1 inch of water on 1,000 square feet
    624 gallons
1 gram per cubic inch
    3.78 pounds per cubic foot
1 board foot (1ft. x 1 ft. x 1 in.)
    1112 cubic foot = 144 cubic inches = 2,359.8 cubic centimeters
1 cord (cd.) of wood
    128 cubic feet (a pile 8 ft x 4 ft x 4 ft) = 3.625 cu. meters

Approximate Rates of Application Equivalents (U.S. Measures)

1 ounce per square foot
    2,722.5 pounds per acre
1 ounce per square yard
    302.5 pounds per acre
1 ounce per 100 square feet
    27.2 pounds per acre
1 pound per 100 square feet
    435.6 pounds per acre
1 pound per 1000 square feet
    43.56 pounds per acre
1 pound per acre
    1 ounce per 2733 square feet (0.37 oz /1000 sq. ft.) = 4 5 grams per gallon = 0.0104 gram per square foot = 1.12 kilograms per hectare
100 pounds per acre
    2.5 pounds per 1000 square feet = 1.04 grams per sq. ft.
5 gallons per acre
    1 pint per 1000 sq. ft. = 0.43 ml per sq. foot
100 gallons per acre
    2.5 gallons per 1000 sq. ft. = 935 liters per hectare
1 quart per 100 gallons (approximate)
    10 ml per gallon
1 pound per gallon
    120 grams per liter
1 kilogram per hectare
    0.89 pound per acre

Dilutions

Dilution required (1 part per %)	Amount to add		Per Qt. of Water
	Per Gal. of Water		
1 part/1000	1/4 tsp.	1/8 oz.	1/16 tsp.
1 part/750	1/3 tsp.	3/16 oz.	3/64 tsp.
1 part/500	1/2 tsp.	1/4 oz.	1/8 tsp.
1 part/250	1 tsp.	1/2 oz.	1/4 tsp.
1 part/200	1-1/4 tsp.	5/8 oz.	1/3 tsp.
1 part/150	1-3/4 tsp.	7/8 oz.	1/2 tsp.
1 part/100(1%)	2-1/2 tsp.	1-1/4 oz.	2/3 tsp.
1 part/50 (2%)	5-1/8 tsp.	2-1/2 oz.	1-1/4 tsp.
1 part/33 (3.3%)	7-3/4 tsp.	3-7/8 oz.	2 tsp.
1 part/25 (4%)	10-1/4 tsp.	5-1/8 oz.	2-1/2 tsp.
1 part/20 (5%)	12-3/4 tsp.	6 oz.	3-1/4 tsp.
1 part/15 (7 1/2%)	17 tsp.	8-1/2 oz.	4-1/4 tsp.
1 part/10 (10%)	16-5/8 tsp.	12-3/4 oz.	6-13/32 tsp.
1 part/5 (20%)	51-1/4 tsp.	25-1/2 oz.	12-3/4 tsp.

Glossary of Landscape Terms

Acid Soil – Soil with a low pH below 7.0.

Aerification – A mechanical process used to cultivate the soil without destruction of the turf.

Alkaline Soil – Soil with a pH above 7.0.

Annual – A plant that completes its life cycle in one growing season.

Apron – The fairway area in front of and around a green.

Bark – The dead, corky, outer layer of woody plants.

Biennial – A plant that completes its life cycle in two years.

Bleeding – The flow of sap from a cut or injured surface of a plant.

Blend – Two or more varieties of the same species in a mixture of seed.

Broad-leaved Evergreen – An evergreen plant with broad leaves that are not needle-shaped.

Broad-leaved Weed – Leaves are wide, not grass- like.

Brushing – See Combing.

Budded – The propagation of a plant by inserting a dormant bud of one plant into the stem of another.

Bunch-Type Growth – A grass that spreads by tillers.

Calcined Clay – A stable clay particle used as a soil amendment.

Caliper – Refers to the diameter of a tree. In nursery-landscape practice, caliper is measured 6 inches above the ground level up to and including 4-inch diameter size and 12 inches above the ground level for larger sizes.

Candle – Refers to early spring growth of pine shoots before needle expansion.

Carbohydrate – Food material produced by photosynthesis.

Central Leader – The main stem of the tree from which other branches develop. In most cases, it is the trunk.

Certified Seed or Sod – Seed or sod that is certified by the Department of Agriculture of the state in which it is grown to be the variety stated on the label.

Clippings – Leaves cut off by mowing.

Collar – The area of the putting green adjoining the putting surface.

Colorant – A dye used to color brown or dormant turf.

Combing – A mechanical device used to lift horizontal stems (stolons) and leaves so they may be cut by the mower. Aids control of grain on putting green.

Compaction – The pressing together of soil particles into a more dense mass.

Contact Pesticide – a pesticide that works when it comes in contact with the target organism.

Cool-Season Turfgrass – Species of turfgrass used primarily in the northern part of the United States such as bluegrass, fescue, bentgrass and ryegrass.

Coring – A method of aerification in which soil cores are removed by hollowtines or spoons.

Crotch – The angle developed between two connecting branches.

Crown – Top of a tree including branches and foliage —part of grass plant near soil surface from which leaves originate.

Cultivar – (See "variety")

Cutting Height – The distance from a flat surface to the bed knife of a reel mower or to the blade of a rotary mower.

Deciduous – Plants that normally have leaves only during the growing season and lose their leaves during the dormant season.

Desiccation – The death of plants by drying out.

Dieback – The dying back of stems due to adverse weather conditions, insects, diseases and other causes.

Dormant – The period of the year when a plant is not growing.

Dormant Seeding – The application of cool-season seed during late fall or early winter for germination the following spring.

Dormant Turf – A brown-colored turf that has ceased growth due to the environment but will renew its growth when environmental conditions are again favorable. Conditions may be either too hot or too cold for growth.

Drop-Crotching – Thinning type of pruning in which a main branch or the leader is removed by cutting to a large lateral. The cut is made at the crotch formed with the portion removed and the lateral remaining.

Dwarfing Root Stock – Root used to reduce the size of a plant on which it is grafted or budded.

Endophytic Fungi – Fungi, present inside some grasses, that may aid in disease and insect resistance.

Espalier – To train a plant on a wire or trellis against a wall or other support.

Fairway – The area between the tee and green.

Fertigation – The application of fertilizer through an irrigation system.

Fertilizer – A liquid or dry material containing one or more of the necessary plant nutrients.

Fertilizer Burn – The death of a plant or plants caused by the over-application of a fertilizer that has a high salt index.

Fibrous – A dense root system made up of a mass of fiber-like roots.

Field Capacity – The amount of water a soil can hold.

Flail Mower – A mower that cuts with loosely mounted T-shaped blades.

Foliar Burn – An injury to the leaves of the plant caused by the application of a chemical.

Footprinting – Discolored areas or impressions in turf leaf from foot traffic when the turf is frosted or in a wilted condition.

French Drain – A drainage device in which a hole or trench is backfilled with sand or gravel.

Fungicide – A chemical used to control plant diseases caused by fungi.

Genus – A group of closely related plants that have certain common traits. For example: Kentucky bluegrass is Poa pratensis. Poa is a genus.

Germination – The first process in the growth of a plant from seed.

Grafted – The propagation of a plant by joining two different plants together by inserting a shoot from a desirable plant into the stem or root of another plant.

Grain – The undesirable horizontally oriented growth of leaves and stems on a putting green.

Grassy Weed – Leaves are narrow-grass like.

Green – A dense, smooth, closely mowed area used for putting the golf ball.

Grooving – See Vertical Mowing.

Heartwood – The hard center wood of a tree.

Herbicide – A chemical used to control weeds.

Herbacious – A plant that is soft and succulent, not woody. Usually dies back to the ground in winter.

Hydroseeding – A method of seeding by mixing seed with water and fertilizer and then spraying the solution into a seedbed.

Insecticide – A chemical used to control insects.

Irrigation, Automatic – Irrigation with the use of preset timing clocks.

Landing Area – The part of the golf course fairway where most tee shots land.

Lapping, Mower – Part of the process of sharpening a reel mower.

Lateral – A branch originating from the main trunk.

Layering, Soil – An undesirable stratification of a soil.

Legginess – Growth that is generally tall without much foliage near the ground, resulting in an open and undesirable plant.

Localized Dry Spot – An area of soil that resists wetting.

Mat – (See "Thatch").

Mixture – Two or more seeded species mixed together.

Mulch – Any material used to cover a soil surface to reduce evaporation or prevent erosion.

Multiple Stemmed Plants – Plants with more than one stem from the base compared to plants with only a central leader.

Narrow-Leaved – An evergreen plant with leaves that are needle-shaped.

Non-selective Herbicide – A chemical that kills all plants it contacts.

Nursery, Turf – A place where replacement sod is grown. May be used for experimentation with new products.

One Year Whip – Refers to a 1-year-old unbranched tree.

Overseeding – Seeding into a dormant turf with cool-season turfgrass in order to provide a playable surface during winter months in the South, or for esthetics. Or a method used to introduce a new turfgrass variety into an old or thin turf.

Perennial – Living more than two years.

Permanent Branch – A branch that is part of the major growth habit of the tree, usually originating from the trunk.

Pesticide – A chemical used to control any plant pest such as weeds, insects and disease.

P.L.S. – Pure Live Seed – percentage of seed in the container that is alive.

Photosynthesis – The production of carbohydrates or food material from carbon dioxide, water and light energy in chlorophyll containing tissue.

Plug – A core or cylinder of sod usually 2 inches or so in diameter. Contains the complete plant, including roots.

Plugging – Establishing turfgrass using plugs of sod.

Poling – Using a pole to remove the dew from the turfgrass leaf blades on a putting green.

Post-emergence herbicide – A chemical used to kill weeds after they come up.

Pre-emergence herbicide – A chemical that kills weeds as they germinate, before they come up.

Pre-germination – The process of germination of seed in a tank of water.

Purity – The percentage of seed in the container that is turfgrass seed.

Radical Branch Spacing – The distribution of branches around the trunk of a tree.

Reel Mower – A mower that cuts turfgrass by means of a series of rotating horizontal blades.

Renovation – Improving a low quality turf usually by upgrading the management system. May require the introduction of new species.

Rhizome – A below-ground stem capable of growing a new plant.

Rotary Mower – A mower that cuts turf with a high- speed blade that runs parallel to the turf surface.

Rough – The part of the golf course bordering the tee, fairway, and green.

Scaffold Branching – A permanent branch originating from the trunk and becoming a part of the major branching or framework of the tree.

Scald – Usually turf that turns brown under shallow standing water.

Scalping – The excessive removal of the top part of the turf plant by mowing.

Seed Priming – Same as pre-germination, but the quantity of water used is limited.

Shearing – Cutting back plants with hedge shears resulting in a very formal habit. Limit shearing to hedges, topiary or where a formal garden is to be maintained.

Shrub – A woody plant with several stems growing from the base.

Slicing – A method of cultivation in which a blade slices intermittently through the turf into the soil.

Slowly-available Fertilizer – A nutrient is slowly available to the plant, metered out over an extended period of time.

Slowly-soluble Fertilizer – (See "slowly-available fertilizer.")

Sod – Plugs, squares or strips of turf with the adhering soil.

Species – A basic unit of classification. A group of plants with similar ancestry. For example: Kentucky bluegrass (Poa pratensis, pratensis is a species).

Spiking – A method of cultivation in which a solid tine or pointed blade penetrates the turf and soil.

Spore – Reproductive organ of fungi similar to a seed.

Sprig – (See "Stolon.")

Sprigging – Establishing turf by means of sprigs or stolons.

Stem – The part of the plant above the ground that supports leaves or flowers.

Sucker – A vigorous, usually undesirable, shoot originating from root or stem tissue below ground.

Syringing – A light application of water used to cool the plant, prevent wilt, or remove due or frost.

Temporary Branch – A branch usually originating from the trunk that is removed by pruning after permanent branches have been selected.

Terminal – Tip ends of branches.

Thatch – A layer of organic material between the crown of the plant and the true soil surface.

Thinning – Removal of connecting branches to point of origin or shortening the length of a branch by cutting to a lateral.

Tiller – A plant that produces a new plant at the base of the parent plant.

Topdressing – A thin layer of soil applied to a turf.

Tracker – A dye added to a spray tank to "track" the application of colorless solutions.

Trained – To dictate the development and growth of a plant by physical means, such as pruning.

Transitional Zone – An east-west zone through the middle of the United States between the northern area favoring cool-season grasses and the southern area favoring warm-season grasses.

Transplanting – Moving a plant from one place to another.

Variety – A plant species may have many varieties. Varieties are usually named. For example: Palmer, Cutter, SR4200 and Gator are all named varieties of perennial ryegrass.

Vertical Branch Spacing – Distribution of branches up and down the trunk of a tree.

Vertical Mowing – The use of a mechanical device with vertically rotating blades for thatch and grain control.

Warm-season Turfgrass – Species of turfgrass such as bermudagrass, St. Augustine, zoysia, and buffalograss used in the southern United States.

Water Sprout – Vigorous shoot, usually undesirable, arising from the trunk or older branches.

Wilt, Dry – The drooping of a plants' leaves caused by a lack of water.

Wilt, Wet – The drooping of a plants' leaves caused by a lack of oxygen

Winter Kill – The loss of a plant to any cause during the winter.

Woody Ornamental – Plants with woody tissue used for their aesthetic value.

Wound – Area where the bark of a plant is cut or damaged.

Wound Dressing – A specially-formulated material applied to tree wounds to protect the wood from cracking.

Index